New York
Progress
Mathematics

7

S® Sadlier School

CCLS

New York
Progress™

Mathematics

Cover: *Series Design:* Studio Montage;
Title design: Quarasan, Inc.

Photo Credits: Cover: age fotostock/Rainer Martini: *right.* Dreamstime.com/Anton Ignatenco: *bottom left inset;* Kmitu: *top left.* Getty Images/David H. Lewis: *bottom left.* Used under license from Shutterstock.com/RoboLab: *background.* Interior: age fotostock/Chromorange: 9. Alamy/K.L. Howard: 141 *bottom.* Corbis/Blend Images/KidStock: 70 *top;* Image Source: 8 *top;* Michael Robinson: 265; Sutton Images: 71. Dreamstime.com/Kmitu: vi *center;* Paul Lemke: 141 *top.* Fotolia.com/peter_waters: vi *bottom right inset.* Getty Images/Jupiterimages: 202 *top;* Abel Mitja Varela: 264 *top.* Used under license from Shutterstock.com/Jana Guothova: 8 *bottom,* 70 *bottom,* 140 *bottom,* 202 *bottom,* 264 *bottom;* Ulrich Mueller: 71 *inset;* Gergo Orban: 203; RoboLab: 1, vi *background;* StudioC: vi *bottom left;* StudioSmart: vi *bottom right;* Yuliyan Velchev: vi *top left.* SuperStock/Exactostock: vi *top right;* Flirt: 140 top.

For additional online resources, go to sadlierconnect.com.

S̸ is a registered trademark of William H. Sadlier, Inc.

William H. Sadlier, Inc.
9 Pine Street
New York, NY 10005-4700

Printed in the United States of America.
ISBN: 978-1-4217-3357-9
1 2 3 4 5 6 7 8 9 WEBC 18 17 16 15 14

Contents

NEW YORK
COMMON CORE
LEARNING STANDARDS

CCLS

Unit 1 Focus on Ratios and Proportional Relationships

Unit 2 Focus on The Number System

Welcome

You have an exciting year ahead of you. You will be learning more about mathematics and how it can help you solve both mathematical and real-world problems.

Did you know that you solve problems and use math all the time? Think about your day. When you play sports, shop at your favorite store, cook a delicious food, build something, or travel in a car, bus, or train, you are using math and applying your understanding to make sense of the world around you.

Common Core Progress will help you become more confident in mathematics as you use it to solve many kinds of problems. That's why it's called *progress*.

Have a great year!

Progress Check

Look at how the Common Core standards you have learned and will learn connect.

It is very important for you to understand the standards from the prior grade level so that you will be able to develop an understanding of ratios and proportional relationships in this unit and be prepared for next year. To practice your skills, go to sadlierconnect.com.

GRADE 6		GRADE 7		GRADE 8
I Can...	Before Unit 1	**Can I?**	After Unit 1	**I Will...**
6.RP.3 Solve unit rate problems **6.NS.1** Divide fractions by fractions	☐	**7.RP.1** Compute unit rates involving ratios of fractions	☐	
6.RP.1 Describe a ratio relationship between two quantities	☐	**7.RP.2** Decide if two quantities are in a proportional relationship	☐	**8.EE.5** Graph proportional relationships Compare proportional relationships represented in different ways
6.RP.3 Plot pairs of values of equivalent ratios on the coordinate plane	☐	Understand that the graph of a proportional relationship is a straight line	☐	**8.SP.2** Use straight lines to model linear relationships on scatter plots
6.RP.2 Understand the concept of a unit rate	☐	**7.RP.2** Identify the constant of proportionality (unit rate) in tables, graphs, equations, diagrams, and verbal descriptions	☐	**8.EE.6** Find the slope of a line **8.F.4** Determine the rate of change and initial value of a function
6.RP.3 Use equations to solve problems involving rates and ratios	☐	**7.RP.2** Represent proportional relationships with equations	☐	**8.F.4** Model linear relationships with functions
6.RP.3 Plot pairs of values of equivalent ratios on the coordinate plane	☐	**7.RP.2** Explain what a point (x, y) on the graph of a proportional relationship means in terms of the situation	☐	**8.F.5** Use graphs to analyze functional relationships
6.RP.3 Solve unit rate problems Find a percent of a quantity or find the whole given a part and the percent	☐	**7.RP.3** Use proportional relationships to solve multi-step ratio and percent problems	☐	**8.SP.3** Solve problems involving the equation of a linear model, interpreting the slope and intercept in context

HOME ◆ CONNECT...

In this unit your child will:

- Compute unit rates involving fractions

- Identify proportional relationships and the constant of proportionality

- Use equations and graphs to represent proportional relationships

- Solve multi-step ratio and percent problems

NOTE: All of these learning goals for your child are based on the Grade 7 Common Core State Standards for Mathematics.

Your child will use ratio thinking to identify and write proportional relationships and use them to solve problems. A proportional relationship can be represented by two equivalent ratios.

In proportional relationship problems, there is one unknown quantity. One way your child will use to determine the unknown quantity is to make a table of equivalent ratios.

Activity: Knowing fraction-percent equivalents is useful for mental math. To help your child remember these, play Match the Percent. Use the fractions and equivalent percents to make a set of 24 cards.

To play the game, use the percent cards and give your child the fraction cards. Show one percent card at a time and ask your child to match it with the equivalent fraction card. You can also switch cards and show your child a fraction. Another way is to place all cards facedown and play a concentration game.

Fraction	$\frac{1}{10}$	$\frac{1}{5}$	$\frac{1}{4}$	$\frac{1}{2}$	$\frac{2}{5}$
Percent	10%	20%	25%	50%	40%

Fraction	$\frac{3}{4}$	$\frac{3}{10}$	$\frac{3}{5}$	$\frac{4}{5}$	$\frac{7}{10}$	$\frac{9}{10}$
Percent	75%	30%	60%	80%	70%	90%

Ways to Help Your Child

Build your child's interest in mathematics by encouraging him or her to join a math club or math circle. Use these searches: *middle school math club* and *middle school math circle* with a search engine. The difference between a club and a circle is that math clubs are usually an extracurricular activity at a middle school while math circles usually involve students meeting with faculty or graduate students at a local college or university. Both provide engaging group mathematics projects to stimulate interest in mathematics.

> **ONLINE**
> **For more Home Connect activities, continue online at** sadlierconnect.com

Focus on Ratios and Proportional Relationships

Essential Question:
Why does recognizing the constant of proportionality help you understand and use proportional relationships?

Essential Question:
How can you compute the unit rate for a ratio of fractions?

7.RP.1

Words to Know:
unit rate
ratio
complex fraction

Guided Instruction

In this lesson, you will learn to compute unit rates for ratios of fractions.

Understand: Unit rates for ratios of fractional quantities with like units

Rachel mixes $\frac{3}{4}$ cup of blue paint with $\frac{2}{3}$ cup of red paint to make purple paint. She wants to make more paint that is exactly the same color purple. How much blue paint should Rachel mix with 1 cup of red paint?

To find the amount of blue paint Rachel needs to mix with 1 cup of red paint, find the unit rate, the number of cups of blue paint per 1 cup of red paint.

The ratio of cups of blue paint to cups of red paint is $\frac{3}{4} : \frac{2}{3}$.

You can find a unit rate for a ratio of fractions using the same methods you used for ratios of whole numbers. Here are two ways to compute the unit rate.

> A is $\frac{3}{4}$ and B is $\frac{2}{3}$. The units of A are cups of blue paint. The units of B are cups of red paint.

Method 1 Find the equivalent ratio for which the second quantity is 1.

To get 1, you multiply $\frac{2}{3}$ by $\frac{3}{2}$. So, to get an equivalent ratio, you multiply $\frac{3}{4}$ by $\frac{3}{2}$ also.

multiply by $\frac{3}{2}$

cups of blue paint	$\frac{3}{4}$	$1\frac{1}{8}$
cups of red paint	$\frac{2}{3}$	1

multiply by $\frac{3}{2}$

$\frac{3}{4} \cdot \frac{3}{2} = \frac{9}{8}$

$= 1\frac{1}{8}$

The unit rate is $1\frac{1}{8}$.

Method 2 To find the unit rate for a ratio $A : B$, divide A by B.

Divide $\frac{3}{4}$ by $\frac{2}{3}$. You can show this division with a complex fraction.

$\dfrac{\frac{3}{4}}{\frac{2}{3}} = \frac{3}{4} \div \frac{2}{3}$

$= \frac{3}{4} \cdot \frac{3}{2}$

$= \frac{9}{8}$

$= 1\frac{1}{8}$

The unit rate is $1\frac{1}{8}$.

> You can show division using a fraction. If the numerator, the denominator, or both are also fractions, the result is a complex fraction.
>
> $\dfrac{\frac{3}{4}}{\frac{2}{3}}$ is a complex fraction.

➡ Rachel needs to mix $1\frac{1}{8}$ cups of blue paint with 1 cup of red paint.

✏ Explain why the two methods result in the same unit rate.

Understand: Unit rates for ratios of fractional quantities with unlike units.

> In $\frac{1}{4}$ hour, Arun walks $\frac{7}{8}$ mile. What is his rate in miles per hour?

You can use the same methods to find the unit rate for unlike units like miles and hours that you used for like units.

To find the unit rate in miles per hour, begin with the ratio of miles : hours. The ratio of miles to hours is $\frac{7}{8} : \frac{1}{4}$

Method 1 Find the equivalent ratio for which the second quantity is 1.

To get 1 hour, you multiply $\frac{1}{4}$ by 4. So, to write an equivalent ratio, you also multiply $\frac{7}{8}$ by 4.

multiply by 4

miles	$\frac{7}{8}$	$3\frac{1}{2}$
hours	$\frac{1}{4}$	1

multiply by 4

$\frac{7}{8} \cdot 4 = \frac{28}{8}$

$\qquad = 3\frac{1}{2}$ ⟵ The unit rate is $3\frac{1}{2}$.

Method 2 To find the unit rate, write the ratio with the two fractions, and then divide.

$\dfrac{\frac{7}{8}}{\frac{1}{4}} = \frac{7}{8} \div \frac{1}{4}$

$\qquad = \frac{7}{8} \cdot 4$

$\qquad = \frac{28}{8}$

$\qquad = 3\frac{1}{2}$ ⟵ The unit rate is $3\frac{1}{2}$.

▶ Arun's rate is $3\frac{1}{2}$ miles per hour.

✏ Which method do you prefer for finding the unit rate? Explain.

Guided Instruction

Connect: **Unit rates with money**

Carl's mother buys $\frac{4}{5}$ pound of Rainier cherries for $2.80 and $\frac{5}{8}$ pound of Bing cherries for $1.50. Which cherries are more expensive?

To find which cherries are more expensive, find the price per pound of each and compare. The price per pound is a unit rate. A unit rate that involves a price is called a unit price.

Step 1

Find the unit price for the Rainier cherries.
The ratio of dollars to pounds is
2.8 dollars to $\frac{4}{5}$ pound.

Rewrite 2.8 as a fraction.

$$2.8 = 2\frac{8}{10} = 2\frac{4}{5} = \frac{14}{5}$$

Divide to find the unit price.

$$\frac{14}{5} \div \frac{4}{5} = \frac{14}{5} \cdot \frac{5}{4}$$
$$= \frac{70}{20}$$
$$= 3\frac{10}{20} \text{ or } 3\frac{5}{10}$$

The unit price is 3.5 dollars or $3.50 per pound.

Step 2

Find the unit price for the Bing cherries.
The ratio of dollars to pounds is
1.5 dollars to $\frac{5}{8}$ pound.

Rewrite 1.5 as a fraction.

$$1.5 = 1\frac{5}{10} = 1\frac{1}{2} = \frac{3}{2}$$

Divide to find the unit price.

$$\frac{3}{2} \div \frac{5}{8} = \frac{3}{2} \cdot \frac{8}{5}$$
$$= \frac{24}{10}$$
$$= 2\frac{4}{10}$$

The unit price is 2.4 dollars or $2.40 per pound.

Step 3

Compare the unit rates.

The unit rate for Rainier cherries is $3.50.
The unit rate for Bing cherries is $2.40.

$3.50 > $2.40

➡ The Rainier cherries cost more per pound, so they are more expensive.

✏ How would you find the number of pounds of cherries for one dollar instead of the number of dollars for one pound of cherries?

Guided Practice

Solve the problems.

1. Ann mixes $\frac{1}{2}$ cup of cranberry juice with $\frac{1}{3}$ cup of orange juice. How much cranberry juice should Ann mix with 1 cup of orange juice?

   The ratio of cups of cranberry juice to cups of orange juice is $\frac{1}{2}$: ____

   Find the unit rate.

Use Method 1 Find the equivalent ratio.

First, to get 1 cup of orange juice, multiply $\frac{1}{3}$ by ____

multiply by $\frac{3}{1}$

cranberry juice	$\frac{1}{2}$	$\frac{3}{2}$
orange juice	$\frac{1}{3}$	

multiply by $\frac{3}{1}$

$\frac{1}{2} \cdot \frac{3}{1} =$ ____

$=$ ____

The unit rate is ____.

Use Method 2 Write the ratio with the fractions and then divide.

Divide $\frac{1}{2}$ by $\frac{1}{3}$.

$\dfrac{\frac{1}{2}}{\frac{1}{3}} = \frac{1}{2} \div \frac{1}{3}$

$= \frac{1}{2} \cdot \frac{3}{1}$

$=$ ____

$=$ ____

The unit rate is ____.

Answer Ann should mix ____ cups of cranberry juice with 1 cup of orange juice.

2. Jeff walks $3\frac{1}{2}$ miles in $\frac{3}{4}$ hour. In $1\frac{1}{4}$ hours, Loralee walks $6\frac{3}{4}$ miles. Who walks faster?

   $3\frac{1}{2} \div \frac{3}{4} = \frac{7}{2} \div$ ____ $6\frac{3}{4} \div 1\frac{1}{4} = \frac{27}{4} \div$ ____

   $=$ ____ $\cdot$ ____ $=$ ____ $=$ _____ $=$ ____ $\cdot$ ____ $=$ ____ $=$ _____

   ____ > ____

   Answer _____

 **Think•Pair•Share**

MP2 3. Explain how you can tell by comparing the two numbers in a ratio whether the unit rate will be greater than, equal to, or less than 1.

Independent Practice

Find the unit rate for each ratio.

1. $\frac{9}{10}$ hour doing math to 2 hours spent reading

   $\frac{9}{10} \div 2$

   $=$ _____ • _____ $=$ _____

   $=$ _____

   _____ hour(s) doing math for every 1 hour spent reading

2. 4 hours walking to $3\frac{1}{3}$ hours jogging

   _____ $\div$ _____

   $=$ _____ • _____ $=$ _____

   $=$ _____

   _____hour(s) walking for every 1 hour jogging

3. $1\frac{2}{3}$ cups of water to $\frac{1}{2}$ cup of juice concentrate

   _____ cup(s) of water for every 1 cup of juice concentrate

4. $0.75 for $\frac{3}{5}$ pound of apples

   _____ per pound of apples

For exercises 5–6, circle the correct answer. Choose all that apply.

5. Jenny mixes $\frac{2}{3}$ pound of almonds with $\frac{3}{5}$ pound of dried fruit. To create more of the same mixture, how many pounds of almonds does Jenny need to mix with one pound of dried fruit?

   a. $\frac{2}{5}$ pound of almonds

   b. $\frac{8}{9}$ pound of almonds

   c. $1\frac{1}{9}$ pounds of almonds

   d. $2\frac{1}{2}$ pounds of almonds

6. Which of the following expresses a unit rate?

   a. miles per hour

   b. 2 centimeters for every 15 meters

   c. $\frac{2}{3}$ ounce of batter for each muffin

   d. cost per pound

Solve the problems.

7. Sally buys $2\frac{1}{2}$ pounds of bananas for $1.50. How much is she paying for one pound of bananas?

Answer _____

8. Ben can type $\frac{2}{5}$ of a page of an essay in $\frac{1}{2}$ minute. How much time would it take him to type one full page of the essay?

Answer _____

For exercises 9–10, use the information below.

To make orange paint, Roger mixed $\frac{5}{8}$ cup of red paint with $\frac{2}{5}$ cup of yellow paint. He really liked the resulting color, and wants to make a larger batch of the orange paint.

9. How much red paint is needed to mix with one cup of yellow paint?

Answer _____

10. How much yellow paint is needed to mix with one cup of red paint?

Answer _____

Independent Practice

MP4 **11.** Explain how unit rates can be helpful at the supermarket.

Solve the problems.

MP6 **12.** Sebastian runs $\frac{1}{4}$ mile in 1.6 minutes. At this rate, how long will it take him to run one mile?

> **Show your work.**

Answer _____

MP3 **13.** Amir walks $\frac{1}{2}$ mile in 15 minutes. Jody walks $\frac{2}{3}$ mile in 20 minutes. Who walks at the faster rate?

Answer _____

> **Justify your answer.**

MP3 **14.** Kami bought $3\frac{1}{2}$ pounds of nectarines for $1.75 and $1\frac{3}{5}$ pounds of oranges for $0.60. Which fruit costs less per pound?

Answer _____

✏ **Justify your answer.**

MP2 **15.** A sign by the pears reads, "Buy $\frac{1}{4}$ pound for only $\frac{1}{2}$ dollar!" Ms. Morales thought that the pears cost more than $1.00 per pound. Her daughter, Jasmine, thought that the pears cost less than $1.00 per pound. Who is correct?

Answer _____

✏ **Justify your answer.**

MP6 **16.** Karl can run $\frac{1}{10}$ mile in $\frac{3}{4}$ minute. To find his unit rate, he found $\frac{3}{4} \div \frac{1}{10}$. Calculate the unit rate. Is the unit rate in miles per minute or minutes per mile?

✏ **Show your work.**

Answer _____

Essential Question:
**How can you decide
whether two quantities
have a proportional
relationship?**

7.RP.2a

Words to Know:
proportional relationship
origin

Guided Instruction

In this lesson, you will learn two methods to test whether two
quantities are in a proportional relationship.

Understand: Using a table to test for a proportional relationship

The table below shows the price and the weight of three bunches of bananas.
Devon wants to find out if each relationship between the price in dollars and
the pounds of bananas is proportional.

Two quantities are in a proportional relationship if the
ratios of the quantities have a constant unit rate, a unit
rate that is the same for each ratio.

Price	Pounds	Unit Rate per pound
$0.90	1.5	$0.60
$1.05	1.75	$0.60
$1.20	2	$0.60

You can compute the unit rate for each ratio pair.
To find the unit rate in dollars per pound, divide the
price in dollars by the number of pounds.

The unit rate is the same for each ratio pair.

▶ The relationship between the two quantities is proportional for each ratio.

The table below shows the price and the number of fluid ounces for three
containers of orange juice. Devon wants to find out if the relationship between
the price in dollars and the number of fluid ounces is proportional.

You can compute the unit rate for each ratio pair.
To find the unit rate in dollars per fluid ounce, divide
the price in dollars by the number of fluid ounces.

The unit rates are not the same for each ratio.

Price	Fluid Ounces	Unit Rate per fluid ounce
$3.84	64	$0.06
$2.24	32	$0.07
$0.80	8	$0.10

▶ The relationship between the two quantities in
each pair is not proportional.

✏️ Explain why it makes sense that the relationship of the quantities in the first
pair is proportional but the relationship of the quantities in the second pair is not.

Guided Instruction

Understand: Using a graph to test for a proportional relationship

Eliza makes these four servings of orange-cranberry juice. If the pairs of quantities in the table are in equivalent proportional relationships, each serving will taste the same. Does the table show proportional relationships that are the same?

Orange Juice (fl oz)	Cranberry Juice (fl oz)
2	3
3	$4\frac{1}{2}$
4	6
5	$7\frac{1}{2}$

You can test to see if there is a proportional relationship by graphing the ratio pairs. If the points lie on a straight line through the point (0, 0), the origin, then the pairs of quantities are in equivalent proportional relationships.

> **Remember!**
> The origin is the point where the two axes cross.

Graph the ordered pairs from the table.

To graph any ratio $A : B$, you use the horizontal or x-axis for the values of B, and the vertical or y-axis for the values of A.

> Notice to plot the quantities of juices from the table of ratios, you represent all the ratios $A : B$ as the ordered pair (B, A). Therefore, the ratio 2 : 3 is written as the ordered pair (3, 2).

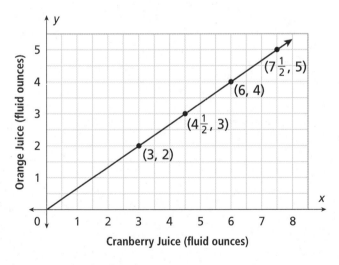

All of the points lie on a straight line that goes through the origin.

➡ Yes. The table shows proportional relationships that are the same.

Continued»

Guided Instruction

Eliza makes the four servings of mango-pear juice shown in the table. Does the table of ratios show equivalent proportional relationships?

Mango Juice (fl oz)	Pear Juice (fl oz)
2	$3\frac{1}{2}$
$2\frac{1}{2}$	4
3	$4\frac{1}{2}$
$4\frac{1}{2}$	6

To determine if the table of ratios show equivalent proportional relationships, graph each ratio from the table on a coordinate plane.

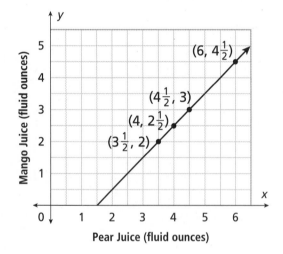

All the points lie on a straight line, however the line does not go through the origin.

➡ No. The table of ratios does not show equivalent proportional relationships.

✏ Do you think the servings of orange-cranberry juice on page 19 all have the same unit rate? Explain.

Guided Instruction

Connect: Comparing two methods to test for a proportional relationship

> Sal makes the four batches of orange paint shown in the table below. If the number of cups of yellow paint and the number of cups of red paint are in a proportional relationship, each batch will be the same color. Will each batch be the same color?

To determine if each batch or mixture of paint will make the same color, you can test for a proportional relationship by either finding the unit rate for all the ratios or making a graph.

Method 1 Find the unit rate for each ratio.

Yellow Paint (cups)	Red Paint (cups)	Unit Rate Cups of Yellow Paint : Cups of Red Paint
2	3	$\frac{2}{3}$
$3\frac{1}{2}$	5	$\frac{7}{10}$
3	$4\frac{1}{2}$	$\frac{2}{3}$
1	$6\frac{1}{2}$	$\frac{2}{13}$

The unit rates are not all the same.

Method 2 Graph the ratios on a coordinate plane.

All the points do not lie on a straight line.

Notice no matter which method you choose, the answer will be the same.

➡ The batches will not all be the same color.

✏ Will any of the batches be the same color? Explain.

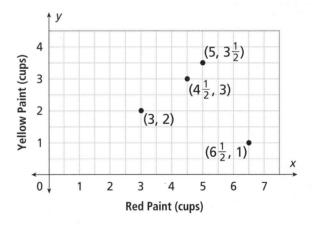

Guided Practice

Find the unit rate for each ratio in the table. Use the unit rates to decide if the table shows a proportional relationship. Circle *yes* or *no*.

1.

Price (dollars)	Gasoline (gallon)	Unit Rate (dollars per gallon)
10.50	3	
14.00	4	
17.50	5	
24.50	7	

Is the relationship proportional?

yes no

2.

Grape Juice (cups)	Cherry Juice (cups)	Unit Rate (cup grape juice per cup cherry juice)
2	5	
3	7	
4	8	
6	9	

Is the relationship proportional?

yes no

Graph the points from the table. Use the graph to decide if the table shows a proportional relationship. Circle *yes* or *no*.

3.

Cups of White Paint	Cups of Red paint
1	$\frac{1}{2}$
3	$1\frac{1}{2}$
4	2
5	$2\frac{1}{2}$

Is the relationship proportional?

yes no

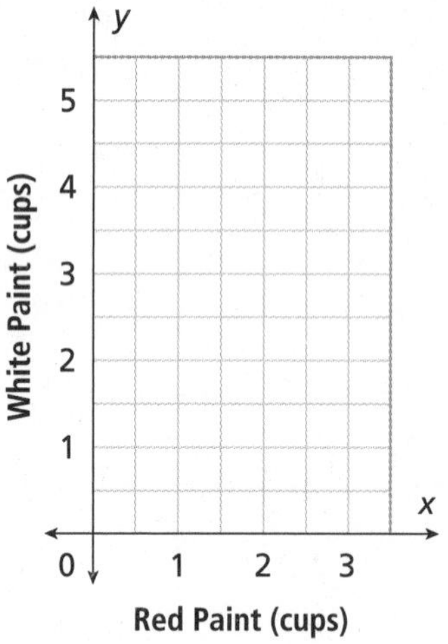

Think•Pair•Share

MP7 **4.** Look at the graph for Exercise 3. How do you think you might use the graph to find the unit rate for the ratios, the number of cups of white paint for each cup of red paint? Explain.

Independent Practice

Find the unit rate for each ratio in the table. Use the unit rates to decide if the table shows a proportional relationship. Circle *yes* or *no*.

1.

Distance (miles)	Time (hour)	Unit Rate (miles per hour)
$1\frac{1}{2}$	$\frac{2}{3}$	
2	$1\frac{1}{4}$	
$2\frac{1}{2}$	$1\frac{1}{2}$	
3	2	

Is the relationship proportional?

yes   no

2.

Price (dollars)	Milk (gallon)	Unit Rate (dollars per gallon)
4.50	2	
6.75	3	
9.00	4	
11.25	5	

Is the relationship proportional?

yes   no

Graph the points from the table. Use the graph to decide if the table shows a proportional relationship. Circle *yes* or *no*.

3.

Cranberry Juice (cups)	Orange Juice (cups)
$\frac{1}{2}$	1
1	2
2	4
$2\frac{1}{2}$	5

Is the relationship proportional?

yes   no

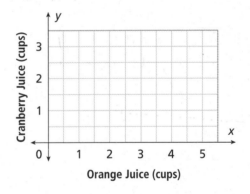

Is the relationship proportional?

4. Which of the following ratios are not proportional to $\frac{11}{4}$?

a. $\frac{22}{8}$

b. $\frac{33}{12}$

c. $\frac{44}{20}$

d. $\frac{11}{3}$

Independent Practice

5. Which of the following graphs shows a proportional relationship?

a.
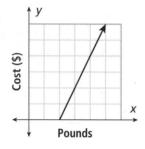

b.
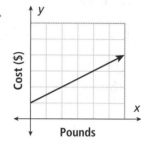

c.
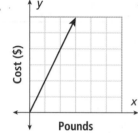

d.
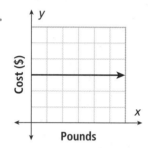

6. Which of the following tables shows a proportional relationship?

a.

Pounds	Dollars
1	2
2	4
4	8

b.

Pounds	Dollars
1	3
3	5
5	7

c.

Pounds	Dollars
$\frac{1}{2}$	2
2	8
3	12

d.

Pounds	Dollars
2	2.50
3	3.50
4	4.50

7. A high-speed train can travel 140 miles in $1\frac{1}{4}$ hours, 224 miles in 2 hours, 308 miles in $2\frac{3}{4}$ hours, and 448 miles in 4 hours. Your friend wants to show that the train travels according to a proportional relationship. Would you recommend that your friend make a graph or use a table? Explain your reasoning.

Answer

Independent Practice

For exercises 8–9, a proportional relationship is shown in the table. What is the value of *n*?

8.

Hours	Miles
2	75
4	150
6	225
8	*n*

Show your work.

Answer _____

9.

Pounds	Dollars
2	9.00
3	13.50
6	27.00
n	49.50

Show your work.

Answer _____

10. Four students in an art class mixed red and blue paint to make purple. The amounts they used are shown in the table. Which student made a different shade of purple than the other students?

Student	Red Paint (cups)	Blue Paint (cups)
Alec	$1\frac{1}{3}$	$\frac{2}{3}$
Rosa	$2\frac{1}{2}$	$1\frac{1}{4}$
Aidan	$4\frac{1}{2}$	2
Zoe	5	$2\frac{1}{2}$

Answer _____

Justify your answer.

Essential Question:
How can you identify the unit rate of a proportional relationship?

7.RP.2b

Words to Know:
constant of proportionality

Guided Instruction

In this lesson, you will learn to identify the unit rate in tables, graphs, equations, diagrams, and verbal descriptions of the proportional relationship.

Understand: Identifying the unit rate from a graph or from an equation

Liam is making whole wheat pancakes. The graph below shows the proportional relationship between the amount of water and the amount of pancake mix. How much water does Liam mix with 1 cup of pancake mix?

To find the amount of water Liam mixes with 1 cup of pancake mix, identify the unit rate using the graph. The number of cups of water for 1 cup of pancake mix is the unit rate, which is also called the constant of proportionality. You can find the unit rate by identifying the y-coordinate when the x-coordinate is 1.

When $x = 1$, $y = \frac{3}{4}$.

So, the unit rate is $\frac{3}{4}$ cup of water per cup of pancake mix.

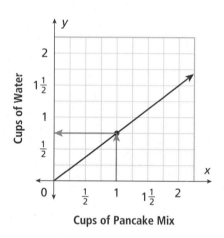

Cups of Pancake Mix

▶ Lian mixes $\frac{3}{4}$ cup of water with 1 cup of pancake mix.

Any proportional relationship can be written as an equation in the form $y = kx$, for which k is the unit rate or the constant of proportionality.

To write the equation that represents the proportional relationship shown in the graph, use $y = kx$, and replace k with $\frac{3}{4}$, which is the unit rate or constant of proportionality for this situation.

The equation for the relationship shown is $y = \frac{3}{4}x$.

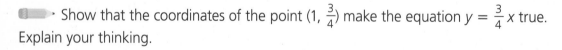 Show that the coordinates of the point $(1, \frac{3}{4})$ make the equation $y = \frac{3}{4}x$ true. Explain your thinking.

Understand: Identifying a unit rate from a double number line diagram

A cinnamon bread recipe calls for $\frac{3}{4}$ cup of flour for every $\frac{1}{4}$ cup of milk. How much flour would be used with 1 cup of milk?

The double number line diagram at the right shows the proportional relationship between the cups of flour and the cups of milk in the recipe.

To find the unit rate, the number of cups of flour for 1 cup of milk, find the point on the top number line that lines up with 1 on the bottom number line.

The point for 3 on the top line lines up with the point for 1 on the bottom line. The unit rate is 3.

> Three cups of flour would be used with 1 cup of milk.

Remember!
A double number line shows equivalent ratios.

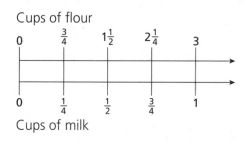

The cinnamon bread recipe calls for $\frac{1}{2}$ tablespoon of cinnamon for every $\frac{1}{4}$ cup of milk. How much cinnamon would be used with 1 cup of milk?

This double number line diagram shows the proportional relationship between tablespoons of cinnamon and cups of milk.

To find the unit rate, the number of tablespoons of cinnamon for 1 cup of milk, you need to extend the number lines so that 1 appears on the bottom number line.

Both number lines start at 0. Each interval on the top number line represents $\frac{1}{2}$ tablespoon of cinnamon. Each interval on the bottom line represents $\frac{1}{4}$ cup milk.

The point for 2 on the top line lines up with the point for 1 on the bottom line. The unit rate is 2.

> Two tablespoons of cinnamon would be used with 1 cup of milk.

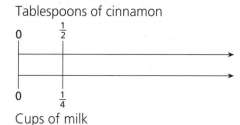

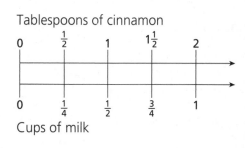

✏️ How could you use the double number line diagram above to find the number of cups of milk for 1 tablespoon of cinnamon?

Guided Instruction

Connect: Different ways to identify a unit rate

> What are some different ways that you have learned to identify the unit rate in a proportional relationship?

➡ You can identify the unit rate for a proportional relationship from a verbal description, a table, a graph, an equation, or a diagram.

Verbal Description

Martin drives 100 miles in 2 hours.

The unit rate is 100 ÷ 2 or 50 miles per hour.

Graph

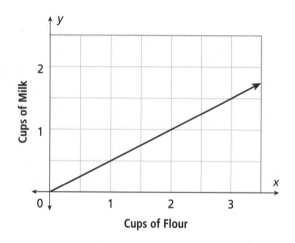

Cups of Flour

The point $(1, \frac{1}{2})$ shows the unit rate. The unit rate is $\frac{1}{2}$ cup of milk per cup of flour.

Table

Feet	Seconds
3	15
4	20
6	30

The unit rate is $\frac{3}{15}$ or $\frac{1}{5}$ foot per second.

Equation

Let x = the number of cups of yellow paint.
Let y = the number of cups of blue paint.

Equation: $y = 4x$

The unit rate is 4 cups of blue paint per cup of yellow paint.

Diagram

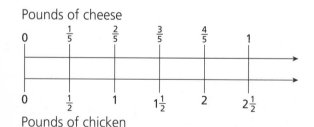

The point for $\frac{2}{5}$ on the top line lines up with the point for 1 on the bottom line.

The unit rate is $\frac{2}{5}$ pound of cheese per pound of chicken.

Identify the unit rate for each of these proportional relationships.

1. To make a smoothie, Kathleen uses $\frac{3}{8}$ cup of blueberries for every banana she uses.

   The unit rate is _____ cup of blueberries per banana.

2. For his smoothie, Clayton puts in $1\frac{1}{2}$ cups of yogurt for every $\frac{1}{2}$ cup of strawberries.

   The unit rate is _____ cups of yogurt per cup of strawberries.

3.

Calories	Servings
10	1
20	2

   The unit rate is _____ calories per serving .

4.

Wheel Revolutions	Minutes
10	4
20	8

   The unit rate is _____ wheel revolutions per minute.

5.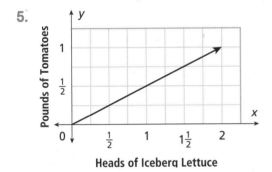

   Heads of Iceberg Lettuce

   The unit rate is _____ pound of tomatoes per head of lettuce.

6.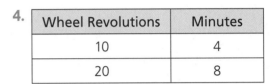

   Cups of cranberries

   The unit rate is _____ cup of raisins for every cup of cranberries.

7. $x =$ the number of bags
   $y =$ the number of apples

   Equation: $y = 12x$

   The unit rate is _____ apples per bag.

8. $x =$ the number of cans of juice
   $y =$ the number of sandwiches

   Equation: $y = 1\frac{1}{4}x$

   The unit rate is $1\frac{1}{4}$ _____

   per _____ .

Think•Pair•Share

MP3 9. Sharon's trail mix contains 4 cups of dried fruit for every 1 cup of almonds. She writes the equation $y = 4x$ to show the proportional relationship. Does x represent the number of cups of dried fruit or the number of cups of almonds? Explain how you know.

Independent Practice

Identify the unit rate for each of these proportional relationships.

1.

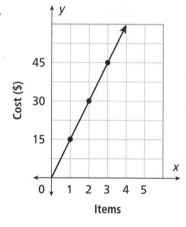

Answer _____ per item.

2.

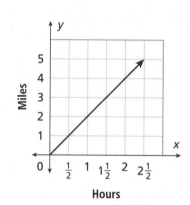

Answer _____ miles per hour.

3.

Cost	People
$20	5
$32	8

Answer _____ per person.

4.

Children	Chaperones
12	4
24	8

Answer _____ children to every chaperone.

5. To make a smoothie, Kerry uses $\frac{1}{4}$ cup of raspberries for each half ounce of mango he uses.

Answer _____ cup of raspberries for each ounce of mango.

6. Cups of red paint

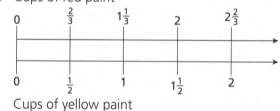

Cups of yellow paint

Answer _____ cups of red paint for each cup of yellow paint.

7. Let x = number of hours driven.
Let y = number of miles traveled.

$y = 52x$

Answer _____ miles per hour.

8. Let x = number of seconds.
Let y = number of yards.

$y = 12\frac{1}{2}x$

Answer _____ yards per second.

Independent Practice

Solve the problems.

MP1 9. Sahir walks $1\frac{1}{2}$ miles in $\frac{3}{4}$ hour. What is his walking speed in miles per hour?

> **Show your work.**

Answer _____

MP4 10. The double number line diagram shows the relationship between the number of pages read and the amount of time Huang needed to read the pages. How much time does Huang need to read one page?

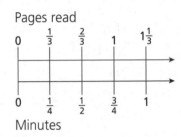

Answer _____

MP5 11. The table shows the prices paid for different amounts of cheddar cheese purchased at a warehouse store. What is the cost of one pound of cheddar cheese?

> **Show your work.**

Pounds	Cost
2.4	$6.60
3	$8.25
4.6	$12.65

Answer _____

For exercises 12–13, circle the correct answer.

12. Which equation shows 6 as the constant of proportionality?

   a. $y = \frac{1}{6}x$ **b.** $y = x + 6$

   c. $y = 6x$ **d.** $y = x - 6$

13. A recipe calls for $\frac{1}{2}$ cup of water for every $\frac{3}{4}$ cup of flour. How much water is needed to mix with 1 cup of flour?

   a. $\frac{2}{3}$ cup   **b.** $\frac{3}{4}$ cup

   c. $1\frac{1}{3}$ cups   **d.** $1\frac{1}{2}$ cups

Independent Practice

MP3 14. Ms. Norton wrote the equation $y = 5x$. She says that x = the number of students in a group and y = the number of colored pencils that will be given to the group. Explain the meaning of the number 5 in this equation. If there are 3 students in a group, how many colored pencils will the group get?

MP5 15. The graph shows the number of cups of red and white paint used to make pink paint. Eliza says that she cannot tell the number of cups of red paint per cup of white paint from the graph because it is difficult to find the exact value of the y-coordinate when $x = 1$. Brad says that he can tell from the graph that the unit rate is $\frac{2}{3}$ cup of red paint for every cup of white paint. Explain how Brad may be using the graph to find the unit rate.

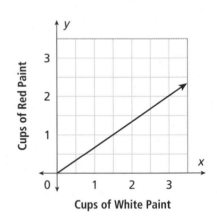

For exercises 16–17, use the table below.

Cost of Organic Potatoes	Pounds of Organic Potatoes
$4.50	3
$7.50	5

MP4 16. Find the constant of proportionality. Then write an equation that relates the total cost y to the number of pounds x.

✏ **Show your work.**

Answer _____

MP5 17. Use your equation from problem 16 to predict the cost for 15 pounds of organic potatoes.

✏ **Show your work.**

Answer _____

MP2 **18.** Juanita and Li buy some oranges. Juanita buys 2.5 pounds for $3.75 and Li buys 5.1 pounds for $8.16. Do they pay the same unit rate?

Answer _____

✏️ **Justify your answer.**

MP5 **19.** To make a cereal-raisin mixture, Yoel uses $\frac{2}{5}$ cup of cereal for every $\frac{1}{4}$ cup of raisins. Make a double number line diagram to find the number of cups of cereal Yoel needs to mix with 1 cup of raisins.

✏️ **Show your work.**

Answer _____

MP3 **20.** From the table, Greg identified the constant of proportionality to be $\frac{5}{2}$ and wrote the equation $y = \frac{5}{2}x$ to represent the relationship. Is Greg correct?

Time, x (hours)	Distance, y (miles)
2	5
5	$12\frac{1}{2}$
8	16

Answer _____

✏️ **Justify your answer.**

Represent Proportional Relationships with Equations

Essential Question:
How can you represent a proportional relationship with an equation?

7.RP.2c

Guided Instruction

In this lesson, you will learn to represent a proportional relationship with an equation and to use equations to solve problems about proportional relationships.

Understand: Representing a proportional relationship with an equation

> Lina buys a new car. She travels 96 miles using 4 gallons of gasoline. Write two equations to represent this proportional relationship.

You can use variables to represent each of the two quantities in the proportional relationship.

Let m = the number of miles Lisa travels.
Let g = the number of gallons of gasoline she uses.

Use the values given in the problem to find the two unit rates for the relationship.

$m = 96$ and $g = 4$

Remember!

Any proportional relationship can be written in the form $y = kx$ where k is the unit rate or the constant of proportionality.

Write the two equations for the relationship using k as the constant of proportionality.

$m = kg$
$m = k \cdot g$
$96 = k \cdot 4$
$\frac{96}{4} = k$
$24 = k$

Remember!

You can divide both sides of an equation by the same number without changing the equality.

$g = km$
$g = k \cdot m$
$4 = k \cdot 96$
$\frac{4}{96} = k$
$\frac{1}{24} = k$

One way to represent the situation is with the equation **$m = 24g$**.
Another way is with the equation **$g = \frac{1}{24} m$**.

➡ The equations **$m = 24g$** and **$g = \frac{1}{24} m$** represent the proportional relationship.

Keep in mind that every word problem presents a unique situation. Therefore, the equation you write to represent a proportional relationship should depend on the information you are given and the information you need to find.

✏️ How far can Lina travel on 1 gallon of gasoline? How many gallons of gasoline will Lina need to travel 1 mile?

Connect: Using an equation to find the unknown in a proportional relationship

> Adam runs 13 miles in 2 hours. If he keeps up the same pace, how far can he run is 5 hours?

To find how far Adam can run in 5 hours, use a proportional relationship. In this proportional relationship, you know two quantities in one ratio and only one quantity in the other ratio.

$$\frac{13 \text{ miles}}{2 \text{ hours}} = \frac{? \text{ miles}}{5 \text{ hours}}$$

You need to find the unknown miles Adam runs in 5 hours.

Step 1

Use the two known quantities in the first ratio to write an equation for the proportional relationship.

Let d = distance in miles.
Let t = time in hours.

$$d = kt$$
$$d = k \cdot t$$
$$13 = k \cdot 2$$
$$\frac{13}{2} = k$$

So, the equation is $d = \frac{13}{2} t$.

Step 2

Use the equation $d = \frac{13}{2} t$ to find the unknown distance, d, Adam runs in 5 hours. Substitute the quantity you know ($t = 5$ hours) into the equation.

$$d = \frac{13}{2} t$$
$$d = \frac{13}{2} \cdot 5$$
$$d = \frac{65}{2}$$
$$d = 32\frac{1}{2}$$

➡ In 5 hours, Adam can run $32\frac{1}{2}$ miles if he keeps up the same pace.

✏️ · Show how you could also use the related equation $t = kd$ to solve the problem.

Guided Practice

Follow the steps to write two equations to represent the proportional relationship.

1. 5 cans of tomato sauce for $10

   Let c = the number of cans. Let d = the number of dollars.

   a. Find two values for the unit rate, k.

   $c = kd$ $\qquad\qquad\qquad\qquad\qquad\qquad$ $d = kc$

   $k =$ _____ $\qquad\qquad\qquad\qquad\qquad\qquad$ $k =$ _____

   b. Use each value of k to write an equation.

   Equations: _____ and _____

Follow the steps to find the unknown quantity in the proportional relationship.

2. $\dfrac{2 \text{ cans of white paint}}{5 \text{ cans of black paint}} = \dfrac{? \text{ cans of white paint}}{4 \text{ cans of black paint}}$

   a. Use the quantities 2 cans of white paint and 5 cans of black paint to write an equation for the proportional relationship.

   Equation: _____

   b. Use your equation from part a and the quantity 4 cans of black paint to find the unknown quantity.

   Answer The unknown quantity is _____ cans of white paint.

Follow the steps to solve the problem.

3. For a potato salad recipe, Jasmine uses 2 cups of salad dressing for every 5 potatoes. How many cups of salad dressing should she use with 12 potatoes?

   a. Complete the proportional relationship below so that it represents the problem. Use a question mark to represent the unknown quantity.

$$\frac{2 \text{ cups of salad dressing}}{5 \text{ potatoes}} = \frac{\rule{2em}{0.4pt} \text{ cups of salad dressing}}{\rule{2em}{0.4pt} \text{ potatoes}}$$

   b. Use the quantities in the known ratio to find the unit rate for the proportional relationship. Use *p* to represent the number of potatoes and *c* to represent the number of cups of salad dressing.

   The unit rate is _____.

   c. Use the unit rate from part b and the variables *p* and *c* to write an equation for the relationship.

   Equation: _____

   d. Use your equation from part c to find the number of cups of salad dressing Jasmine will use with 12 potatoes.

   Answer _____

 Think•Pair•Share

MP2 4. Martin mixes green paint and blue paint in a proportional relationship that can be represented by the equation $g = 5b$, where *g* is the number of cups of green paint and *b* is the number of cups of blue paint. To make this same color, should Martin mix 5 cups of blue paint for every 1 cup of green paint or 5 cups of green paint for every 1 cup of blue paint? Explain.

Independent Practice

For exercises 1–4, write two equations to represent the proportional relationship.

1. A car travels 100 miles in 2 hours.

   Let m = the number of miles traveled.
   Let h = the number of hours spent traveling.

   Equations: _____ and _____

2. 12 child tickets cost $72.00.

   Let t = the number of tickets for children.
   Let c = the total cost of the tickets.

   Equations: _____ and _____

3. Xian reads 7 pages in 20 minutes.

   Let m = the number of minutes spent reading.
   Let p = the number of pages read.

   Equations: _____ and _____

4. 5 pounds of oranges cost $2.00.

   Let p = the number of pounds of oranges.
   Let c = the total cost in dollars of the oranges.

   Equations: _____ and _____

Independent Practice

Solve the problems.

5. On a family trip, the Batistas drive 110 miles in 2 hours. At this rate, how far would they drive in 7 hours?

   ✏️ **Show your work.**

   Answer _____

6. A snail moves 9 feet in 3 days. At this rate, how long will it take for the snail to move 15 feet?

   ✏️ **Show your work.**

   Answer _____

7. Bill hikes 8 miles in 3 hours. At this rate, how many miles will he hike after 2 hours?

   ✏️ **Show your work.**

   Answer _____

For problems 8–9, circle the correct answer. Circle all that apply.

8. Bea mixes 3 cups of cereal with 2 cups of trail mix to make a snack for her family. To make more of the same mix, how many cups of cereal would she mix with 24 cups of trail mix?

   a. 16 cups

   b. 25 cups

   c. 36 cups

   d. 72 cups

9. Usain can run 3 miles in 20 minutes. Which of the following could be the constant of proportionality, k, that relates the number of miles run and the number of minutes it takes?

   a. $\frac{3}{20}$

   b. $\frac{20}{3}$

   c. 23

   d. 60

Independent Practice

MP3 10. Melanie mixes water with plant fertilizer in a proportional relationship that can be represented by the equation $w = 3p$, where w is the number of quarts of water and p is the number of tablespoons of plant fertilizer. To keep this suggested ratio, should Melanie mix 1 quart of water for every 3 tablespoons of fertilizer or 3 quarts of water for every 1 tablespoon of fertilizer? Explain.

Answer _____

MP7 11. Angelo says that if you know one unit rate in a proportional relationship, the other unit rate is always the multiplicative inverse of the unit rate you know. Is Angelo correct? Explain.

MP2 12. The table shows a proportional relationship between the number of cups of cranberry juice and the number of cups of orange juice in a recipe for punch. What is the value of x? What does it represent?

Cups of Cranberry Juice	Cups of Orange Juice
5	12
x	30

▭ **Show your work.**

Answer _____

MP3 13. To improve her cardiovascular capacity, Mia wants to increase the distance she walks each day. She now walks $\frac{1}{2}$ mile in $8\frac{1}{2}$ minutes. If Mia keeps the same pace, will she be able to walk $1\frac{1}{2}$ miles in less than $\frac{1}{2}$ hour?

Answer _____

▭ **Justify your answer.**

MP6 14. Victor can ride his bike 15 miles in 2 hours. He uses this ratio, 15 : 2, to write an equation that shows the relationship between the distance he bikes and the time it takes. Victor's work is shown below. Is his equation correct?

Let m = number of miles.
Let h = number of hours.

$h = km$
$15 = k \cdot 2$
$7.5 = k$
So, the equation is $h = 7.5\,m$.

Answer _____

✏️ **Justify your answer.**

MP6 15. On Monday, Val walked 4 miles in $1\frac{1}{2}$ hours. On Tuesday, she walked 3 miles in $\frac{9}{10}$ hour. Did Val walk at the same rate on both days?

Answer _____

✏️ **Justify your answer.**

MP1 16. Laurie and Anna are running a 3-mile race. After 5 minutes, Laurie has run $\frac{3}{5}$ mile and Anna has run $\frac{7}{10}$ mile. If both ladies can keep their same pace for the remainder of the race, how many minutes ahead of Laurie will Anna cross the finish line?

✏️ **Show your work.**

Answer _____

Interpret Graphs of Proportional Relationships

Essential Question:
What do the points on the graph of a proportional relationship mean in terms of the situation?

7.RP.2d

Guided Instruction

In this lesson, you will learn to explain the meaning of the points on a graph of a proportional relationship.

Understand: **The meaning of the points on the graph of a proportional relationship**

When Marta cooks, she often uses liquid egg whites instead of eggs. The graph shows how many cups of egg whites she uses to replace the eggs in a recipe. What do the points $(0, 0)$, $(1, \frac{1}{4})$, $(2, \frac{1}{2})$, and $(3, \frac{3}{4})$, mean?

The graph shows the number of eggs on the *x*-axis and the number of cups of egg whites on the *y*-axis.

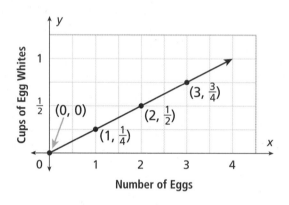

▶ The meaning of each of the points is described below.

The graph of a proportional relationship always contains the point $(0, 0)$, however the point $(0, 0)$ does not represent a ratio since by definition, in the ratio A to B, B cannot be 0.

- The point $(0, 0)$ show that if Marta wants to use 0 eggs, she should use 0 cups of egg whites.

- The point $(1, \frac{1}{4})$ shows that if Marta wants to use 1 egg, she should use $\frac{1}{4}$ cup of egg whites. So, the unit rate is $\frac{1}{4}$ cup of egg whites per egg.

- The point $(2, \frac{1}{2})$ shows that if Marta wants to use 2 eggs, she should use $\frac{1}{2}$ cup of egg whites.

- The point $(3, \frac{3}{4})$ shows that if Marta wants to use 3 eggs, she should use $\frac{3}{4}$ cup of egg whites.

▬▶ What does the point $(4, 1)$ show?

Connect: Drawing a graph to show a proportional relationship

The equation $y = 1\frac{1}{2}x$ shows the relationship between x, the number of servings of soup, and y, the number of potatoes used. Draw a graph to show how the two quantities are related.

To draw a graph and show how the two quantities are related, follow the steps below.

Step 1

Label the axes for the two variables.
Label the x-axis *Number of Servings* and
the y-axis *Number of Potatoes*.

Step 2

To draw the graph, you need just two points. Choose any two values for x and find the corresponding values for y.

$x = 2$

$y = 1\frac{1}{2}x$

$y = 1\frac{1}{2} \cdot 2$

$y = \frac{3}{2} \cdot 2$

$y = \frac{6}{2}$

$y = 3$

$x = 4$

$y = 1\frac{1}{2}x$

$y = 1\frac{1}{2} \cdot 4$

$y = \frac{3}{2} \cdot 4$

$y = \frac{12}{2}$

$y = 6$

Draw the graph through (2, 3) and (4, 6).

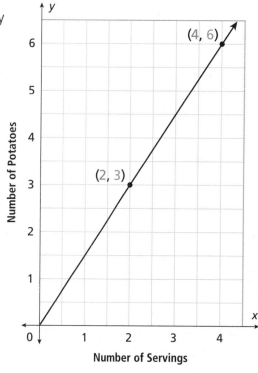

The graph shows the proportional relationship.

Could you have used the coordinates of the point (0, 0) when drawing the graph? Explain.

Guided Practice

Use the graph to complete the sentences in exercises 1–6.

The graph shows the proportional relationship between the number of yards of fabric bought and the cost of the fabric in dollars.

1. The point (2, 3) shows that _____ yards of

   fabric cost _____.

2. The point _____ shows that 3 yards of fabric cost $4.50.

3. The cost of $4\frac{1}{2}$ yards of fabric is _____.

4. The point (0, 0) shows that the cost of

   _____ yards of fabric is _____ dollars.

5. The unit rate is _____ per yard. The point

   _____ shows this unit rate.

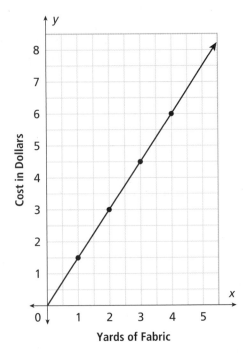

6. If x = the number of yards of fabric and y = the total cost in dollars,

   the equation for the proportional relationship is y = _____.

Circle the best answer.

7. Use the graph at the right. What does the point (2, 10) represent?

   a. The unit rate is every 2 items purchased earns 10 reward points.

   b. 2 items purchased earns 10 reward points.

   c. 10 items purchased earns 2 reward points.

   d. The unit rate is 10 reward points for every item purchased.

Store Reward Earnings

For exercises 8–12, use the information below.

The equation $d = 2.5p$ represents the relationship between p, the number of pounds of cheese bought, and d, the cost of the cheese in dollars.

8. Draw a graph to represent this proportional relationship.

9. The point (0, 0) shows that if Alan buys _____ pounds of cheese, the cost will be _____ dollars.

10. Two pounds of cheese cost _____.

11. The unit rate is _____ per pound of cheese.

12. The point _____ shows the unit rate from exercise 11.

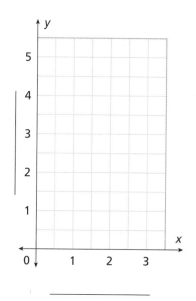

_____

For exercises 13–15 and the Think Pair Share, use the information below.

Daniel mixes 2 tablespoons of strawberry jam with 4 cups of butter to make strawberry butter.

13. Draw a graph to represent the proportional relationship.

14. The unit rate is _____ tablespoon(s) of jam per cup of butter.

15. The equation for the graph is $y =$ _____.

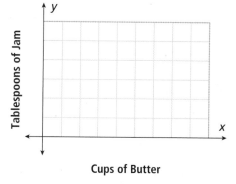

Think•Pair•Share

MP3 16. How much butter should Daniel mix with 1 tablespoon of jam? Explain how you can use the graph to find the answer.

Independent Practice

Use the graph for exercises 1–7.

The graph shows the proportional relationship between the number of hours Richie runs and the number of miles he runs.

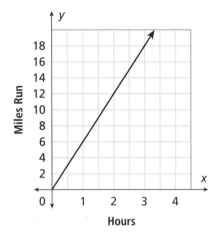

1. The point (2, 12) shows that in _____ hours Richie runs _____ miles.

2. In 3 hours how far does Richie run? _____

3. The unit rate for Richie's running is _____.

4. The point (0, 0) shows that after _____ Richie runs _____.

5. How far does Richie run in $2\frac{1}{2}$ hours? _____

6. If x = the number of hours run and y = the total distance covered in miles, the equation for the proportional relationship shown in the graph

   is $y =$ _____.

7. Write another real-world situation that could be represented using the graph above. State what x and y represent in your situation by choosing specific coordinates to explain your reasoning.

For exercises 8–12, use the information below.

The equation $c = 5f$ represents relationship between f, the length of a board in feet, and c, the cost of the board in dollars at a lumber shop.

8. Draw a graph to represent this proportional relationship.

9. The point (0, 0) shows that if Neil buys a board with a length of _____ feet, the board will cost _____ dollars.

10. A board with a length of 3 feet will cost _____.

11. The unit rate is _____ per foot of board.

12. The point _____ shows the unit rate from exercise 11.

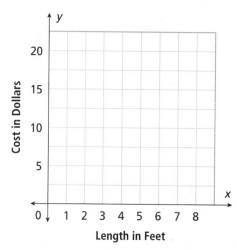

For exercises 13–15, use the information below.

For Daniel's printer there is a proportional relationship between the number of pages it prints and the number of seconds it takes to print them. Daniel found that the printer printed 10 pages in 20 seconds.

13. Draw a graph to represent the proportional relationship.

14. Use the graph to choose the best estimate for the number of pages that can be printed in 5 seconds.

   a. between 2 and 3 pages

   b. between 4 and 5 pages

   c. between 6 and 7 pages

   d. between 8 and 9 pages

15. Explain how to find the exact unit rate in pages per second.

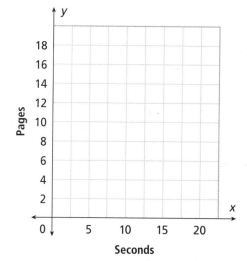

Answer _____

Independent Practice

MP3 **16.** Dawid says that if he has an equation for a proportional relationship, he needs to find only one point to draw the graph. Mariko says that she needs two points to draw the graph. Who is correct? Use an example to explain.

Answer _____

✏ **Justify your answer.**

For exercises 17–18, use the graph.

MP4 **17.** The graph shows that Rex and Ed each bikes at his own constant speed. Who bikes faster?

Answer _____

✏ **Justify your answer.**

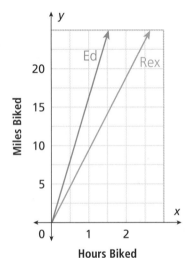

MP2 **18.** Jaden bikes faster than either Ed or Rex. Describe where a line representing Jaden's speed would appear on the graph.

Answer _____

✏ **Justify your answer.**

Solve the problems.

MP5 **19.** Chefs Arun, Belle, and Carl all make buttermilk biscuits. Arun's recipe uses 5 cups of buttermilk and 9 cups of flour. Belle's recipe uses 6 cups of buttermilk and 14 cups of flour. Carl makes a batch of biscuits using 3 cups of buttermilk and 7 cups of flour. Is Carl using Arun's recipe or Belle's recipe?

Answer _____

▸ **Justify your answer.**
Explain using both a graph and words.

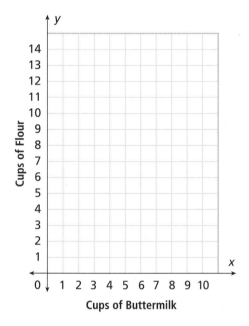

MP6 **20.** The points (2, 1.1) and (5, 2.75) represent a proportional relationship between the number of pounds of apples bought and the total cost of the apples in dollars. Norma thinks that she can buy 7 pounds of apples for $3.75. Noah thinks that he can buy 3 pounds of apples for $1.65. One person is correct. Who is correct?

Answer _____

▸ **Justify your answer.**

Problem Solving: Multi-step Ratio Problems

Guided Instruction

In this lesson, you will learn different ways to solve multi-step ratio problems.

Understand: **Using equations to solve multi-step ratio problems**

> To make her favorite fruit salad, Charlotte mixes $\frac{1}{2}$ cup of blueberries with $\frac{3}{4}$ cup of raspberries. She wants to make a 10-cup batch that has the same ratio of blueberries to raspberries. How many cups of blueberries should Charlotte use? How many cups of raspberries should she use?

To find how many cups of blueberries and raspberries Charlotte needs to use, follow the steps below and on the next page.

Step 1

Write a proportional relationship that has just one unknown quantity.

You know one ratio: $\frac{1}{2}$ cup of blueberries to $\frac{3}{4}$ cup of raspberries. But you don't know either quantity to make a second equivalent ratio.

The only other quantity you know is 10 cups, the number of cups in the total batch.

You can use this proportional relationship:

$$\frac{\text{cups of blueberries in original batch}}{\text{cups of fruit in original batch}} = \frac{?\text{ cups of blueberries in large batch}}{10\text{ cups of fruit in large batch}}$$

You don't know the total number of cups of fruit in the original batch, but you can find that quantity using the quantities you do know.

To find the number of cups of fruit in the original batch, add $\frac{1}{2} + \frac{3}{4}$.

$$\frac{1}{2} + \frac{3}{4} = \frac{2}{4} + \frac{3}{4} = \frac{5}{4}$$

Now you can write in the 3 quantities you know and use a question mark to show the unknown quantity.

$$\frac{\frac{1}{2}\text{ cup of blueberries in original batch}}{\frac{5}{4}\text{ cups of fruit in original batch}} = \frac{?\text{ cups of blueberries in large batch}}{10\text{ cups of fruit in large batch}}$$

Step 2

Find the unknown quantity, the number of cups of blueberries in the 10-pound batch.

You can use equations.

Using the two quantities of the first ratio, you can write an equation to find k, the unit rate.

> **Remember!**
> Another name for unit rate is the constant of proportionality.

Let b = the number of cups of blueberries.
Let f = the number of cups of fruit.

$$b = k \cdot f$$
$$\frac{1}{2} = k \cdot \frac{5}{4}$$
$$\frac{1}{2} \div \frac{5}{4} = k$$
$$\frac{1}{2} \cdot \frac{4}{5} = k$$
$$\frac{4}{10} = k$$

Then write another equation using the value you found for k. Substitute the quantity you know from the second ratio and find the unknown quantity.

$$b = \frac{4}{10} \cdot f$$
$$b = \frac{4}{10} \cdot 10$$
$$b = \frac{40}{10}$$
$$b = 4$$

So, the unknown quantity is 4. There are 4 cups of blueberries in the 10-cup batch.

Step 3

Find the number of cups of raspberries in the 10-cup batch.

Subtract 4 from 10. $10 - 4 = 6$
There are 6 cups of raspberries in the 10-cup batch.

▶ Charlotte should use 4 cups of blueberries and 6 cups of raspberries in the 10-cup batch.

✏️ Suppose you wanted to first find the number of cups of raspberries in the 10-cup batch. What would you do differently?

Guided Instruction

Connect: Using other methods to find the unknown quantity in a proportional relationship

What are two other methods to find the unknown quantity in this proportional relationship?

$$\frac{\frac{1}{2} \text{ cup of blueberries in original batch}}{\frac{5}{4} \text{ cups of fruit in original batch}} = \frac{? \text{ cups of blueberries in large batch}}{10 \text{ cups of fruit in large batch}}$$

Method 1 Reason about unit rates.

Use the ratio you know to calculate the unit rate. $\frac{1}{2}$ cup of blueberries $\div \frac{5}{4}$ cups of fruit $= \frac{1}{2} \cdot \frac{4}{5} = \frac{4}{10}$ cup of blueberries per cup of fruit.

For every $\frac{4}{10}$ cup of blueberries, there is 1 cup of fruit. Multiply the unit rate, $\frac{4}{10}$, by 10 to find the number of cups of blueberries in 10 cups of fruit. $10 \cdot \frac{4}{10} = \frac{40}{10} = 4$

Method 2 Use cross products.

Every pair of ratios has two cross products. When two ratios are equivalent, those two cross products are equal.

$$\frac{\frac{1}{2} \text{ cup of blueberries in original batch}}{\frac{5}{4} \text{ cups of fruit in original batch}} = \frac{? \text{ cup of blueberries in large batch}}{10 \text{ cups of fruit in large batch}}$$

$$\frac{1}{2} \cdot 10 = \frac{5}{4} \cdot ?$$

Use the cross products to write and solve an equation.

$$\frac{1}{2} \cdot 10 = \frac{5}{4}x$$

$$5 = \frac{5}{4}x$$

$$5 \div \frac{5}{4} = x$$

$$5 \cdot \frac{4}{5} = x$$

$$\frac{20}{5} = 4 = x$$

➡ The unknown quantity is 4 cups of blueberries.

✏ Three different methods were used on pages 51 and 52 to find the unknown in the proportional relationship. What is the same about all three methods?

Follow the steps to solve the problem.

1. Julie mixes $\frac{5}{6}$ cup of red paint and $\frac{1}{3}$ cup of white paint to make a sample of pink paint. She decides it is exactly the color pink that she wants. So, she mixes 2 gallons of white paint with some red paint to make the same color. How many gallons of red paint does she use? How many gallons of pink paint does she make?

Use this proportional relationship.

$$\frac{\frac{5}{6} \text{ cup of red paint}}{\frac{1}{3} \text{ cup of white paint}} = \frac{? \text{ gallons of red paint}}{2 \text{ gallons of white paint}}$$

a. Show two different ways to find the unknown quantity.

The unknown quantity is _____.

b. Use the quantity you found in part a to answer both of the questions in the problem.

Julie uses _____ gallons of red paint. She makes _____ gallons of pink paint.

 **Think•Pair•Share**

Use the information in exercise 1 to answer.

MP3 2. Sam wrote the proportional relationship at the right and says that x represents the number of gallons of red paint Julie uses. Do you agree with Sam? Why or why not?

$$\frac{\frac{5}{6}}{\frac{1}{3}} = \frac{2}{x}$$

Independent Practice

Follow the steps to solve the problem.

1. Marco's makes his famous salad dressing by mixing $5\frac{1}{4}$ ounces of olive oil with $1\frac{1}{2}$ ounces of vinegar. How much vinegar should Marco mix with a 28-ounce bottle of olive oil to make his salad dressing? How much salad dressing will he make?

   a. Complete this proportional relationship that can be used in solving the problem. Use a question mark for the unknown quantity.

   $$\frac{5\frac{1}{4} \text{ ounces of olive oil}}{\underline{\hspace{1.5cm}} \text{ ounces of vinegar}} = \frac{28 \text{ ounces of olive oil}}{\underline{\hspace{1.5cm}} \text{ ounces of vinegar}}$$

   b. Find the unknown quantity.

   c. Use your answer from part b to find the amount of salad dressing Marco will make.

Independent Practice

In exercises 2–5, circle the equation that correctly shows the proportional relationship in the problem. Choose all that apply.

2. Elsie drives 146 miles on $3\frac{3}{8}$ gallons of gasoline. How many gallons of gasoline will Elsie use to drive 225 miles?

   a. $\dfrac{146 \text{ miles}}{3\frac{3}{8} \text{ gallons}} = \dfrac{225 \text{ miles}}{? \text{ gallons}}$

   b. $\dfrac{3\frac{3}{8} \text{ gallons}}{146 \text{ miles}} = \dfrac{225 \text{ miles}}{? \text{ gallons}}$

   c. $\dfrac{146 \text{ miles}}{3\frac{3}{8} \text{ gallons}} = \dfrac{? \text{ gallons}}{225 \text{ miles}}$

   d. $\dfrac{225 \text{ miles}}{? \text{ gallons}} = \dfrac{146 \text{ miles}}{3\frac{3}{8} \text{ gallons}}$

3. In softball, Robert struck out 8 batters in the $5\frac{1}{3}$ innings he pitched. If Robert continues at this same rate, how many innings would it take Robert to strike out 100 batters?

   a. $\dfrac{5\frac{1}{3} \text{ innings}}{8 \text{ batters}} = \dfrac{100 \text{ batters}}{? \text{ innings}}$

   b. $\dfrac{100 \text{ batters}}{? \text{ innings}} = \dfrac{8 \text{ batters}}{5\frac{1}{3} \text{ innings}}$

   c. $\dfrac{8 \text{ batters}}{5\frac{1}{3} \text{ innings}} = \dfrac{100 \text{ batters}}{? \text{ innings}}$

   d. $\dfrac{? \text{ innings}}{100 \text{ batters}} = \dfrac{8 \text{ batters}}{5\frac{1}{3} \text{ innings}}$

4. Ronnie gets paid \$186.25 for working 16.4 hours each week. How much will Ronnie make if she cuts down to $10\frac{1}{4}$ hours a week?

   a. $\dfrac{? \text{ dollars}}{10\frac{1}{4} \text{ hours}} = \dfrac{16.4 \text{ hours}}{186.25 \text{ dollars}}$

   b. $\dfrac{10\frac{1}{4} \text{ hours}}{? \text{ dollars}} = \dfrac{186.25 \text{ dollars}}{16.4 \text{ hours}}$

   c. $\dfrac{10\frac{1}{4} \text{ hours}}{? \text{ dollars}} = \dfrac{16.4 \text{ hours}}{186.25 \text{ dollars}}$

   d. $\dfrac{? \text{ dollars}}{10\frac{1}{4} \text{ hours}} = \dfrac{186.25 \text{ dollars}}{16.4 \text{ hours}}$

5. Jana mixes 2 cups of black paint and 3 cups of white paint to make gray paint. How many gallons of black paint will she use to make 4 gallons of the same gray paint?

   a. $\dfrac{2 \text{ cups of black paint}}{5 \text{ cups of gray paint}} = \dfrac{? \text{ gallons of black paint}}{4 \text{ gallons of gray paint}}$

   b. $\dfrac{2 \text{ cups of black paint}}{3 \text{ cups of gray paint}} = \dfrac{? \text{ gallons of black paint}}{4 \text{ gallons of gray paint}}$

   c. $\dfrac{2 \text{ cups of black paint}}{3 \text{ cups of white paint}} = \dfrac{? \text{ gallons of black paint}}{4 \text{ gallons of gray paint}}$

   d. $\dfrac{2 \text{ cups of black paint}}{3 \text{ cups of white paint}} = \dfrac{4 \text{ gallons of black paint}}{? \text{ gallons of gray paint}}$

Independent Practice

MP3   **6.** Marti claims that if two quantities are in proportion and she knows both quantities for one ratio and just one of the quantities in the other ratio, she can always find the unknown quantity. Do you agree with Marti?

MP2   **7.** Complete the proportional relationship below by making up your own labels for the quantities. Then write and solve a word problem that could be represented by the proportional relationship.

$$\frac{6 \rule{3cm}{0.4pt}}{30 \rule{3cm}{0.4pt}} = \frac{? \rule{3cm}{0.4pt}}{80 \rule{3cm}{0.4pt}}$$

Solve the problems.

MP5   **8.** In Hawaii's Kona Iron Man competition, Gretchen swims the first $\frac{7}{8}$ of a mile in 70 minutes. At this pace, how many minutes will it take for Gretchen to swim the entire $2\frac{2}{5}$-mile course?

⟫ **Show your work.**

Answer _____

MP1   **9.** At the furniture shop, Javier earned $97.60 in commission when he sold a desk for $1,220. At this rate of commission, how many dollars worth of furniture does Javier need to sell to make $200 in commission?

⟫ **Show your work.**

Answer _____

Independent Practice

MP1 **10.** For his dog Bowser, Max mixes a 14-pound bag of Gravy Treat dog food with a 10-pound bag of Hungry Chops dog food. Then Max puts the mixture into small bags that each weigh $1\frac{1}{2}$ pounds. If the proportional relationship between the quantities of the two dog foods remains constant, how many pounds of Gravy Treat would each small bag contain?

✏ **Show your work.**

Answer _____

MP6 **11.** After $4\frac{1}{6}$ hours, Winnie's tablet has only $\frac{1}{3}$ of its battery power left. At that rate, if Winnie recharges the battery fully, can she use her tablet for 7 hours?

Answer _____

✏ **Justify your answer.**

MP6 **12.** It starts raining at 9:00 A.M. By 10:30 A.M., $4\frac{3}{8}$ centimeters of rain has fallen. If it keeps raining at this rate until midnight, will the total amount of rain for the day break the current record of 42 centimeters? If so, by how much?

Answer _____

✏ **Justify your answer.**

Problem Solving: Multi-step Percent Problems

Essential Question:
How can you use proportional relationships to solve multi-step percent problems?

7.RP.3

Words to Know:
percent decrease
percent increase
percent error

Guided Instruction

In this lesson, you will learn different ways to solve multi-step percent problems.

Understand: Solving percent decrease problems

Samantha buys a laptop computer on sale for 25% off the original price. The sale price is $300. What was the original price of the computer?

To solve this problem, first use a tape diagram to represent the situation. Then you can write an equation or a proportional relationship.

After a 25% discount, the price is $300. The price has gone down or decreased. The 25% can be called the percent decrease.

This means that 100% − 25%, or 75%, of the original price is $300.

100% = original price
x dollars

| 25% | 25% | 25% | 25% |

75% = discounted price
300 dollars

Method 1 Use an equation.

Let x = the original price

75% of x = 300

$$\frac{75}{100}x = 300$$

$$\frac{3}{4}x = 300$$

$$x = 300 \div \frac{3}{4}$$

$$x = 300 \cdot \frac{4}{3}$$

$$x = 100 \cdot 4$$

$$x = 400$$

> **Remember!**
> A percent is a rate per hundred.
> $75\% = \frac{75}{100} = 0.75 = \frac{3}{4}$

Method 2 Use the proportional relationship of the percent and the prices.

$$\frac{75}{100} = \frac{300}{x}$$

$75x = 100 \cdot 300$ ⟵ Use cross products.

$$x = \frac{100 \cdot 300}{75}$$

$$x = \frac{25 \cdot 4 \cdot 300}{25 \cdot 3}$$

$$x = 4 \cdot \frac{300}{3}$$

$$x = 4 \cdot 100$$

$$x = 400$$

➡ The original price of the computer is $400.

✏ How much money does Samantha save by buying the computer on sale? What percent of $400 is this amount? How can you check that you are correct?

Guided Instruction

Understand: Solving percent increase problems

> Samantha's state has a sales tax of 10%. How much will Samantha pay for the $300 computer when the sales tax has been added?

You can use a tape diagram to see how to write an equation or a proportional relationship.

The price will go up or increase. The 10% can be called the percent increase.

To find the price of the computer after sales tax, find 110% of $300. Since 100% of $300 is $300, 110% of $300 will be more than $300.

100% = price before tax
300 dollars

10%	10%	10%	10%	10%	10%	10%	10%	10%	10%	10%

110% = price after tax
x dollars

Method 1 Use an equation.

Let x = the price plus sales tax.

110% of 300 = x

$$\frac{110}{100} \cdot 300 = x$$

$$\frac{11}{10} \cdot 300 = x$$

$$11 \cdot \frac{300}{10} = x$$

$$11 \cdot 30 = x$$

$$330 = x$$

Method 2 Use the proportional relationship between percents and prices.

$$\frac{110}{100} = \frac{x}{300}$$

$100x = 110 \cdot 300$ ⟵ Use cross products.

$$x = \frac{110 \cdot 300}{100}$$

$$x = 110 \cdot 3$$

$$x = 330$$

➡ The price with sales tax is $330.

✏ Ethan says that since 110% of 300 is 330, then 90% of 330 must be 300. Is this true? Explain.

Guided Instruction

Understand: Solving percent error problems

Each bag of Campfire Popcorn is marked 300 grams. However, some bags will have a little more than 300 grams, and some will have a little less. Robert determines that his bag has a mass of 306 grams. How can Robert describe how close that is to the desired measurement?

You can find the percent error to describe how close the measured value of 306 grams is to the desired value of 300 grams.

Percent error tells how close a measured value is to an actual value or a desired value. To calculate percent error, find the difference between the two values, use a fraction to represent the difference, and then express the fraction as a percent.

Step 1

Find the difference between the desired value and the measured value.

Subtract the lesser value from the greater value.

$306 - 300 = 6$

Step 2

Write a fraction. Use the difference between the two values as the numerator. Use the desired value as the denominator.

$\dfrac{6}{300}$

Step 3

Multiply the fraction by 100 to write it as a percent.

$\dfrac{6}{300} \cdot 100 = \dfrac{6}{3}$

$\qquad\qquad = 2\%$

➡ The percent error is 2%.

Jonathan's bag of Campfire Popcorn has a mass of 294 grams. He says that the percent error is the same as for Robert's bag. Do you agree? Explain.

Guided Instruction

Connect: Using percents in comparisons

> Star Auto Rental rents cars and vans. This week they rented 50% more cars than vans. They rented 500 vehicles in all. How many cars did they rent? How many vans did they rent?

You can write and solve an equation to find the number of vans they rented.

Let x = the number of vans they rented.

The number of vans rented is 100% of x.

The number of cars rented is 150% of x. ← number of cars = number of vans + 50% of number of vans

$$= 100\% \text{ of } x + 50\% \text{ of } x$$
$$= 150\% \text{ of } x$$

100% of x + 150% of x = 500

250% of x = 500

To solve this equation for x, you can think about 250% as $\frac{250}{100}$, $2\frac{50}{100}$, $2\frac{5}{10}$, 2.5, or $2\frac{1}{2}$.

Method 1 Use fractions to solve for x.

250% of x = 500

$$2\frac{1}{2}x = 500$$
$$x = 500 \div 2\frac{1}{2}$$
$$x = 500 \div \frac{5}{2}$$
$$x = 500 \cdot \frac{2}{5}$$
$$x = 200$$

Method 2 Use decimals to solve for x.

250% of x = 500

$$2.5x = 500$$
$$x = 500 \div 2.5$$
$$x = 200$$

They rented 200 vans. Since they rented 500 vehicles altogether, they rented 500 − 200, or 300 cars.

➤ Star Auto Rental rented 200 vans and 300 cars.

✏ How can you check the answer?

Guided Practice

Find the unknown percent or money amount.

1. original price: $140
   percent discount: 10%

   sale price: _____

2. original price: $50
   sale price: $40

   percent discount: _____

3. percent sales tax: 7%
   price before tax: $250

   price with tax: _____

4. price with tip: $46
   percent tip: 15%

   total bill before tip: _____

5. measured distance: 270 m
   actual distance: 250 m

   percent error: _____

6. measured value: 57 in.
   actual value: 60 in.

   percent error: _____

Solve the problem.

7. The glee club has 5% more girls than boys. There are 82 students in the glee club. How many are boys? How many are girls?

   Answer _____

Think•Pair•Share

MP7 8. Julian and Amanda each use a bathroom scale to measure the weight of their dog Fido. Then they take Fido to a veterinarian who gets a more precise weight, 50 pounds. Julian's measurement was 105% of 50 pounds and Amanda's measurement was 95% of 50 pounds. How many pounds off was Julian's measurement? How many pounds off was Amanda's measurement? Did they both have the same percent error?

Find the unknown percent or money amount.

1. price: $125
   percent sales tax: 8%

   total cost: _____

2. measured value: 23.5 cm
   actual value: 25 cm

   percent error: _____

3. original value: 540
   new value: 604.8

   percent increase: _____

4. original price: $195
   sale price: $136.50

   percent discount: _____

5. cost including tip: $84
   percent tip: 20%

   cost before tip: _____

6. price: $220 price
   including tax: $236.50

   percent tax: _____

Solve the problem.

7. In an election, Rollo got 10% fewer votes than Alvarez. If 475 people voted,
   how many votes did each candidate get?

Answer _____

Independent Practice

For exercises 8 and 9, circle each equation that correctly represents the problem. Choose all that apply.

8. The Cellular Connection buys new model Z-Phones for $80 each and sells them for $200. What is the percent markup, n, for the model Z-Phone?

   a. $\dfrac{120}{80} = \dfrac{n}{100}$

   b. $\dfrac{80}{120} = \dfrac{n}{100}$

   c. $\dfrac{80}{200} = \dfrac{n}{100}$

   d. $\dfrac{120}{200} = \dfrac{n}{100}$

9. Nick paid $240 for his karate lessons plus 15% fees. What is f, the amount of the fees in dollars?

   a. $f = 240 + (0.15 \cdot 240)$

   b. $f = 0.15 \cdot 240$

   c. $\dfrac{15}{100} = \dfrac{f}{240}$

   d. $\dfrac{15}{100} = \dfrac{240}{f}$

MP3 10. Greg claims that percents greater than 100% do not make sense. His example is that it is impossible for a candidate to get more than 100% of the votes in an election. Gemma says that there are situations in which percents greater than 100% do make sense. Who is correct? Explain.

MP6 11. The price of gold increased by 20 percent. Shortly afterward, the new price decreased by 20 percent. Francesca says that the price is "right back where it started." Is Francesca correct? Use an example to explain.

Independent Practice

Solve the problems.

MP4 **12.** Wendy took her brother Eliot to lunch at a restaurant. The cost of the food was $40 before the tax or tip. The tax was 4% of the cost of the food and the tip was 16% of the pre-tax amount. What was the total cost of eating lunch at the restaurant?

✏️ **Show your work.**

Answer _____

MP8 **13.** Wade invested money at a simple interest rate of 6 percent for 1 year and ended up with $23,320. How much money did Wade invest originally?

✏️ **Show your work.**

Answer _____

MP6 **14.** A 60-gram ring is made of 14-carat gold. Fourteen-carat gold is made of gold mixed with copper and has about 40 percent more gold than copper. Is there more than 40 grams of pure gold in the ring?

Answer _____

✏️ **Justify your answer.**

For exercises 1–3, circle the correct answer or answers.

1. Which equation shows 2.4 as the constant of proportionality?

   a. $a = 2.4 + b$ b. $a = \frac{12}{5}b$ c. $a = 2.4b$ d. $a = 2\frac{1}{4}b$

2. Rafe burns $4\frac{1}{2}$ calories in $\frac{2}{3}$ of a minute riding his bike. What is Rafe's unit rate?

   a. $6\frac{3}{4}$ calories per minute b. $6\frac{3}{4}$ minutes per calorie

   c. $\frac{27}{4}$ calories per minute d. $\frac{4}{27}$ calories per minute

3. The football game had $20\frac{2}{3}$ minutes of commercials in the first $1\frac{1}{4}$ hours it was on. At that rate, how many minutes of commercials would be shown in a full $3\frac{1}{2}$ hour game? Which equation correctly shows the proportional relationship?

   a. $\dfrac{20\frac{2}{3}\text{ min}}{1\frac{1}{4}\text{ hr}} = \dfrac{m\text{ min}}{3\frac{1}{2}\text{ hr}}$ b. $\dfrac{20\frac{2}{3}\text{ min}}{1\frac{1}{4}\text{ hr}} = \dfrac{3\frac{1}{2}\text{ hr}}{m\text{ min}}$

   c. $\dfrac{1\frac{1}{4}\text{ hr}}{20\frac{2}{3}\text{ min}} = \dfrac{3\frac{1}{2}\text{ hr}}{m\text{ min}}$ d. $\dfrac{1\frac{1}{4}\text{ hr}}{20\frac{2}{3}\text{ min}} = \dfrac{m\text{ min}}{3\frac{1}{2}\text{ hr}}$

For exercises 4–6, does the table show a proportional relationship? Write _yes_ or _no_.

4.

Points	Minutes
5	6
6	7
8	9

5.

Points	Minutes
10	2.5
16	4
21	5.25

6.

Points	Minutes
$\frac{1}{2}$	3
1	6
$1\frac{1}{2}$	9

_____   _____   _____

7. A dog eats 3 cans of dog food in 12 days. Write an equation to represent the proportional relationship. Then find k, the constant of proportionality.

   Let c = _____   Let d = _____

   Equation: _____   ____ = $k \cdot$ ____

   $k =$ ____

8. Measured distance: 84 feet
   Actual distance: 80 feet

   Percent error: _____

Solve the problems.

MP2 **9.** Nick dissolved $3\frac{3}{8}$ grams of sodium chloride in $\frac{9}{16}$ liter of water. To make 1 liter of this same solution, how many grams of sodium chloride does Nick need?

• **Show your work.**

Answer _____

MP2 **10.** The world-wide sea level has risen 22.75 mm in the past 6.5 years. At this rate, how much higher will the level be 8 years from now?

• **Show your work.**

Answer _____

MP6 **11.** Jeb paid $35 to rent a kayak for $1\frac{3}{4}$ hours.

a. Write an equation to show the relationship between h, time in hours, and d, cost in dollars.

Equation: _____

b. Graph the equation and show where the unit cost for renting a kayak is on the graph.

Unit cost: _____

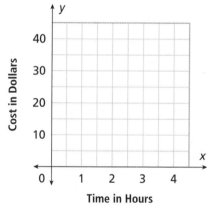

MP2 **12.** Bailey finished reading $2\frac{1}{2}$ books in $3\frac{1}{3}$ weeks. On the average, how many books per week does Bailey read?

• **Show your work.**

Answer _____

MP2 **13.** Roscoe's family has dinner at a restaurant. The total cost is $103.80. This includes 5% tax and 15% tip on the pre-tax amount. How much was the bill before tax and tip?

✏️ **Show your work.**

Answer _____

MP6 **14.** Two construction companies are building 1,100 foot tall skyscrapers. Company A has finished 550 feet of construction in $5\frac{1}{2}$ months. Company B has finished 385 feet of construction in $3\frac{1}{2}$ months. If both companies continue to build at the same rate, which company will reach the top first?

Answer _____

✏️ **Justify your answer.**

MP2 **15.** In cooking school, 4 students made secret sauce. One of the students made a mistake in the recipe. Who was it?

Answer _____

✏️ **Justify your answer.**

Student	Mayonnaise	Mustard
Hal	4 ounces	2.5 ounces
Moncef	7.5 ounces	5 ounces
Sheena	$2\frac{2}{5}$ ounces	$1\frac{1}{2}$ ounces
Claire	12 ounces	7.5 ounces

Progress Check

Look at how the Common Core standards you have learned and will learn connect.

It is very important for you to understand the standards from the prior grade level so that you will be able to develop an understanding of the number system in this unit and be prepared for next year. To practice your skills, go to sadlierconnect.com.

GRADE 6 — I Can...

6.NS.5
Use positive and negative numbers to represent real-world quantities

6.NS.6
Understand opposites of numbers and locate them on a number line

6.NS.2
Fluently divide multi-digit whole numbers

6.NS.3
Fluently add, subtract, multiply, and divide multi-digit decimals

Before Unit 2 / GRADE 7 — Can I ? / After Unit 2

7.NS.1
Describe real-world situations where opposite quantities combine to make 0

Show that a number and its opposite are additive inverses (have a sum of zero)

7.NS.1
Represent addition and subtraction of rational numbers on a number line

Understand subtraction of rational numbers as adding the additive inverse

Add and subtract rational numbers

Relate sums and differences of rational numbers to real world contexts

7.NS.2
Multiply and divide rational numbers

Relate products and quotients of rational numbers to real-world contexts

Convert a rational number to a decimal; understand that the decimal form ends in 0s or repeats

7.NS.3
Solve real-world and mathematical problems involving the four operations with rational numbers

GRADE 8 — I Will...

8.NS.1
Understand that all numbers have decimal expansions

Show that the decimal expansion of a rational number eventually terminates or repeats

Express a repeating decimal expansion as a rational number

In this unit your child will:

- Build conceptual understanding of the operations of addition, subtraction, multiplication, and division with rational numbers

- Carry out the operations of addition, subtraction, multiplication, and division with rational numbers

- Convert rational numbers in fraction form to decimal form

- Use all four operations to solve problems involving rational numbers

NOTE: All of these learning goals for your child are based on the Grade 7 Common Core State Standards for Mathematics.

Your child will understand and perform the four operations of addition, subtraction, multiplication, and division on rational numbers. Rational numbers include the integers (the whole numbers including zero and their opposites) and positive and negative fractions and decimals. Understanding the rules for calculations and identifying the correct sign for the result is important. These examples show how your child will be applying these rules.

$$+5 + (-2) = +3 \qquad -5 - (+2) = -7 \qquad -6 \cdot (-2) = +12$$
$$-3 + (-5) = -8 \qquad -3 - (-3) = 0 \qquad +18 \div (-3) = -6$$

Activity: Play Rational Operations with your child. Make one set of cards numbered from −6 to 6: −6, −5, −4, −3, −2, −1, 0, 1, 2, 3, 4, 5, and 6. Shuffle the cards and place the playing stack facedown. Take turns. On each turn, one player takes 2 cards and the other player names one of the four operations: *Add*, *Subtract*, *Multiply*, or *Divide*. The first player gives the result and the second tells whether it is correct. Then the cards go into a discard stack. The game is over when only one card is left in the playing stack.

Since 0 cannot be used as a divisor, when the zero card is drawn and the operation is Divide, the zero must be used as the dividend.

Ways to Help Your Child

Use a search engine to find videos and online games for rational numbers and the number system so that you can watch them with your child. Topics to search include: the number system, rational numbers, and number system games. An interesting project that could be used as a Science Fair project is to compare our number system with a number system used in earlier times, such as the Babylonian, Egyptian, or Roman systems.

ONLINE

For more Home Connect activities, continue online at sadlierconnect.com

Focus on The Number System

12:19.10

Essential Question:
How do properties of operations apply to adding, subtracting, multiplying, and dividing within the system of rational numbers?

Essential Question:
How can you add integers?
7.NS.1a; 7.NS.1b

Words to Know:
rational numbers
integers
absolute values
additive inverses

Guided Instruction

In this lesson, you will learn to add integers.

Understand: Using a number line to add integers

Five students are playing a game. They score points by drawing integer cards. The chart at the right shows the cards that each student has drawn so far. How many points does each student have?

Student	Cards
Alice	+4, +2
Raven	−3, −2
Colin	+6, −4
Tyrone	−5, +2
Sam	−4, +4

To find the number of points for each student, add the numbers on that student's cards.

You can use a number line to find the sum of each pair of rational numbers. In this lesson, you will work with rational numbers that are integers.

To add numbers on the number line, always start at 0.
To add a positive number, move to the right.
To add a negative number, move to the left.

> **Remember!**
> Rational numbers include positive numbers, negative numbers, and 0. Integers are the rational numbers that are whole numbers, their opposites, or 0.

Alice's Points: +4 + (+2)

- Start at 0. Draw an arrow 4 units to the right to show +4.

- Begin at the end of the first arrow. Draw another arrow 2 units to the right for +2.

- The final position is +6, so +4 + (+2) = +6.

Raven's Points: −3 + (−2)

- Start at 0. Draw an arrow 3 units to the left to show −3.

- Begin at the end of the first arrow. Draw another arrow 2 units to the left for −2.

- The final position is −5, so −3 + (−2) = −5

Colin's Points: +6 + (−4)

- Start at 0. Draw an arrow 6 units to the right to show +6.

- Begin at the end of the first arrow. Draw another arrow 4 units to the left for −4.

- The final position is +2, so +6 + (−4) = +2.

Tyrone's Points: −5 + (+2)

- Start at 0. Draw an arrow 5 units to the left to show −5.

- Begin at the end of the first arrow. Draw another arrow 2 units to the right for +2.

- The final position is −3, so −5 + (+2) = −3.

Sam's Points: +4 + (−4)

- Start at 0. Draw an arrow 4 units to the right to show +4.

- Begin at the end of the first arrow. Draw another arrow 4 units to the left for −4.

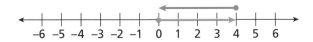

- The final position is 0, so +4 + (−4) = 0.

➡ Alice has +6 points, Raven has −5 points, Colin has +2 points, Tyrone has −3 points, and Sam has 0 points.

✏ If you add +6 + (−2), how many units will be between +6 and the sum? Will the sum be to the right or to the left of +6? How do you know?

Guided Instruction

Understand: Using absolute values to add two integers

How can you add two integers without drawing a number line?

Sometimes it may not make sense to draw a number line to add. You can think about the number line in your head. After a while, you will begin to see patterns. These three rules show those patterns.

Adding integers with like signs:

- Add the absolute values of the numbers.

- For the sum, use the same sign as the addends.

Remember!
The absolute value of a rational number is its distance from 0 on the number line.
$|-7| = 7$ $|+7| = 7$

Examples:

$+4 + (+1) = +5$

$-5 + (-2) = -7$

$+25 + (+30) = +55$

$-45 + (-50) = -95$

Adding integers with unlike signs:

- Subtract the lesser absolute value from the greater absolute value.

- For the sum, use the sign of the number with the greater absolute value.

Examples:

$+3 + (-5) = -2$

$-5 + (+2) = -3$

$+30 + (-20) = +10$

$-45 + (+50) = +5$

Adding any integer and its opposite:

- The sum of any integer and its opposite is 0.

Because a number and its opposite have a sum of 0, they are called additive inverses.

Remember!
Opposites are the same distance from 0, but in opposite directions, on the number line.

Examples:

$+3 + (-3) = 0$

$-5 + (+5) = 0$

$+25 + (-25) = 0$

$-82 + (+82) = 0$

➡ You can use the three rules above for adding any two integers.

✏️ Choose one of the examples above. Show the addition on a number line to check the sum.

Connect: Using addition of integers in real world situations

> An elevator starts on the ground floor. It goes up 6 floors and then down
> 8 floors. What floor is it on now?

To find what floor the elevator is on now, add $+6 + (-8)$.

- The addends have unlike signs. Subtract
  the lesser absolute value from the
  greater absolute value. $|-8| - |+6| = 8 - 6 = 2$

- The sum is negative because you use the sign
  of the integer with the greater absolute value. $+6 + (-8) = -2$

⇨ The elevator is now 2 floors below the ground floor.

> A hydrogen atom has one proton with a charge of +1 and one electron with a
> charge of −1. What is the total charge of a hydrogen atom?

To find the total charge, add $+1 + (-1)$.

- +1 and −1 are opposites or additive inverses. $+1 + (-1) = 0$

⇨ The hydrogen atom has a total charge of 0.

> Eric is playing miniature golf. He records his scores as above or below *par*, the
> number of expected strokes for a given hole. He scores −2, or 2 below par, on
> the first hole and −3, or 3 below par, on the second hole. What is his combined
> score after the first two holes?

To find Eric's score, add $-2 + (-3)$.

- The addends have like signs. Add the
  absolute values of the numbers. $|-2| + |-3| = 2 + 3 = 5$

- The sum is negative because both addends
  are negative. $-2 + (-3) = -5$

⇨ Eric's combined score after the first two holes is −5, or 5 below par.

Guided Practice

Use the number line to find each sum.

1. +2 + (+3) = _____

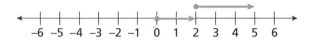

2. −4 + (−1) = _____

3. −6 + (+8) = _____

4. +4 + (−3) = _____

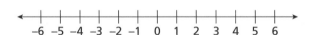

5. +2 + (−2) = _____

Use any method to find each sum.

6. −4 + (−2) =

_____

7. +6 + (−5) =

_____

8. +18 + (−18) =

_____

9. +10 + (+15) =

_____

10. −2 + (−2) + (−2) =

_____

11. +8 + (−9) + (−3) =

_____

Use integers to write an addition equation for the problem. Solve the problem.

12. A hot air balloon is at an elevation of 650 feet. After it descends 120 feet, what is the elevation of the balloon?

Equation _____

Answer _____

 **Think•Pair•Share**

MP2 **13.** Describe a real world situation for the equation +4 + (−4) = 0.

Independent Practice

For exercises 18–20, use the information below.

Barney started a savings account on May 1 by depositing $600. He then recorded all his transactions for the rest of the month, but he forgot to record whether they were deposits or withdrawals.

Date	May 1	May 4	May 13	May 26
Amount	$600	$116	$250	$234
Deposit (D) or Withdrawal (W)	D	?	?	?

MP2 **18.** What is the most Barney could have in his account on May 26?

⬤▶ **Show your work.**

Answer _____

MP2 **19.** Could Barney end up with $0 in the account on May 26?

Answer _____

⬤▶ **Justify your answer.**

MP2 **20.** Barney finds out that he has $732 in his account. What kind of transactions would produce this result?

Answer _____

⬤▶ **Justify your answer.**

Understand Subtraction of Integers

Essential Question:
How can you subtract integers?

7.NS.1c

Guided Instruction

In this lesson, you will learn to subtract integers.

Understand: Subtracting integers

> Connie records the outside temperature at 9:00 A.M. and at noon every day. Today the 9:00 A.M. temperature was −2°F and the noon temperature was +1°F. What was the change in temperature from 9:00 A.M to noon today?

Find the change in temperature by subtracting the 9:00 A.M. temperature from the noon temperature.

noon temperature − 9:00 A.M. temperature = change in temperature
$$+1 - (-2) = ?$$

Here are two methods that you can use to subtract integers.

Method 1 Think about subtraction as finding an unknown addend.

Because of the relationship between addition and subtraction, if $+1 - (-2) = ?$, then $-2 + ? = +1$.

You have learned how to use a number line to add. You can also use a number line to find an unknown addend.
$$-2 + ? = +1$$

- Start at 0. Draw an arrow to show the first addend, −2.

- Place a dot above the sum, +1.

- Draw an arrow to represent the unknown addend. Begin at the first addend and end at the dot.

The second arrow is 3 units long and it points to the right.

It represents the integer +3. This means that the missing addend is +3.

So, $-2 + (+3) = +1$ and because of the relationship between addition and subtraction, $+1 - (-2) = +3$.

> The length of the second arrow also represents the absolute value of the difference between the two numbers in the subtraction problem. It is the distance between those numbers on the number line. −2 and +1 are 3 units apart on the number line.

Method 2 Think about subtraction as adding the additive inverse.

Another way to subtract an integer is to add the opposite of the integer or its additive inverse.

$+1 - (-2) = ?$ ⟵ Think: What is the opposite of −2?

$+1 + (+2) = +3$ ⟵ Follow the rules for addition. If two integers are both positive, the sum is positive.

So, $+1 - (-2) = +3$

The answer to the subtraction is the same with both methods, +3.

⮞ The change in temperature is +3 degrees.

Check that the sign of the answer makes sense. Think about the situation. The temperature increased, so the change should be positive. The answer makes sense.

✎ How can you find the distance between two numbers on the number line by looking at their difference?

Connect: Using subtraction of integers in real-world situations

> Jason is playing a game. At the beginning of his turn, he has a score of −250 points. At the end of his turn, he has −150 points. How many points did Jason gain or lose during his turn?

To find the number of points he gained or lost, subtract his beginning score, −250, from his end score, −150: $-150 - (-250)$

- To subtract an integer, add its opposite. $\qquad -150 + (+250)$

- The addends have unlike signs.
  Subtract the lesser absolute value $\qquad |+250| - |-150| = 250 - 150 = 100$
  from the greater absolute value.

- The sum is positive because $|+250| > |-150|$. $\qquad -150 + (+250) = +100$
  $\qquad$ So, $-150 - (-250) = +100$

⮞ Jason gained 100 points during his turn.

Check that the sign of the answer makes sense. Jason had more points at the end of his turn ($-150 > -250$), so the change should be positive. The answer makes sense.

Guided Practice

1. Follow the steps to find $+4 - (-3)$.

   a. Complete the unknown-addend equation that relates to the subtraction equation.

Subtraction equation	**Unknown-addend equation**
$+4 - (-3) = ?$	_____ $+ ? =$ _____

   b. On the number line below, show how to find the unknown addend.

   • Start at 0.

   • Draw an arrow to show the first addend.

   • Place a dot above the sum.

   • Draw a second arrow from the first addend to the sum to show the unknown addend.

   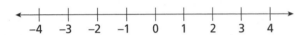

   c. How many units long is the second arrow? _____ units

   d. Is the second arrow pointing *to the left* or *to the right*? _____

   e. The missing addend is _____. So, $+4 - (-3) =$ _____.

2. Follow the steps to find $-3 - (-2)$.

   a. Write the related unknown-addend equation for the subtraction. Use a question mark for the unknown addend.

   _____

   b. Show how to use the number line to find the unknown addend.

   c. The missing addend is _____. So, $-3 - (-2) =$ _____.

Complete the sentences.

3. If $-8 + (-4) = -12$, then $-12 - (-4) =$ _____.

4. Subtracting $+6$ has the same result as adding _____.

5. If $-9 - (+5) = -14$, then -9 and $+5$ are _____ units apart on the number line.

Complete the first equation. Then use the first equation to complete the second equation.

6. $-3 +$ _____ $= -7$

   $-7 - (-3) =$ _____

7. $-8 + (-5) =$ _____

   $-8 - (+5) =$ _____

Subtract. Use any method.

8. $-4 - (-3) =$ _____

9. $+2 - (-5) =$ _____

10. $0 - (-2) =$ _____

11. $+12 - (+20) =$ _____

12. $+12 - (+10) =$ _____

13. $+87 - (+87) =$ _____

Use integers to write a subtraction equation for the problem. Solve the problem.

14. A hiker begins at 2,000 feet above sea level and takes a break at 1,600 feet above sea level. What is the hiker's change in elevation?

    Equation _____

    Answer _____

15. On a marathon course, Andrew is 3 miles behind Ben, and Carl is 2 miles ahead of Ben. How far apart are Andrew and Carl?

    Equation _____

    Answer _____

Think•Pair•Share

MP5 16. The number line at the right is vertical, rather than horizontal. Show how to use the vertical number line to find the missing addend in this equation: $-3 + ? = +2$. How is using a vertical number line different from using a horizontal number line?

$-3 +$ _____ $= +2$

Independent Practice

1. Follow the steps to find $-3 - (+5)$.

   a. Write the related unknown-addend equation for the subtraction. Use a question mark for the unknown addend.

   _____

   b. Show how to use the number line to find the unknown addend.

   c. The missing addend is _____ . So, $-3 - (+5) =$ _____.

Complete the first equation. Then use the first equation to complete the second equation.

2. $-12 +$ _____ $= -7$

   $-7 - (-12) =$ _____

3. $+6 + (-7) =$ _____

   $+6 - (+7) =$ _____

Subtract. Use any method.

4. $-5 - (+8) =$

   _____

5. $+2 - (+9) =$

   _____

6. $6 - (-0) =$

   _____

7. $-40 - (-30) =$

   _____

8. $-13 - (-7) =$

   _____

9. $26 - (-13) =$

   _____

10. $+7 - (+7) =$

    _____

11. $-32 - (+15) =$

    _____

12. $55 - (+22) =$

    _____

13. $+14 - (+21) =$

    _____

14. $-25 - (-50) =$

    _____

15. $+9 - (-9) =$

    _____

16. $+300 - (-250) =$

    _____

17. $-162 - (-12) =$

    _____

18. $260 - (+161) =$

    _____

19. $-288 - (+112) =$

    _____

20. $+999 - (+111) =$

    _____

21. $-456 - (+544) =$

    _____

Independent Practice

For exercises 22 and 23, circle the correct answer or answers.

22. Which expression has the same value as $(-6) + (-5)$?

    a. $(-5) + (-6)$

    b. $(-5) - (+6)$

    c. $(-6) - (+5)$

    d. $(+6) - (-5)$

23. Customers rate service at Jenna's Bike shop from -10 to $+10$ with $+10$ being best and -10 being worst. Last year Bruce gave the shop a -7. This year he gave it a -2. Which equation shows the change in Bruce's rating from last year to this year?

    a. $-2 - (-7) = +5$

    b. $-7 - (-2) = -5$

    c. $-2 - (+7) = -9$

    d. $-7 - (+2) = -5$

MP2 24. Gina subtracted integer B from integer A to get integer C. Then Gina added B and C and got A. Give an example of integers A, B, and C for which this works. Will this work for any integers A, B, and C? Explain.

MP8 25. Ned says that if you want to know the difference between two integers and you don't care whether the difference is positive or negative, you can just count the number of units on the number line between the two integers. Explain how you know Ned is right.

Independent Practice

**Use integers to write a subtraction equation for the problem.
Solve the problem.**

MP1 **26.** Ned and Sam are playing a game. Ned has −3 points. Sam has −8 points. How many more points does Ned have than Sam?

Equation _____

Answer _____

MP5 **27.** One elevator is on the 8th floor (8 floors above the ground floor) and the other elevator is one floor below the ground floor. How many floors apart are the two elevators?

Equation _____

Answer _____

MP6 **28.** A weather balloon is released and reaches a maximum altitude of 5000 meters. A week later, the balloon is recovered at 3750 meters. What was the change in altitude between the maximum height and the height at which the balloon was recovered?

Equation _____

Answer _____

Solve the problems.

MP4 **29.** Coach Cathy gives out plus and minus points to her soccer players based on attendance at practice and games. At the end of the first week of the season, Riley had +15 points. During the second week Riley missed a practice and the game. At the end of the second week he had −19 points. How many points did Riley gain or lose during the second week?

Equation _____

Answer _____

✎ **Explain how you can tell that your answer is reasonable.**

Independent Practice

MP6 **30.** Thom's factory makes electric razors. Thom sets a target number of completed razors for his team each day. The table shows the team's performance for 7 days. A positive score shows the number by which the team exceeds its daily target. A negative score shows the number by which the team falls short of the target.

Day	1	2	3	4	5	6	7
Score	−6	+7	0	−2	+8	−1	+7

a. Which days show an increase over the previous day? Which days show a decrease from the previous day?

Answer _____

b. On which day does the team show the greatest increase over the day before?

Answer _____

> **Justify your answer.**

c. On which day does the team show the greatest decrease from the day before?

Answer _____

> **Justify your answer.**

10 Add and Subtract Rational Numbers

Essential Question:
How can you add and subtract rational numbers that are not integers?

7.NS.1d

Guided Instruction

In this lesson, you will learn to add and subtract rational numbers that are not integers.

Understand: Adding rational numbers that are not integers

> On Monday morning, when Victoria put some water in her swimming pool, the water level rose $2\frac{1}{2}$ inches. By Tuesday morning, some water had evaporated and the level went down $\frac{3}{4}$ inch. What was the change in water level from Monday morning to Tuesday morning?

Represent the rise in the water level by a positive number. Represent the decrease in the water level by a negative number. To find the change, add $2\frac{1}{2} + (-\frac{3}{4})$.

Use the same rules to add any rational numbers that you use to add integers.

- The addends have unlike signs. Subtract the lesser absolute value from the greater absolute value.

$$2\frac{1}{2} - \frac{3}{4}$$

$$\frac{5}{2} - \frac{3}{4} = \frac{10}{4} - \frac{3}{4}$$

$$= \frac{7}{4} = 1\frac{3}{4}$$

> To save time, you can calculate absolute values mentally as you work with them.

- The sum is positive because $|+2\frac{1}{2}| > |-\frac{3}{4}|$.

$$2\frac{1}{2} + (-\frac{3}{4}) = +1\frac{3}{4}$$

⟹ During that time, the change in the water level was $+1\frac{3}{4}$ inches.

> Emma is \$14.36 overdrawn on her checking account. She writes a check for \$6.85. What is the balance in her checking account now?

Represent the amount overdrawn and the amount of the check as negative numbers. To find the balance (in dollars) in her checking account now, add $-14.36 + (-6.85)$.

- The addends have like signs. Add the absolute values of the numbers.

$$\begin{array}{r} 14.36 \\ +\ \ 6.85 \\ \hline 21.21 \end{array}$$

- The sum is negative because both addends are negative.

$$-14.36 + (-6.85) = -21.21$$

⟹ The balance in Emma's checkbook is −\$21.21.

Understand: Subtracting rational numbers that are not integers

Jo Ann's suitcase weighs $5\frac{1}{4}$ pounds under the limit set by the airline. Jeff's suitcase is $2\frac{3}{8}$ pounds over the limit. How much more does Jeff's suitcase weigh than Jo Ann's?

To represent the differences in weight from the limit, you can use a negative number for Jo Ann's suitcase and a positive number for Jeff's suitcase.

To find how much more Jeff's suitcase weighs than Jo Ann's suitcase, subtract $2\frac{3}{8} - (-5\frac{1}{4})$.

Use the same rules to subtract any rational numbers that you use to subtract integers.

- To subtract a rational number, add its opposite. $\qquad$ $2\frac{3}{8} + (+5\frac{1}{4})$

- The addends have like signs. Add the absolute values. $\qquad$ $2\frac{3}{8} + 5\frac{1}{4}$

$$2\frac{3}{8} + 5\frac{2}{8}$$

$$= 7\frac{5}{8}$$

- The sum is positive because both addends are positive. $\qquad$ $2\frac{3}{8} - (-5\frac{1}{4}) = +7\frac{5}{8}$

➡ Jeff's suitcase weighs $7\frac{5}{8}$ pounds more than Jo Ann's suitcase.

Mercury is one of few elements that is a liquid at room temperature. The melting point of mercury is $-37.89°$F. Its boiling point is $+674.11°$F. How many degrees higher is the boiling point of mercury than its melting point?

To find how much higher the boiling point is than the melting point, subtract $+674.11 - (-37.89)$.

- To subtract a rational number, add its opposite. $\qquad$ $+674.11 + (+37.89)$.

- The addends have like signs. Add the absolute values.

$$\begin{array}{r} 674.11 \\ +37.89 \\ \hline 712.00 \end{array}$$

- The sum is positive because both addends are positive. $\qquad$ $+674.11 - (-37.89) = 712$

➡ The boiling point of mercury is 712 degrees higher than its melting point.

Guided Instruction

Connect: Solving a two-step problem involving rational numbers

> Jayden has a lemonade stand. On Saturday he spends $4.50 on supplies and collects $3.75 in sales. On Sunday, he again spends $4.50 on supplies, but collects $6.70 in sales. How much more profit does Jayden make on Sunday than on Saturday?

Step 1

Find the amount of profit Jayden makes on Saturday and on Sunday.

To find Saturday's profit, represent his expenses as a negative number of dollars and his sales as a positive number of dollars. Add $-4.50 + (+3.75)$.

- The addends have unlike signs.
  Subtract the lesser absolute value
  from the greater absolute value.

$$4.50 - 3.75$$
$$\begin{array}{r} 4.50 \\ -3.75 \\ \hline 0.75 \end{array}$$

- The sum is negative because $|-4.50| > |+3.75|$.

$$-4.50 + (3.75) = -0.75$$

To find Sunday's profit, represent his expenses as a negative number of dollars and his sales as a positive number of dollars. Add $-4.50 + (+6.70)$.

- The addends have unlike signs.
  Subtract the lesser absolute value
  from the greater absolute value.

$$6.70 - 4.50$$
$$\begin{array}{r} 6.70 \\ -4.50 \\ \hline 2.20 \end{array}$$

- The sum is positive because $|+6.70| > |-4.50|$.

$$-4.50 + (6.70) = 2.20$$

Step 2

Subtract the amount of profit Jayden makes on Saturday from the amount of profit he makes on Sunday. Subtract $2.20 - (-0.75)$.

- To subtract a rational number, add its opposite.

$$+2.20 + (+0.75)$$

- The addends have like signs. Add the absolute values.

$$\begin{array}{r} 2.20 \\ +0.75 \\ \hline 2.95 \end{array}$$

- The sum is positive because both addends are positive.

$$2.20 - (-0.75) = 2.95$$

▶ Jayden makes $2.95 more profit on Sunday than on Saturday.

Independent Practice

Write an expression for each exercise. Then solve the problem.

MP5 **18.** The temperature in Lucy's refrigerator is 2.74°C. The temperature in the freezer section of her refrigerator is –19.4°C. How much colder is the freezer temperature?

Expression _____

✏ **Show your work.**

Answer _____

MP1 **19.** In a pro golf tournament, the scores are reported as they relate to par, 72. On Saturday, the players shot an average score of 69.81. How much above or under par was the average?

Expression _____

✏ **Show your work.**

Answer _____

MP3 **20.** Icebergs are large chunks of ice that break off from glaciers and float in the ocean. Small icebergs are called *growlers*. But icebergs can also be huge. As little as one-eighth of an iceberg is visible above the water. Most of the iceberg lies below the surface of the water. Suppose an iceberg has a height of $6\frac{1}{2}$ feet above the water with the bottom tip of the iceberg at $-42\frac{3}{4}$ feet. What is the height of that iceberg from bottom tip to top?

Expression _____

✏ **Show your work.**

Answer _____

Independent Practice

MP2 21. Lee claims that to evaluate an expression such as $4.8 + (-2\frac{3}{10})$, the best strategy is to first convert the fraction to a decimal. Roger claims the opposite—that it is easier to work with fractions, so he converts the decimal to fraction form. Who is right? Explain.

MP3 22. Roxie says that the difference between -8.6 and $-12\frac{6}{10}$ is $+4$. Hank says the difference is -4. Can both students be correct? Use examples to explain.

Write an expression for each exercise. Then solve the problem.

MP1 23. A geologist found two underground wells that contained large deposits of water. The first well was $46\frac{2}{3}$ meters below the surface. The second well had more water, and was $77\frac{5}{6}$ meters deeper than the first well. How deep below the surface was the second well?

Expression _____

✏️ **Show your work.**

Answer _____

MP1 24. The average daytime temperature on the moon is $+160.6°F$. At night, the moon's temperature drops to $-243.4°F$. How much warmer is the moon during the day than at night?

Expression _____

✏️ **Show your work.**

Answer _____

Solve the problems.

MP6 **25.** On December 31, a senator had an approval rating of 52.6%. The diagram at the right shows how his approval rating changed during January, February, and March.

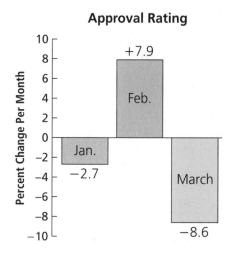

a. What was the senator's approval rating at the end of January?

✏ **Show your work.**

Answer _____

b. At the end of which month was the senator's approval rating highest?

Answer _____

✏ **Justify your answer.**

c. What was the senator's approval rating at the end of March?

✏ **Show your work.**

Answer _____

Understand Multiplication of Integers

Essential Question:
How can you multiply integers?
7.NS.2a

Guided Instruction

In this lesson, you will learn to multiply integers.

Understand: Using properties of rational numbers to multiply two integers

> Use repeated addition to find $+3 \cdot +4$ and $+3 \cdot -4$.

You can think about multiplication by a positive integer as repeated addition.

$+3 \cdot +4 = (+4) + (+4) + (+4)$ $+3 \cdot -4 = (-4) + (-4) + (-4)$

$(+4) + (+4) + (+4)$ $(-4) + (-4) + (-4)$
$(+8) + (+4) = +12$ $(-8) + (-4) = -12$
So, $+3 \cdot +4 = +12$.   So, $+3 \cdot -4 = -12$.

> When you use the multiplication dot, •, you do not have to put signed numbers in parentheses.

➡ Using repeated addition, $+3 \cdot +4 = +12$ and $+3 \cdot -4 = -12$.

> Use the Commutative Property of Multiplication to find $-4 \cdot +3$.

Because the Commutative Property of Multiplication holds for all rational numbers, it holds for integers.

Since $+3 \cdot -4 = -12$, $-4 \cdot +3 = -12$.

> **Remember!**
> The Commutative Property of Multiplication states that
> $a \cdot b = b \cdot a$.

➡ Using the Commutative Property of Multiplication, $-4 \cdot +3 = -12$.

> Use the Distributive Property to find $-3 \cdot -4$.

Because the Distributive Property holds for all rational numbers, it holds for integers.

$-3 \cdot [5 + (-4)] = (-3 \cdot 5) + (-3 \cdot -4)$
$-3 \cdot (+1) = -15 + (-3 \cdot -4)$
$-3 = -15 + (-3 \cdot -4)$
Since $-3 = -15 + (+12)$, $-3 \cdot -4 = +12$.

> **Remember!**
> The Distributive Property of Multiplication over Addition states that
> $a \cdot (b + c) = a \cdot b + a \cdot c$.

➡ Using the Distributive Property, $-3 \cdot -4 = +12$.

Guided Instruction

Use the multiplication property of 0 to find +3 • 0, −3 • 0, 0 • +3, or 0 • −3.

The multiplication property of 0 states that if 0 is a factor, the product is always 0.

$$+3 \cdot 0 = 0 \qquad -3 \cdot 0 = 0 \qquad 0 \cdot +3 = 0 \qquad 0 \cdot -3 = 0$$

▶ Using the multiplication property of 0, $+3 \cdot 0 = 0$, $-3 \cdot 0 = 0$, $0 \cdot +3 = 0$, and $0 \cdot -3 = 0$.

Understand: Using rules to multiply two integers

What are the rules for multiplying two integers?

You can use these rules to multiply two integers.

Multiplying two integers with like signs:

• Multiply the absolute values of the numbers.

• The product is positive.

Examples:

$+3 \cdot +4 = +12$

$-5 \cdot -2 = +10$

Multiplying two integers with unlike signs:

• Multiply the absolute values of the numbers.

• The product is negative.

Examples:

$-4 \cdot +5 = -20$

$+8 \cdot -10 = -80$

Multiplying two integers when one factor is 0:

• The product is 0.

Examples:

$0 \cdot +3 = 0 \qquad 0 \cdot -9 = 0$

$+4 \cdot 0 = 0 \qquad -8 \cdot 0 = 0$

▶ These three rules are the rules for multiplying any two integers.

✏ Sam says that $(-76) \cdot (+84)$ and $(+76) \cdot (-84)$ have the same product. Do you agree? Explain your thinking.

Guided Instruction

Connect: Using multiplication of a negative integer by a positive integer in real-world situations

The temperature drops 2 degrees each hour for 4 hours. What integer represents the change in temperature over those 4 hours?

To find the integer for the change over 4 hours, multiply $+4 \cdot -2$.

$+4 \cdot -2 = -8$

> The integers have unlike signs, so the product is negative.

➡ The change over 4 hours can be represented by -8.

✏ Show how you could use repeated addition to check that the answer to $4 \cdot (-2)$ is -8.

A stock falls 6 points each day for 3 days. What integer represents the change in stock price for the 3 days?

To find the integer for the change over 3 days, multiply $+3 \cdot -6$.

$+3 \cdot -6 = -18$

➡ The change over 3 days can be represented by -18.

Each month Tina has $25 deducted from her bank account for the newspaper. What integer represents the deduction for the year?

To find the integer for the deduction for the year, multiply $+12 \cdot -25$.

$+12 \cdot -25 = -300$

> **Remember!**
>
> There are 12 months in a year.

➡ The deduction for the year can be represented by -300.

Write the multiplication as repeated addition.

1. +4 • +7 = _____

2. +3 • −8 = _____

Write + if the product is positive, − if the product is negative, and 0 if the product is zero.

3. −5 • −7 = _____

4. −2 • +8 = _____

5. +5 • 0 = _____

Write the product.

6. −8 • −2 = _____

7. −9 • +4 = _____

8. +3 • +15 = _____

9. −4 • 0 = _____

10. +15 • −16 = _____

11. −3 • −2 • −3 = _____

12. −3 • −3 • −3 = _____

13. $(−3)^4$ = _____

14. $(−2)^3$ = _____

Use integers to write a multiplication expression for the problem. Then solve the problem.

15. An airplane descends at an average speed of 235 feet per second for 5 seconds. What is the plane's change in altitude during those 5 seconds?

    Expression _____

    Answer _____

 **Think•Pair•Share**

MP2 16. Describe a real world situation for the equation +5 • −3 = −15.

Independent Practice

Write the multiplication as repeated addition.

1. $+3 \cdot +6 = $ _____

2. $+2 \cdot -4 = $ _____

3. $+5 \cdot -7 = $ _____

4. $+4 \cdot -2 = $ _____

Write + if the product is positive, − if the product is negative, and 0 if the product is zero.

5. $+4 \cdot +6 = $ ____

6. $+7 \cdot -2 = $ ____

7. $-10 \cdot +7 = $ ____

8. $-9 \cdot -6 = $ ____

9. $+20 \cdot -5 = $ ____

10. $0 \cdot -6 = $ ____

11. $+5 \cdot +14 \cdot +5 = $ ____

12. $-3 \cdot +10 \cdot -11 = $ ____

13. $-9 \cdot -8 \cdot -7 = $ ____

Write the product.

14. $+7 \cdot +2 = $ _____

15. $+8 \cdot -4 = $ _____

16. $-4 \cdot +9 = $ _____

17. $+14 \cdot -3 = $ _____

18. $-13 \cdot 0 = $ _____

19. $-12 \cdot -4 = $ _____

20. $+3 \cdot +4 \cdot +5 = $ _____

21. $+5 \cdot -2 \cdot +7 = $ _____

22. $-4 \cdot +6 \cdot -5 = $ _____

23. $-8 \cdot -5 \cdot -4 = $ _____

24. $-3 \cdot 0 \cdot -13 = $ _____

25. $(+3)^3 = $ _____

26. $(-5)^4 = $ _____

27. $(-2)^7 = $ _____

28. $(-3)^5 = $ _____

Several students are playing a game. They draw 3 cards and find the product of the cards to get their score. Find the score for each player.

A −2	B +2	C −4	D +6	E 0	F −10

29. Rosemary draws cards A, C, and F. Her score is _____.

30. Tanner draws cards B, D, and F. His score is _____.

31. Katie draws cards A, B, and D. Her score is _____.

32. Jayden draws cards D, E, and F. His score is _____.

33. The player with the greatest score wins. That player is _____.

Independent Practice

For exercises 34–39, circle the correct answer or answers.

34. Which multiplication expression is modeled on the number line?

a. −7 • (−2)

b. −2 • (−7)

c. +2 • (+7)

d. +2 • (−7)

35. Which of the following models shows 3 • (−5)?

a.

b.

c.

d.
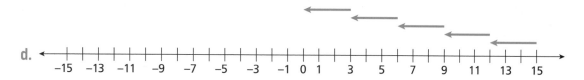

36. Which of the following is the product of −11 • (+8)?

a. −3

b. −88

c. +88

d. +3

37. Which of the following expressions has the same product as −3 • (+2) • (−1)?

a. +3 • (+2) • (−1)

b. +3 • (+2) • (+1)

c. +3 • (−2) • (−1)

d. −3 • (−2) • (+1)

Independent Practice

38. Which of the following expressions has the same product as $-7 \cdot (+4)$?

    a. $+4 \cdot (-7)$ **b.** $-7 \cdot (-4)$

    c. $+7 \cdot (-4)$ **d.** $+7 \cdot (+4)$

39. Which of the following expressions has the same product as $-3 \cdot [+4 \cdot (-5)]$?

    a. $-3 \cdot [-4 \cdot (-5)]$ **b.** $[-3 \cdot (+4)] \cdot (-5)$

    c. $+3 \cdot [+4 \cdot (-5)]$ **d.** $+3 \cdot [(+4) \cdot (+5)]$

Use integers to write a multiplication expression for the problem. Then solve the problem.

40. The water in a fish tank drains out at a rate of 325 milliliters per minute. What is the change in the volume of the water after 8 minutes?

Expression _____

✏ **Show your work.**

Answer _____

41. A climber descends 445 feet per hour. What is the change in altitude after 4 hours?

Expression _____

✏ **Show your work.**

Answer _____

MP3 **42.** Maggie claims that multiplication of integers is just like multiplication of whole numbers except for the sign of the product. Explain. Use examples.

MP3 **43.** Without doing any calculating, Manny says that the product shown below must be negative. Explain how Manny may have determined this.

$$+2 \cdot (+3) \cdot (-4) \cdot (+5) \cdot (-6) \cdot (-7)$$

Solve the problem.

MP7 **44.** The Obstacle Fitness Course is scored by awarding 12 points for every station that is passed and by deducting 8 points for every station that is failed. Stations that are not tried do not affect the score. Monica passed 7 stations and failed 4 stations. Julie passed 9 stations and failed 7 stations. Who got a higher score?

Answer _____

➤ **Justify your answer.**

Understand Division of Integers

Guided Instruction

In this lesson, you will learn to divide integers.

Understand: Using a rule to divide integers

> How can you use what you know about multiplying integers to divide integers?

The examples below show a pattern that leads to the rules for dividing integers.

Multiplication Equation	Related Division Equations
$+3 \cdot +4 = +12$	$+12 \div +3 = +4$ $+12 \div +4 = +3$
$-5 \cdot -2 = +10$	$+10 \div -2 = -5$ $+10 \div -5 = -2$
$-4 \cdot +5 = -20$	$-20 \div -4 = +5$ $-20 \div +5 = -4$
$-8 \cdot 0 = 0$	$0 \div -8 = 0$ You cannot divide 0 by 0, because division by 0 is undefined.
$+8 \cdot 0 = 0$	$0 \div +8 = 0$ You cannot divide 0 by 0, because division by 0 is undefined.

The rules for dividing integers are similar to the rules for multiplying integers.

Dividing two integers with like signs:

- Divide the absolute values of the numbers.
- The quotient is positive.

$+12 \div +3 = +4$

$+12 \div +4 = +3$

$-20 \div -4 = +5$

Dividing two integers with unlike signs:

- Divide the absolute values of the numbers.
- The quotient is negative.

$+10 \div -2 = -5$

$+10 \div -5 = -2$

$-20 \div +5 = -4$

Dividing 0 by any non-zero integer:

- The quotient is 0.

$0 \div -8 = 0$

$0 \div +8 = 0$

Dividing by 0 is undefined.

You cannot divide any number by 0.

➡ You can use the rules on page 104 for dividing any two integers.

✏ Write two related division equations for $-8 \cdot -3 = +24$.

Understand: Dividing two integers when the quotient is not an integer

> When you divide two integers is the quotient always an integer?

You know that when you divide two whole numbers, the quotient may be a rational number that is not a whole number. This example shows the result of dividing 15 by 4.

$$15 \div 4 = 3\frac{3}{4}$$

When you divide two integers, the quotient may be a rational number that is not an integer. Look at these examples for -15 and -4, -15 and $+4$, and $+15$ and -4.

$$-15 \div -4 = +3\frac{3}{4} \qquad -15 \div +4 = -3\frac{3}{4} \qquad +15 \div -4 = -3\frac{3}{4}$$

➡ When you divide two integers, the quotient is not always an integer.

✏ What is $-2 \div -3$? Is the quotient an integer? Is the quotient a rational number?

Understand: Fractional notation for division of integers

> How are $-\frac{2}{3}$, $\frac{-2}{3}$, and $\frac{2}{-3}$ related?

$$\frac{-2}{3} = -2 \div 3$$
$$= -\frac{2}{3}$$

$$\frac{2}{-3} = 2 \div -3$$
$$= -\frac{2}{3}$$

Remember!

$$\frac{a}{b} = a \div b$$

It is not necessary to show the positive signs.

Since $\frac{-2}{3}$ and $\frac{2}{-3}$ are both are equivalent to $-\frac{2}{3}$, the three expressions are equivalent.

➡ $-\frac{2}{3}$, $\frac{-2}{3}$, and $\frac{2}{-3}$ are equivalent.

✏ Write three expressions in fraction notation that are equivalent to $-5 \div 6$.

Guided Instruction

Connect: Using division of integers to solve real-world and mathematical problems

> Over a period of 5 years, the enrollment at Watertown Middle School has a change of −80. What is the average change per year? What does this mean?

To find the average change per year, divide −80 ÷ 5.

−80 ÷ 5 = −16
The quotient is negative because the dividend and the divisor have unlike signs.

➡ The average change per year is −16. This means that there were 16 fewer students each year.

> The temperature drops 4 degrees Fahrenheit over a period of 3 hours. What is the average change in temperature each hour?

To find the average change in temperature per hour, divide −4 ÷ 3.
$-4 \div 3 = -\frac{4}{3}$ or $-1\frac{1}{3}$

➡ The average change in temperature per hour is $-1\frac{1}{3}$ degrees Fahrenheit.

> The product of a number and −8 is +72. What is the number?

−8 • ? = +72

Divide to find the missing factor. +72 ÷ −8 = −9

➡ The number is −9.

🔲 · In which of the three problems above is the answer a rational number? In which problems is the answer an integer?

Write two related division equations for the multiplication equation.

1. $+7 \cdot -8 = -56$

   _____ $\div -8 = +7$

   $-56 \div$ _____ $=$ _____

2. $-8 \cdot -9 = +72$

   _____

   _____

Write + if the quotient is positive, − if the quotient is negative, and 0 if the quotient is zero.

3. $-15 \div -3 =$ _____

4. $0 \div -7 =$ _____

5. $\dfrac{-16}{+2} =$ _____

Write the quotient.

6. $-8 \div -2 =$ _____

7. $-3 \div -4 =$ _____

8. $0 \div -9 =$ _____

9. $-84 \div -2 =$ _____

10. $\dfrac{+125}{-5} =$ _____

11. $\dfrac{-861}{-21} =$ _____

Use integers to write a division expression for the problem. Then solve the problem.

12. The average temperature dropped 16 degrees over a period of 5 weeks. What is the average change in temperature per week?

    Expression _____

    Answer _____

 **Think•Pair•Share**

MP2 **13.** Describe a real world situation for the equation $-200 \div +4 = -50$.

Independent Practice

Write two related division equations for the multiplication equation.

1. $+3 \cdot +6 = +18$

   _____ $\div +6 = +3$

   $+18 \div$ _____ $=$ _____

2. $+9 \cdot -7 = -63$

   _____

   _____

3. $-12 \cdot -8 = +96$

   _____ $\div -8 = -12$

   $+96 \div$ _____ $=$ _____

4. $-6 \cdot +15 = -90$

   _____

   _____

5. $+16 \cdot -9 = -144$

   _____ $\div -9 = +16$

   $-144 \div$ _____ $=$ _____

6. $-20 \cdot -36 = +720$

   _____

   _____

Write + if the quotient is positive, − if the quotient is negative, and 0 if the quotient is zero.

7. $-28 \div +7 =$ _____

8. $+80 \div -10 =$ _____

9. $-49 \div -2 =$ _____

10. $-250 \div -6 =$ _____

11. $\dfrac{0}{-58} =$ _____

12. $\dfrac{-168}{+38} =$ _____

Write the quotient.

13. $-28 \div +4 =$ _____

14. $-32 \div -16 =$ _____

15. $-20 \div -5 =$ _____

16. $+64 \div -16 =$ _____

17. $-80 \div +5 =$ _____

18. $\dfrac{-133}{-7} =$ _____

19. $-120 \div -8 =$ _____

20. $\dfrac{+207}{-9} =$ _____

21. $0 \div -27 =$ _____

22. $-156 \div +13 =$ _____

23. $+625 \div +25 =$ _____

24. $-238 \div -14 =$ _____

25. $-1,004 \div -251 =$ _____

26. $-1,250 \div +50 =$ _____

27. $+144 \div 0 =$ _____

28. $-182 \div +28 =$ _____

29. $+5 \div -8 =$ _____

30. $-42 \div -8 =$ _____

For exercises 31–33, circle the correct answer or answers.

31. Which of the following has a quotient of −7?

   a. $-84 \div (-12)$ b. $-490 \div (+7)$ c. $+490 \div (-70)$ d. $-84 \div (+12)$

32. Which of the following has the least quotient?

    a. $0 \div (-199)$ **b.** $0 \div (+1{,}998)$ **c.** $-198 \div (-11)$ **d.** $+198 \div (-11)$

33. Which of the following has the quotient with the greatest absolute value?

    a. $\dfrac{-360}{-6}$ **b.** $\dfrac{-360}{-60}$ **c.** $\dfrac{-360}{+60}$ **d.** $\dfrac{-3{,}600}{-600}$

Use integers to write a division expression for the problem. Then solve the problem.

34. If I multiply a number by -2, the product will be -56. What is the number?

    Expression _____

    Answer _____

35. On her bank statement, Marie saw 6 identical withdrawals that came to a total of $190. By how much did each withdrawal change Marie's account?

    Expression _____

    Answer _____

MP2 36. Elena wants to be able to use her calculator to divide integers. What directions can you provide for her to use? Use an example.

MP2 37. Rodrigo claims that the quotient of two integers is always an integer. Van claims that sometimes the quotient is an integer, but not always. Who is correct? Explain.

Independent Practice

Solve the problems.

MP2 **38.** This formula can be used to calculate electric current in a circuit.

current	=	**voltage**	÷	**resistance**
(amperes)		(volts)		(ohms)

a. In a circuit with a voltage of −12 volts, the resistance is +15 ohms. How many amperes of current will flow through this circuit?

➤ **Show your work.**

Answer _____

b. In a circuit, voltage and current can have either a positive or negative value. Resistance, on the other hand, always has a positive value. What does this tell you about voltage and current? Can one be positive and the other negative? Explain.

MP1 **39.** A raindrop takes 9 seconds to fall 396 meters from a cloud.

a. What is the average speed of the fall in meters per second?

➤ **Show your work.**

Answer _____

b. After 11 seconds, the raindrop has now fallen a total of 594 meters. By how many meters per second has the raindrop's speed changed from its speed after 9 seconds?

✏️ **Show your work.**

Answer _____

MP1 **40.** In football, positive plays gain yardage and negative plays lose yardage. The Stallions post the following plays during their final drive of the game.

Play	1	2	3	4	5	6	7	8
Play type	Run	Pass	Pass	Run	Pass	Run	Penalty	Pass
Yardage	+4	−8	+16	−3	−12	+1	+5	−15

a. What is the average number of yards gained or lost per play?

✏️ **Show your work.**

Answer _____

b. The Stallions have enough time for one more play before the game ends. Based on their average yardage per pass and their average yardage per run, should the team choose to pass or run?

Answer _____

✏️ **Justify your answer.**

Essential Question:
How can you multiply and divide rational numbers that are not integers?

7.NS.2c

Guided Instruction

In this lesson, you will learn to multiply and divide rational numbers that are not integers.

Understand: Multiplying and dividing rational numbers that are not integers

> Water is being drained from a large tank. After 5 minutes, the change in the amount of water is $-34\frac{1}{2}$ gallons. What is the average change per minute?

To find the average change per minute, divide $-34\frac{1}{2}$ by 5. Use the same rules to divide rational numbers that you use to divide integers.

- Divide the absolute values.

$$34\frac{1}{2} \div 5 = \frac{69}{2} \div \frac{5}{1}$$
$$= \frac{69}{2} \cdot \frac{1}{5}$$
$$= \frac{69 \cdot 1}{2 \cdot 5} = \frac{69}{10} = 6\frac{9}{10}$$

- The quotient is negative because the dividend and the divisor have unlike signs.

$$-34\frac{1}{2} \div 5 = -6\frac{9}{10}$$

You can check using multiplication.

If $5 \cdot -6\frac{9}{10}$ equals $-34\frac{1}{2}$, then your computation is correct.

$$5 \cdot 6\frac{9}{10} = 5 \cdot \frac{69}{10}$$
$$= \frac{5 \cdot 69}{10} = \frac{345}{10} = 34\frac{5}{10} = 34\frac{1}{2}$$

$5 \cdot -6\frac{9}{10} = -34\frac{1}{2}$ ⟵ The product is negative because the factors have unlike signs.

The check shows the computation is correct.

➡ The average change in the amount of water is $-6\frac{9}{10}$ gallons per minute.

✏ Find the quotient of $-34\frac{1}{2} \div -6\frac{9}{10}$. Tell how you know you are correct.

After 3 weeks of cutting grass, Stan's business had a profit of −$96.45. What was the average profit (gain or loss) per week?

To find the average profit per week in dollars, divide −96.45 ÷ 3.

- Divide the absolute values.

```
        32.15
    3)96.45
      −9
      ──
       06
      − 6
      ──
        0 4
       − 3
       ──
         15
        − 15
        ──
          0
```

- The quotient is negative because the dividend and the divisor have unlike signs.

$-96.45 \div 3 = -32.15$

You can check by using multiplication.

If 3 • −32.15 equals −96.45, then your computation is correct.

```
      32.15
    ×     3
    ──────
      96.45
```

3 • −32.15 equals −96.45. ◀── The product is negative because the factors have unlike signs.

The check shows that the computation is correct.

➤ The average profit per week was −$32.15.

✎ Use the division above to find the quotient of −9.645 ÷ 0.3. Explain your thinking.

Guided Instruction

Connect: Using division of rational numbers

> Martin walks $\frac{3}{4}$ mile in $\frac{1}{2}$ hour. At that rate, how far will Martin walk in 1 hour?

To find the unit rate, the number of miles Martin walks in 1 hour, divide $\frac{3}{4}$ by $\frac{1}{2}$.

$$\frac{\frac{3}{4}}{\frac{1}{2}} = \frac{3}{4} \div \frac{1}{2}$$

$$= \frac{3}{4} \cdot \frac{2}{1}$$

$$= \frac{3 \cdot 2}{4 \cdot 1} = \frac{6}{4} = 1\frac{2}{4} = 1\frac{1}{2}$$

Remember!

You can use a complex fraction to show division. A complex fraction is a fraction in which both the numerator and the denominator are fractions.

➡ At that rate, Martin will walk $1\frac{1}{2}$ miles in 1 hour.

> If a number is multiplied by $\frac{1}{2}$, the result is $-\frac{4}{5}$. What is the number?

To find the number, find the missing factor in $\frac{1}{2} \cdot ? = -\frac{4}{5}$.

You can find the value of $-\frac{4}{5} \div \frac{1}{2}$ to find the missing factor.

You can also represent this division by a complex fraction: $\dfrac{-\frac{4}{5}}{\frac{1}{2}}$

- Divide the absolute values.

$$\frac{4}{5} \div \frac{1}{2} = \frac{4}{5} \cdot \frac{2}{1}$$

$$= \frac{4 \cdot 2}{5 \cdot 1} = \frac{8}{5} = 1\frac{3}{5}$$

- The quotient is negative because the factors have unlike signs.

$$-\frac{4}{5} \div \frac{1}{2} = -1\frac{3}{5}$$

➡ The number is $-1\frac{3}{5}$.

✏ Find the value of $\dfrac{\frac{1}{2}}{-\frac{2}{3}}$.

Guided Practice

Find each product or quotient.

1. $+\dfrac{2}{9} \cdot -\dfrac{3}{5} =$ _____

2. $-\dfrac{1}{2} \cdot -\dfrac{3}{7} =$ _____

3. $-5\dfrac{1}{2} \cdot +2\dfrac{2}{3} =$ _____

4. $+\dfrac{4}{9} \div +\dfrac{5}{9} =$ _____

5. $-\dfrac{3}{5} \div -\dfrac{1}{5} =$ _____

6. $+2\dfrac{1}{2} \div -1\dfrac{1}{3} =$ _____

7. $-1.8 \div +6 =$

_____

8. $-2.5 \cdot -3.92 =$

_____

9. $+5.75 \div -0.25 =$

_____

10. $\dfrac{\frac{1}{2}}{-\frac{1}{4}} =$ _____

11. $\dfrac{-\frac{5}{6}}{\frac{2}{3}} =$ _____

12. $\dfrac{-\frac{5}{2}}{-\frac{1}{2}} =$ _____

Use rational numbers to write an expression to represent the problem. Solve the problem.

13. Over a period of 5 hours, the temperature had an average change of $-1\dfrac{1}{2}$ degrees Fahrenheit per hour. What was the total change in temperature over the 5-hour period?

Expression _____

Answer _____

 **Think•Pair•Share**

MP6 **14.** Calculate $5\dfrac{1}{4} \div -\dfrac{7}{8}$. Use multiplication to check.

Independent Practice

Find each product or quotient.

1. $-\dfrac{4}{5} \cdot +\dfrac{15}{16} =$ _____

2. $+\dfrac{5}{9} \cdot -\dfrac{3}{10} =$ _____

3. $-3\dfrac{5}{9} \cdot -1\dfrac{1}{8} =$ _____

4. $-\dfrac{2}{3} \div -\dfrac{5}{12} =$ _____

5. $+\dfrac{5}{8} \div -\dfrac{15}{16} =$ _____

6. $-4\dfrac{1}{6} \div +1\dfrac{7}{18} =$ _____

7. $+36 \div -7.2 =$ _____

8. $+4.8 \cdot +17.5 =$ _____

9. $-102.24 \div +3.6 =$ _____

10. $\dfrac{\frac{3}{10}}{-\frac{9}{20}} =$ _____

11. $\dfrac{-\frac{5}{12}}{-\frac{25}{36}} =$ _____

12. $\dfrac{-\frac{3}{7}}{\frac{21}{30}} =$ _____

**Use rational numbers to write an expression to represent the problem.
Solve the problem.**

13. The price of gold dropped a total of $-\$18$ in $4\dfrac{1}{2}$ hours. What was the average change in price per hour?

    Expression _____

    ✏️ **Show your work.**

    Answer _____

Solve the problems.

MP7 **23.** In $\frac{2}{3}$ of a minute, Aaron's 5-liter mountain bike tire lost $\frac{8}{9}$ of a liter of air. If the tire continues to lose air at this rate, how long will it take for the tire to be completely flat?

✏️ **Show your work.**

Answer _____

MP1 **24.** A red-tailed hawk dives at a constant rate in which its altitude changes by $-7\frac{1}{2}$ meters in $\frac{15}{100}$ second. How long will it take the hawk to dive -70 meters?

✏️ **Show your work.**

Answer _____

MP1 **25.** A 4-ton dump truck pours out $\frac{3}{8}$ of a ton of sand in $2\frac{7}{10}$ minutes. If the truck continues to pour at this rate, will there be any sand left after 30 minutes?

Answer _____

✏️ **Justify your answer.**

Convert Rational Numbers to Decimal Form

Essential Question:
How can you convert rational numbers to decimal form?

7.NS.2d

Words to Know:
terminating decimal
repeating decimal

Guided Instruction

In this lesson, you will learn to convert rational numbers to decimal form.

Understand: Converting rational numbers to terminating decimals

Before 2001, fractions were used to report changes in stock prices. What is the decimal equivalent for an increase of $\frac{3}{8}$ in a stock price?

To find the decimal equivalent for $\frac{3}{8}$, divide 3 by 8.

```
      0.375
  8) 3.000   ←—— Keep writing zeros in the dividend until the remainder is 0.
    −2 4
      60
     −56
      40
     −40
       0   ←—— The remainder is 0.
```

Remember!
$$\frac{a}{b} = a \div b$$

Because the division comes to an end (the remainder is 0), the decimal is called a terminating decimal.

➡ The decimal equivalent for a price increase of $\frac{3}{8}$ is 0.375.

What is the decimal equivalent for an increase of $\frac{1}{16}$ in the price of a stock?

To find the decimal equivalent for $\frac{1}{16}$, divide 1 by 16.

```
       0.0625
  16) 1.0000   ←—— Keep writing zeros in the dividend until the remainder is 0.
    − 96
      40
     −32
      80
     −80
       0   ←—— The remainder is 0.
```

➡ The decimal equivalent for a price increase of $\frac{1}{16}$ is 0.0625.

✏ Where would the point for $\frac{1}{16}$ be on a number line marked in tenths?

Understand: Converting rational numbers to repeating decimals

> A store advertises a sale in which sale prices are $\frac{1}{3}$ off the regular prices.
> What is the decimal equivalent for $\frac{1}{3}$?

To find the decimal equivalent for $\frac{1}{3}$, divide 1 by 3.

$$
\begin{array}{r}
0.333 \\
3\overline{)1.000} \\
-9 \\
\hline
10 \\
-9 \\
\hline
10 \\
-9 \\
\hline
1
\end{array}
$$

← The digit 3 keeps repeating.

← The remainder will never be 0.

> To show that the digits repeat, place a bar over the digits that repeat.
> $\frac{1}{3} = 0.\overline{3}$

Because the division does not come to an end (the remainder will never be 0), but the digits in the quotient repeat, the decimal is called a repeating decimal.

▶ The decimal equivalent for $\frac{1}{3}$ is $0.\overline{3}$.

Any rational number can be written either as a terminating or a repeating decimal.

> At Franklin School today, $\frac{2}{11}$ of the students were absent. What is the
> decimal equivalent for $\frac{2}{11}$?

To find the decimal equivalent for $\frac{2}{11}$, divide 2 by 11.

$$
\begin{array}{r}
0.1818 \\
11\overline{)2.0000} \\
-11 \\
\hline
90 \\
-88 \\
\hline
20 \\
-11 \\
\hline
90 \\
-88 \\
\hline
2
\end{array}
$$

← The digits 1 and 8 keep repeating.

← The remainder will never be 0.

> To show that the digits repeat, place a bar over the digits that repeat.
> $\frac{2}{11} = 0.\overline{18}$

▶ The decimal equivalent for $\frac{2}{11}$ is $0.\overline{18}$.

✏ · Where would the point for $\frac{1}{3}$ lie on a number line marked in tenths?

Guided Instruction

Connect: Converting mixed numbers and negative rational numbers to decimal form

> How do you write decimals for rational numbers that are mixed numbers or rational numbers that are negative?

Begin by writing the fraction part as a terminating or repeating decimal.

Then study the patterns below to write decimals for rational numbers that are mixed numbers or rational numbers that are negative.

$\frac{3}{8} = 0.375$	$\frac{1}{3} = 0.\overline{3}$
$5\frac{3}{8} = 5.375$	$2\frac{1}{3} = 2.\overline{3}$
$-\frac{3}{8} = -0.375$	$-\frac{1}{3} = -0.\overline{3}$
$-5\frac{3}{8} = -5.375$	$-2\frac{1}{3} = -2.\overline{3}$

Notice that the only change is in the fraction part of the number. The sign of a rational number does not change. The whole number part of a rational mixed number does not change.

➡ You can rewrite the fraction parts as terminating or repeating decimals and then follow the patterns shown above.

Connect: Using decimals to compare rational numbers

> The seventh and eighth grades at Diamond Middle School both have the same number of students. In the seventh grade, $\frac{7}{12}$ of the students are girls. In the eighth grade, $\frac{11}{18}$ of the students are girls. Which grade has more girls?

You can compare fractions by writing them as decimals.

Seventh grade: $\frac{7}{12}$ **girls**

$$12\overline{)7.0000} \quad \frac{0.5833}{}$$

$\frac{7}{12} = 0.58\overline{3}$

Eighth grade: $\frac{11}{18}$ **girls**

$$18\overline{)11.0000} \quad \frac{0.6111}{}$$

$\frac{11}{18} = 0.6\overline{1}$

Since $0.6\overline{1} > 0.58\overline{3}$, there are more girls in the eighth grade.

➡ The eighth grade has more girls.

✎ Which is greater: $-\frac{7}{12}$ or $-\frac{11}{18}$? Explain.

Independent Practice

Solve the problems.

MP1 **23.** Jenean took a pumpkin from her garden that weighed 18.4125 pounds and cut off the top. The top part weighed $\frac{13}{16}$ pound. How much did the remaining part of the pumpkin weigh?

Answer _____

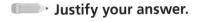 **Show your work.**

MP7 **24.** In the City Council, in order for a bill to pass, $\frac{2}{3}$ of the members must vote in favor of it. Sixty-two of the 94 City Council members vote in favor of a bill. Does it pass?

Answer _____

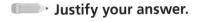 **Justify your answer.**

MP7 **25.** Brock just bought a new tennis racquet that weighs $9\frac{7}{12}$ ounces. Brock's new racquet feels heavier than his old racquet, which weighed $9\frac{9}{16}$ ounces, but Brock is not sure if it is actually heavier. Is the new racquet heavier?

Answer _____

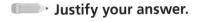 **Justify your answer.**

Apply Rational-Number Operations

Essential Question:
How can you use rational numbers to solve mathematical and real world problems?

7.NS.3

Words to Know:
order of operations

Guided Instruction

In this lesson, you will learn to use rational-number operations to solve mathematical and real world problems.

Understand: Evaluate mathematical expressions using the order of operations

What is the result when you evaluate the expression $[6 + (-\frac{3}{5})] \cdot [5 + (-\frac{1}{2})]$ using the order of operations?

The rules for the order of rational-number operations are the same rules you used for order of operations with positive numbers.

$$[6 + (-\tfrac{3}{5})] \cdot [5 + (-\tfrac{1}{2})]$$

Evaluate the expressions within brackets.

$$5\tfrac{2}{5} \cdot 4\tfrac{1}{2}$$

Multiply.

$$\frac{27}{5} \cdot \frac{9}{2}$$
$$= \frac{243}{10}$$

Order of Operations

1. Do operations within grouping symbols.
2. Evaluate powers.
3. Do multiplication and division, left to right.
4. Do addition and subtraction, left to right.

➡ The value of the expression is $\frac{243}{10}$ when you use order of operations.

What is the result when you evaluate the expression $-4 \cdot (-\frac{1}{2})^3$ using the order of operations?

$$-4 \cdot (-\tfrac{1}{2})^3$$

Evaluate the power first.

$$-4 \cdot (-\tfrac{1}{8})$$

Multiply.

$$\frac{4}{8}$$

➡ The value of the expression is $\frac{4}{8}$ when you use order of operations.

Guided Instruction

What is the result when you evaluate the expression $-4 - (+5) + 6 \cdot (-3)$ using the order of operations?

$$-4 - (+5) + 6 \cdot (-3)$$

Multiply first. $\qquad -4 - (+5) + (-18)$

Add and subtract, left to right. $\qquad -4 + (-5) + (-18)$

$$-9 + (-18)$$

$$-27$$

➡ The value of the expression is -27.

What is the result when you evaluate the expression $\dfrac{(-\frac{1}{5}) + (-\frac{2}{5})}{+\frac{3}{4} - (+\frac{1}{4})}$ using the order of operations?

$$\dfrac{(-\frac{1}{5}) + (-\frac{2}{5})}{+\frac{3}{4} - (+\frac{1}{4})}$$

Evaluate the numerator. $\qquad \dfrac{-\frac{3}{5}}{+\frac{3}{4} - (+\frac{1}{4})}$

> Think about the numerator and the denominator as having grouping symbols around them.

Evaluate the denominator. $\qquad \dfrac{-\frac{3}{5}}{+\frac{1}{2}}$

Divide. $\qquad -\dfrac{3}{5} \div \dfrac{1}{2}$

$$-\dfrac{3}{5} \cdot \dfrac{2}{1}$$

$$-\dfrac{6}{5}$$

$$-1\dfrac{1}{5}$$

➡ The value of the expression is $-1\dfrac{1}{5}$.

✏ • Is the value of $(-\frac{1}{5}) + (-\frac{2}{5})$ the same as the value of $-\frac{1}{5} - \frac{2}{5}$? Explain.

Guided Instruction

Connect: Apply rational-number operations to solve mathematical problems

> What is the result when the product of 4 and $-2\frac{1}{2}$ is divided by the sum of $-\frac{5}{6}$ and $+2\frac{5}{6}$?

You can solve this problem by writing and evaluating an expression.

Write the expression.

$$\frac{4 \cdot -2\frac{1}{2}}{-\frac{5}{6} + 2\frac{5}{6}}$$

Evaluate the numerator.

$$\frac{-10}{-\frac{5}{6} + 2\frac{5}{6}}$$

Evaluate the denominator.

$$\frac{-10}{2}$$

Divide.

$$-5$$

➡ The result is -5.

✏ Instead of using the fraction bar, Ron writes and evaluates the expression $4 \cdot -2\frac{1}{2} \div -\frac{5}{6} + 2\frac{5}{6}$. What is the value of Ron's expression? How can you change Ron's expression so it has the same value as the expression in the example above?

Connect: Apply rational-number operations to solve real world problems

> Abigail records the low temperature every day for a week. The low temperature is $-2°C$ on three days, $0°C$ on two days, and $-5°C$ and $-3°C$ on the other two days. What is the average low temperature for the week?

You can solve this problem by writing an expression and then evaluating the expression.

Write the expression.

$$\frac{3 \cdot (-2) + 2 \cdot 0 + (-5) + (-3)}{7}$$

Evaluate the numerator.
Begin with the multiplication.

$$\frac{-6 + 0 + (-5) + (-3)}{7}$$

Add to evaluate the numerator.

$$\frac{-14}{7}$$

Divide.

$$-2$$

➡ The average low temperature for the 7 days is $-2°C$.

For exercises 9–13, circle the correct answer or answers.

9. Which operation should you perform first in evaluating the expression below?

$$3\frac{2}{3} + (-\frac{5}{6}) \cdot \frac{7}{10} \div (-\frac{1}{2})$$

a. multiplication: $(-\frac{5}{6}) \cdot \frac{7}{10}$

b. division: $\frac{7}{10} \div (-\frac{1}{2})$

c. addition: $3\frac{2}{3} + (-\frac{5}{6})$

d. subtraction: $3\frac{2}{3} - \frac{5}{6}$

10. Which expressions are equivalent to $25 - [-2 - (+3)]^2$?

a. $25 - (+25)$

b. $25 - [-2 - (+9)]$

c. $25 - [-2 - (-9)]$

d. $25 - [-5]^2$

11. Which expressions are equivalent to $[(3)^3 + (-25)]^2$?

a. $27 - (25)^2$

b. 2^2

c. $(27 - 25)(27 - 25)$

d. 4

12. Which expressions are equivalent to $\dfrac{\frac{3}{8} - (+6)}{-\frac{2}{5} \cdot 10}$?

a. $-5\frac{5}{8} \cdot (-4)$

b. $\dfrac{-5\frac{5}{8}}{-4}$

c. $-5\frac{5}{8} \div (-\frac{1}{4})$

d. $-5\frac{5}{8} \div (-4)$

13. Which expressions are equivalent to the square of the product of $-8\frac{4}{5}$ and $+9$ divided by the sum of $\frac{5}{6}$ and $-\frac{3}{4}$?

a. $(-8\frac{4}{5} \cdot 9)^2 \div [\frac{5}{6} + (-\frac{3}{4})]$

b. $\dfrac{(-8\frac{4}{5} \cdot 9)^2}{\frac{5}{6} - \frac{3}{4}}$

c. $(-8\frac{4}{5})^2 \cdot (9) \div [\frac{5}{6} + (-\frac{3}{4})]$

d. $\dfrac{(-8\frac{4}{5} \cdot 9)^2}{(\frac{5}{6} - \frac{3}{4})^2}$

Independent Practice

MP3 **14.** The equation below is false, but you can make it true by inserting a set of parentheses. Show where to place the parentheses. Then show the steps for evaluating the expression on the left side of the equation to show that it has a value of 0.

$$3\frac{4}{5} + 2\frac{1}{5} \cdot \frac{1}{2} - 3 = 0$$

MP7 **15.** Matt claims that working left to right to evaluate an expression is not really important if an expression has only multiplication and division. Mindy says that failing to work left to right will give you the wrong answer. Who is correct? Explain using the expression $40 \div 5 \cdot 4$.

Solve the problems.

MP1 **16.** On Monday morning, Grace ran $2\frac{5}{8}$ miles in $\frac{1}{3}$ of an hour. Her afternoon run took only $\frac{1}{6}$ of an hour, but it was $1\frac{1}{4}$ miles shorter than her morning run. What was Grace's average speed for the day?

▭▸ **Show your work.**

Answer _____

MP1 **17.** To make concrete, Rita dumped two bags of gravel each weighing $3\frac{3}{4}$ kg into a wheelbarrow. Then she added a $1\frac{7}{8}$ kg bag of cement. What percent of the weight of the mixture is the weight of the gravel?

✎▸ **Show your work.**

Answer _____

MP1 **18.** An episode of an hour-long TV show has three commercials each lasting $1\frac{1}{3}$ minutes. The intro for the show lasts $1\frac{1}{2}$ minutes and the credits last $\frac{3}{4}$ minute. How many minutes does the actual show last when commercials, intro, and credits are taken out?

✎▸ **Show your work.**

Answer _____

MP1 **19.** A large barrel of oil is $\frac{1}{4}$ full. Then, for $7\frac{1}{2}$ minutes, oil is added to the barrel at a rate of 4 gallons per minute. Then, for $6\frac{1}{2}$ minutes, some of the oil is removed at a rate of $-3\frac{1}{2}$ gallons per minute. Is the barrel now more or less than $\frac{1}{4}$ full?

Answer _____

✎▸ **Justify your answer.**

Find the sum, difference, product, or quotient.

1. $-48 \div (+6) =$ _____

2. $4\frac{3}{8} - (+2\frac{5}{6}) =$ _____

3. $-9 \cdot (+10) =$ _____

4. $80 \div (-50) =$ _____

5. $-10 - (-12) =$ _____

6. $-5\frac{1}{2} \div (-2) =$ _____

7. $(4.8) \cdot (-7.5) =$ _____

8. $-13 + (-7) =$ _____

9. $2\frac{1}{6} - (+3\frac{2}{9}) =$ _____

Use the order of operations to evaluate each expression.

10. $-6 + (-2) \cdot 5 =$ _____

11. $(-3 + 8)^2 =$ _____

12. $-\frac{1}{2} \cdot (-4)^4 =$ _____

Write the decimal equivalent for each rational number. If the decimal repeats, use a bar to show the digits that repeat.

13. $-\frac{1}{3} =$ _____

14. $+2\frac{1}{8} =$ _____

15. $-6\frac{4}{15} =$ _____

For exercises 16–18, circle the correct answer or answers.

16. Jamie is playing a game. On his first turn, he gains 3 points. On his second turn, he loses 3 points. Which expression represents Jamie's score at the end of his second turn?

    a. $+3 + (-3)$

    b. $+3 \cdot (-3)$

    c. $+3 - (-3)$

    d. $+3 \div (-3)$

17. Which of the following represent the number of units between -5 and -2 on the number line?

    a. $|-5 - (-2)|$

    b. $|-5 + (-2)|$

    c. $|-2 - (-5)|$

    d. $|-2 + (-5)|$

18. Which addition expression is shown on the number line?

    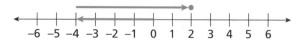

    a. $-4 + (+2)$

    b. $-4 + (+6)$

    c. $+4 + (-6)$

    d. $-4 + (-6)$

Solve the problems.

MP2 **19.** A seagull is gliding $74\frac{1}{2}$ feet above the surface of the water. It then dives 80 feet to catch a fish. How many feet below the surface of the water does the seagull dive?

✎ **Show your work.**

Answer _____

MP1 **20.** The ratings for the TV show *I Want to Be a Rock Star* drop a total of 9 points in 6 weeks. What rational number represents the average change in points per week?

✎ **Show your work.**

Answer _____

MP3 **21.** In a math competition, contestants receive +8 points for every correct answer and −5 points for every incorrect answer. Boris has 23 correct answers and 5 incorrect answers; Bridget has 32 correct answers and 19 incorrect. Who has the higher score?

Answer _____

✎ **Justify your answer.**

MP3 **22.** Chuck has 8.25 gigabytes on his hard drive. Chuck wants to load 3 movies on the drive that take up 3.6, 2.8, and 4.1 gigabytes each. To make room for the movies, Chuck plans to delete a 2.3-gigabyte movie. Does Chuck have enough space for the 3 new movies?

Answer _____

✎ **Justify your answer.**

MP2 **23.** Sara made 3 slow motion films of a honeybee beating its wings. In film 1, Sara counted 24 beats over a time period of $\frac{1}{8}$ second. In film 2, Sara counted 30 beats in $\frac{1}{6}$ second. In film 3, she counted 18 beats in $\frac{1}{12}$ second. What was the average number of beats per second for the bee in the 3 films?

✏️ **Show your work.**

Answer _____

MP1 **24.** Darrel has a section of counter top granite that measures $48\frac{2}{3}$ feet in length. Darrel needs to cut a $6\frac{1}{6}$-foot piece off for the trim. Then he needs to take what remains and divide it into slabs that measure $4\frac{1}{4}$ feet in length each. How many $4\frac{1}{4}$-foot slabs can Darrel cut? Will there be any granite left over? If so, how much?

✏️ **Show your work.**

Answer _____

MP1 **25.** Focus tests suggest that customers love the new gPhone X1, but they think the 5.82-inch long screen is too long. The engineers come back with a design they called the gPhone X2 with a screen that is $\frac{5}{8}$ inch shorter than the X1. Will the new X2 be shorter than its main competitor, the $5\frac{1}{5}$-inch Rover 6?

Answer _____

✏️ **Justify your answer.**

Progress Check

Look at how the Common Core standards you have learned and will learn connect.

It is very important for you to understand the standards from the prior grade level so that you will be able to develop an understanding of expressions and equations in this unit and be prepared for next year. To practice your skills, go to sadlierconnect.com.

UNIT 3

GRADE 6		GRADE 7		GRADE 8
I Can...	Before Unit 3	**Can I ?**	After Unit 3	**I Will...**
6.EE.2 Write, read, and evaluate expressions in which letters stand for numbers	☐	**7.EE.1** Add, subtract, factor, and expand linear expressions with rational coefficients	☐	
6.EE.3 Generate equivalent algebraic expressions using properties of operations	☐	**7.EE.2** Understand that rewriting an expression in different forms can shed light on a problem	☐	
6.EE.1 Write and evaluate numerical expressions involving whole-number exponents	☐	**7.EE.3** Solve multi-step problems posed with rational numbers	☐	**8.EE.4** Perform operations with numbers expressed in scientific notation in the context of real-world and mathematical problems
6.EE.7 Write and solve one-step addition equations; for example, solve $x + 4 = 6$ for x Write and solve one-step multiplication equations; for example, solve $3x = 5$ for x	☐ ☐	**7.EE.4** Solve word problems leading to two-step linear equations in one variable Solve two-step linear equations fluently	☐ ☐	**8.EE.7** Determine if a linear equation has one solution, infinitely many solutions, or no solutions Solve multi-step linear equations with rational coefficients
6.EE.8 Write simple inequalities for real-world or mathematical problems; for example, $x < 6$	☐	**7.EE.4** Solve word problems leading to two-step linear inequalities in one variable	☐	

HOME ◆ CONNECT...

In this unit your child will:

- Add, subtract, factor, and expand linear expressions

- Solve multi-step problems with rational numbers

- Use various methods to solve linear equations

- Write and solve linear equations to solve word problems

- Use various methods to solve linear inequalities

- Write and solve linear inequalities to solve word problems

NOTE: All of these learning goals for your child are based on the Grade 7 Common Core State Standards for Mathematics.

Your child will work first with linear expressions and then with linear equations.

The expression $5x + 4 - 3x - 2 + 1$ is a linear expression. Your child will simplify linear expressions by collecting like terms. For example, the linear expression $5x + 4 - 3x - 2 + 1$ simplifies to $2x + 3$. He or she will also evaluate expressions for a given value of the variable. For example, when $x = 5$, both $5x + 4 - 3x - 2 + 1$ and $2x + 3$ are equal to 13.

The equation $5x + 4 = 3x - 2 + 1$ is a linear equation. Your child will solve linear equations by working with the equation to move the variable so it is by itself on one side and its value is on the other side. When $5x + 4 = 3x - 2 + 1$ is solved, $x = -2.5$.

Activity: Your child can build both math and language arts skills by describing a problem situation that matches a given equation. Write an equation on a sheet of paper and then ask your child to write a word problem that can be solved using the equation.

Equations you can use: $3x + 7 = 16$, $5s - 4 = 10$, $2p + 6 = 20$, and $4q - 8 = 8$.

This example shows how the activity works. For $3x + 7 = 16$, your child might write: Josie bought 3 pens that were the same price but different colors and a book that cost $7. She spent $16 in all. How much did each pen cost?

Ways to Help Your Child

It is likely that you use mathematics in some way in your job—you may use a computer to do calculations, solve equations, make measurements, collect data, or use other aspects of mathematics. If so, discuss with your child what you do and why the mathematics is important. If not, ask a friend who does use mathematics in his or her job to talk with your child about this. Knowing that people need to use mathematics in their work can give your child an appreciation of the value of mathematics in everyday life.

ONLINE

For more Home Connect activities, continue online at sadlierconnect.com

Focus on Expressions and Equations

Ride Coupons **$1.25** PER COUPON Ride Coupons

120 COUPONS **$100** SAVE $50.00
55 COUPONS **$50** SAVE $18.75
21 COUPONS **$20** SAVE $6.25

All Rides Require More Than One (1) Coupon Each

Essential Question:
How does using rational numbers in expressions, equations, and inequalities help you represent real-world situations?

BEST DEAL TODAY
120 COUPONS: $100
SAVE $50.00

8

Combine Like Terms to Simplify Linear Expressions

Essential Question:
How can you apply the distributive property to combine like terms to simplify an expression and how can writing expressions in different forms help you see different ways to solve a problem?

7.EE.1, 7.EE.2

Guided Instruction

In this lesson, you will learn to use the distributive property to combine like terms to simplify a linear expression. You will also learn how writing expressions in different forms can help you see different ways to solve a problem.

Words to Know:
- linear expression
- terms
- variable terms
- coefficient
- like terms
- constant terms
- simplify

Understand: Combining like terms to simplify expressions

> Simplify the expression $3x + 4 - 5x - 2 + 3$.

The expression $3x + 4 - 5x - 2 + 3$ is a linear expression in the variable x. A linear expression is the sum of terms that are either rational numbers or the product of a rational number and a variable.

The expression $3x + 4 - 5x - 2 + 3$ has five terms: $3x$, 4, $-5x$, -2, and 3.

You can think about each term as an addend, but the plus signs are not necessary.
$3x + 4 - 5x - 2 + 3$ is equivalent to $(3x) + (+4) + (-5x) + (-2) + (+3)$.

- The terms $3x$ and $-5x$ are variable terms. They are the product of a rational number (called the coefficient) and a variable. Since $3x$ and $-5x$ contain the same variable, they are like terms.

- The terms $+4$, -2, and $+3$ are constant terms. They are rational numbers. All constant terms are like terms.

To simplify an expression, rewrite the expression as an equivalent expression that has only one variable term, only one constant term, or one variable term and one constant term.

To simplify the expression $3x + 4 - 5x - 2 + 3$, combine the like terms.

$3x + 4 - 5x - 2 + 3$ ⟵ Rewrite the expression so that the like terms
$3x - 5x + 4 - 2 + 3$ are grouped together.

$x(3 - 5) + 4 - 2 + 3$ ⟵ Use the distributive property to combine the
$x \cdot -2 + 4 - 2 + 3$ variable terms.
$-2x + 4 - 2 + 3$

$-2x + 5$ ⟵——————— Combine the constant terms.

⟹ When you simplify $3x + 4 - 5x - 2 + 3$, the result is $-2x + 5$.

Because of the associative property of addition, you can change the order of the terms.

$3 - 5$ is equivalent to $3 + (-5)$.

$+4 - 2 + 3$ is equivalent to $+4 + (-2) + (+3)$.

Simplify the expression $-\frac{1}{2}a + 5 + \frac{3}{4}a - \frac{1}{2} + a$.

To simplify the expression $-\frac{1}{2}a + 5 + \frac{3}{4}a - \frac{1}{2} + a$, combine like terms.

$-\frac{1}{2}a + \frac{3}{4}a + a + 5 - \frac{1}{2}$ ◀—— Rewrite the expression so that the like terms are grouped together.

$a\left(-\frac{1}{2} + \frac{3}{4} + 1\right) + 5 - \frac{1}{2}$ ◀—— Use the distributive property to combine the variable terms.

$a \cdot 1\frac{1}{4} + 5 - \frac{1}{2}$

$1\frac{1}{4}a + 5 - \frac{1}{2}$

Remember!

$a = 1a$

$1\frac{1}{4}a + 4\frac{1}{2}$ ◀—————— Combine the constant terms.

▶ The simplified expression is $1\frac{1}{4}a + 4\frac{1}{2}$.

The expression given for each side of this triangle represents the length of that side in feet. What is the simplified expression for the perimeter of this triangle?

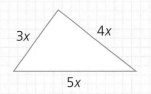

$3x$ $4x$ $5x$

$3x + 4x + 5x$ ◀—— Use addition to write an expression for the perimeter of the triangle. Simplify the expression.

$3x + 4x + 5x$ ◀—— The three terms of the expression are variable terms and they are like terms. Use the distributive property to combine the terms.

$x(3 + 4 + 5)$

$x \cdot 12$

$12x$

▶ The simplified expression for the perimeter of the triangle is $12x$ feet.

✏ What is the simplified expression for the perimeter of a triangle with these side lengths in feet: $\frac{1}{2}s$, $4\frac{1}{2}s$, and 7?

Guided Instruction

Connect: Expressions in different forms show different ways to solve a problem

> The cost of a pizza at Pizza Palace is $7.50. If you have a coupon, you can get $2 off the price of each pizza. Write an expression to show the final cost in dollars of p pizzas when using the coupon.

You can write different expressions depending upon the method you use to solve the problem.

Method 1

Find the total cost in dollars of p pizzas without the coupon.

The cost in dollars is 7.50p.

Find the total number of dollars you save on p pizzas by using the coupon.

You save 2p dollars.

Subtract the total number of dollars you save on p pizzas from the total cost in dollars of p pizzas without the coupon. The result is the cost of the pizza in dollars when using the coupon.

The final cost in dollars is 7.50p − 2p.

Method 2

Find the cost in dollars of one pizza when using the coupon.

The cost is in dollars is 7.50 − 2.

Find the cost in dollars of p pizzas when using the coupon.

The final cost in dollars is (7.50 − 2)p.

➡ The expressions 7.50p − 2p and (7.50 − 2)p both show the final cost in dollars of p pizzas.

Simplifying each expression shows that the expressions are equivalent.

• The simplified form of 7.50p − 2p is 5.50p.

• The simplified form of (7.50 − 2)p is 5.50p.

✏ Use either Method 1 or Method 2 to find the cost of 4 pizzas using a coupon. Which method did you use?

MP1 **22.** Moxie earns a salary of $40 a day as a window salesman. In addition, he earns $12.50 for every window he sells and $2.25 for every window that includes a warranty. To get from job-to-job, Moxie must pay $18.25 a day to rent a car.

    a. On Monday, Moxie sells w windows that all include a warranty. Write a simplified expression to represent the total amount in dollars Moxie makes on Monday.

    ▭▬ **Show your work.**

    Answer _____

    b. If $w = 9$, how much money does Moxie make?

    ▭▬ **Show your work.**

    Answer _____

MP1 **23.** Brenda wants to create a formula for computing the total cost of any restaurant dinner bill that includes a 6% sales tax on the bill, a 15% tip on the pre-tax amount, $5 for parking, and $2.50 for a coat check.

    a. Write a simplified expression that can be used to calculate the total cost of a dinner that cost d dollars before tax and tip are added. Simplify the expression.

    ▭▬ **Show your work.**

    Answer _____

    b. If dinner before tax and tip comes to $42.50, how much would the total cost be?

    ▭▬ **Show your work.**

    Answer _____

Lesson 17

Expand and Factor Linear Expressions

Essential Question:
How can you expand and factor linear expressions and how can writing expressions in different forms help you see different ways to solve a problem?

7.EE.1, 7.EE.2

Words to Know:
expand
factor

Guided Instruction

In this lesson, you will learn to expand a linear expression to simplify it and how to factor an expression.

Understand: Expand to simplify an expression

The expressions in this figure represent the length and width of the rectangle in meters. What is the simplified expression for the area of this rectangle?

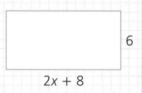

6

$2x + 8$

To find the area, multiply the length times the width. So, the expression $6(2x + 8)$ represents the area of the above rectangle in square meters.

An expression that has been simplified has no parentheses. You can use the distributive property to expand the expression and to eliminate the parentheses.

$6(2x + 8) = 6 \cdot 2x + 6 \cdot 8$ ←——— Expand the expression, that is, use the distributive property to find the product.

$= 12x + 48$ ←——— This is the simplified expression.

▶ The simplified expression for the area of the rectangle is $12x + 48$ square meters.

> Simplify the expression $-7(3m - 9)$.

Use the distributive property to eliminate the parentheses.

$-7(3m - 9) = -7 \cdot 3m + -7 \cdot -9$
$\qquad\qquad\quad = -21m + 63$

> It is important to multiply both terms in the parentheses by −7, not by +7.

▶ The simplified expression is $-21m + 63$.

> Simplify the expression $-(-6n + 8)$.

Again, use the distributive property to eliminate the parentheses. You can think of the negative sign as meaning "multiply each term by −1."

> Multiplying by −1 is the same as finding the opposite.

$-(-6n + 8) = -1 \cdot -6n + -1 \cdot +8$
$\qquad\qquad\quad = +6n - 8$

▶ The simplified expression is $+6n - 8$.

Understand: Expand _and_ combine like terms to simplify an expression

Simplify $5m - 6(2m + 7)$.

In this example, you will need to both expand the expression and combine like terms.

$5m - 6(2m + 7)$ ◄——— Expand $-6(2m + 7)$.
$5m - 12m - 42$

$5m - 12m - 42$ ◄——— Combine like terms.
$-7m - 42$ ◄——————— The simplified expression is $-7m - 42$.

Write a simplified expression for the length (in inches) of segment _AC_.

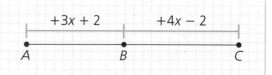

To find the length of segment _AC_, add the length of segment _AB_, $+3x + 2$, and the length of segment _BC_, $+4x - 2$.

$+3x + 2 + (+4x - 2)$ ◄——— Write the expression.
$+3x + 2 + (+4x - 2)$ ◄——— Simplify.
$+3x + 2 + 4x - 2$ ◄——— This is like multiplying by $+1$.
$+3x + 2 + 4x - 2$
$+3x + 4x + 2 - 2$ ◄——— Combine like terms.
$+7x$ ◄——————— The length of segment _AC_ is $7x$ inches.

Write a simplified expression (in inches) for the length of segment _YZ_.

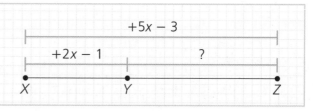

To find the length of segment _YZ_, subtract the length of segment _XY_, $+ 2x - 1$, from the length of segment _XZ_, $+ 5x - 3$.

$+5x - 3 - (+2x - 1)$ ◄——— Write the expression.
$+5x - 3 - (+2x - 1)$ ◄——— Simplify.
$+5x - 3 - 2x + 1$ ◄——— This is like multiplying by -1.
$+5x - 3 - 2x + 1$
$+5x - 2x - 3 + 1$
$+3x - 2$ ◄——————— The length of segment _YZ_ is $3x - 2$ inches.

✏️➤ Simplify $4x - 3(-2x + 8)$.

Guided Instruction

Understand: Factoring an expression

> Write the expression $6x + 18$ as a product of factors. Use the greatest common factor (GCF) as one of the factors.

Sometimes you are given an expression in simplest form and you are asked to factor the expression, that is, write it as a product of factors. This is the opposite of what you do when you expand an expression.

To write $6x + 18$ as the product of factors, think about the common factors of $6x$ and 18. The common factors are 1, 2, 3, and 6. 6 is the GCF. Divide each term by 6.

$6x + 18$

$\dfrac{6x}{6} + \dfrac{18}{6}$ ←——— Divide.

$x + 3$ ←——— So, one factor is 6 and the other factor is $x + 3$.

▶ $6x + 18$ can be written as the product of factors in this way: $6(x + 3)$.

> Write the expression $9x - 15x$ as a product of factors. Use the greatest common factor (GCF) as one of the factors.

To write $9x - 15x$ as the product of factors, think about the common factors of $9x$ and $-15x$. The common factors are -1, -3, 1, 3, $-3x$, and $3x$. $3x$ is the GCF. Divide each term by $3x$.

$9x - 15x$

$\dfrac{9x}{3x} - \dfrac{15x}{3x}$ ←——— Divide.

$3 - 5$ ←——— So, one factor is $3x$ and the other factor is $3 - 5$, or -2.

▶ $9x - 15x$ can be written as the product of factors in this way: $(3x)(-2)$.

✏ What is the GCF of $4x$ and $-10x$? Use the GCF to write $4x - 10x$ as the product of two factors.

Independent Practice

Simplify each expression.

1. $3(2x - 5)$

_____

2. $-2(a + 7)$

_____

3. $-\frac{2}{3}(9a - 30)$

_____

4. $7b + 4(-b + 3)$

_____

5. $-c - 8(4c - 5) - (-18c)$

_____

6. $-11(-7p + 8) - 22(2p - 3)$

_____

7. $-\frac{3}{5}(35x - 30) - (-x - 8)$

_____

8. $-\frac{5}{8}(+24r - 40) - (-r - 15)$

_____

9. $-(-\frac{3}{8}r - \frac{1}{2}) + 5(-\frac{7}{8}r - \frac{3}{10})$

_____

Write each expression as a product of two factors. Use the greatest common factor (GCF) of the terms as one of the factors.

10. $7y + 21$

_____

11. $15n - 25$

_____

12. $9n - 36n$

_____

Solve the problems.

13. The figure shows the length and width of a rectangle in feet. What is an expression in simplest form for the perimeter of the rectangle?

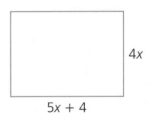

$4x$

$5x + 4$

Answer _____

14. Tree A has a height of $8h - 1$ feet. Tree B has a height of $6h - 11$ feet. How much taller in feet is Tree A than Tree B?

Answer _____

Independent Practice

For exercises 15–16, circle the correct answer or answers.

15. Which of the following is equivalent to $-6 - 2(3x - 3)$?

    a. $-6 - 6x - 6$　　　b. $-6 - x$　　　　　c. $-6 - 6x + 6$　　　d. $-6x$

16. Which of the following is equivalent to $18k - 30 + 12k$?

    a. $6k(3 - 5 + 2)$　　b. $6(3k - 5 + 2k)$　　c. $6(5k - 5)$　　　　d. $3(6k - 10 + 2k)$

MP2　17. Rolando simplified the expression $8 - 5(-2a + 1)$ as shown below.

$$8 - 5(-2a + 1) = 3(-2a + 1)$$
$$= -6a + 3$$

Rolando says that he did not make any errors in simplifying. Carolyn claims
Rolando made an error in using the distributive property. Who is correct? Explain.

Solve the problems.

MP4　18. A square measuring $3x$ inches on each
side is increased by 2 inches in length
and decreased by 1 inch in width.

$3x$　　　　　　$3x + 2$

$3x - 1$

a. Write two different expressions to
show the perimeter of the rectangle
that is formed. Explain how each
expression shows a different way to find the perimeter of the rectangle.

Expression 1 _____

Expression 2 _____

b. Simplify each of your expressions from part a. Do you get the same
simplified expression?

Answer _____

c. Use either method to calculate the perimeter if $x = 5$.

Answer _____

Independent Practice

MP2 **19.** The figure shows the lengths of segment *AC* and segment *AB* in centimeters.

$$AC = 16x + 40$$

$$AB = 10x - 2 \qquad BC = \text{?}$$

A   *B*   *C*

    a. Write a simplified expression for the length of segment *BC*.

       ✏️ **Show your work.**

       Answer _____

    b. If $x = 11$, which is longer, segment *AB* or segment *BC*?

       Answer _____

       ✏️ **Justify your answer.**

MP4 **20.** An equilateral triangle measuring 8*s* feet on a side is changed into an isosceles triangle by decreasing the length of one side by 5 feet and increasing the length of the other two sides by 3 feet.

    a. Write a simplified expression for the perimeter of the isosceles triangle.

       ✏️ **Show your work.**

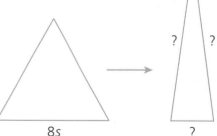

8*s*

       Answer _____

    b. Is the perimeter of the isosceles triangle greater or less than the perimeter of the equilateral triangle?

       Answer _____

       ✏️ **Justify your answer.**

Problem Solving: Multi-step Problems with Rational Numbers

Essential Question:
How can you solve mathematical and real-life problems containing rational numbers and use estimation to assess the reasonableness of your answers?

7.EE.3

Guided Instruction

In this lesson, you will learn to solve mathematical and real-life problems containing rational numbers. You will calculate with numbers in both fraction and decimal form and use estimation and mental math to assess the reasonableness of your answers.

Understand: Estimating with rational numbers

Use estimation to choose the correct answer.

Evaluate. $\dfrac{70\frac{4}{5} + 7\frac{1}{10}}{8.2} - (-4.8)$

a. 0.143   **b.** 1.43   **c.** 14.3   **d.** 143

When you estimate with rational numbers, you replace the numbers in a problem with numbers that are easy to calculate with. An estimate can give you an idea about whether your answer is reasonable.

Step 1

Estimate $70\frac{4}{5} + 7\frac{1}{10}$.

$70\frac{4}{5}$ is about 71.

$7\frac{1}{10}$ is about 7.

$71 + 7 = 78$ which is about 80.

Step 2

Use 80 for the value of $70\frac{4}{5} + 7\frac{1}{10}$.

Estimate. $\dfrac{80}{8.2}$ is about $\dfrac{80}{8}$ or 10.

Step 3

Use 10 for $\dfrac{70\frac{4}{5} + 7\frac{1}{10}}{8.2}$.

Estimate. $10 - (-4.8)$ is about $10 + 5$ or 15.

Based on this estimate of 15, the correct answer would be 14.3.

➡ The correct answer is **c**, 14.3.

✏ Show how to find the exact value of $\dfrac{70\frac{4}{5} + 7\frac{1}{10}}{8.2} - (-4.8)$.

Connect: Solve real-life problems and assess the reasonableness of answers

> Wenshu is hanging a framed mirror on the wall. The frame is $21\frac{1}{8}$ inches wide. She wants the mirror to be centered. The wall measures $59\frac{1}{2}$ inches across. How far from each edge of the wall should Wenshu hang the mirror?

Write an expression to represent the problem, estimate the value of the expression, find the exact answer, and then compare the exact answer to your estimate to see if it is reasonable.

You can make a drawing to help you understand the problem so that you can write an expression to represent it.

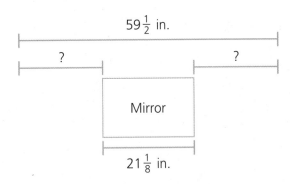

Step 1

Write an expression. Then estimate the value.

Using the drawing, you can see that you need to subtract $21\frac{1}{8}$ from $59\frac{1}{2}$ to find the width of the wall that won't be covered by the mirror. Then you can divide by 2, since if the mirror is centered, there will be equal space on each side.

The expression $\dfrac{59\frac{1}{2} - 21\frac{1}{8}}{2}$ represents the problem.   Estimate: $\dfrac{60 - 20}{2} = \dfrac{40}{2} = 20$

The mirror will be about 20 inches from each side of the wall.

Step 2

Find the exact value of the expression.

Evaluate the numerator of the fraction.

$59\frac{1}{2} - 21\frac{1}{8}$

$59\frac{4}{8} - 21\frac{1}{8} = 38\frac{3}{8}$

Divide the value of the numerator by 2.

$38\frac{3}{8} \div 2$

$\dfrac{307}{8} \cdot \dfrac{1}{2}$

$\dfrac{307}{16} = 19\frac{3}{16}$

Step 3

Compare the exact value with the estimate. $19\frac{3}{16}$ is close to 20, so the answer is reasonable.

➡ Wenshu should hang the mirror $19\frac{3}{16}$ inches from each edge of the wall.

Guided Instruction

> Four friends go out to dinner. The total cost of the food is $49.80. They must pay 5% tax on that amount and want to leave 15% of the pre-tax amount as a tip. If the four friends split the bill equally, how much will each owe?

Write an expression to represent the problem, estimate the value of the expression, find the exact answer, and then compare the exact answer to your estimate to see if your answer is reasonable.

Step 1

Write an expression.

You first need to add the cost of the food, the tax, and the tip.

- The cost of the food in dollars is 49.8.

- The tip in dollars is 0.15 • 49.8.

- The tax in dollars is 0.05 • 49.8.

> The problem states that the tip is 15% of the pre-tax price.

You can write the expression $49.8 + 0.15 • 49.8 + 0.05 • 49.8$ to represent the cost of the food, the tax, and the tip.

Then you need to divide by 4, since 4 friends will share the cost.

The expression $\dfrac{49.8 + 0.15 • 49.8 + 0.05 • 49.8}{4}$ can represent the problem.

Step 2

Estimate the value of the expression.

$$\dfrac{49.8 + 0.15 • 49.8 + 0.05 • 49.8}{4} \longrightarrow \dfrac{50 + (0.15)50 + 0.05(50)}{4}$$

$$\dfrac{50 + 7.5 + 2.5}{4} = \dfrac{60}{4} = 15 \qquad \text{Each friend will owe about \$15.}$$

Step 3

Find the exact value of the expression.

$$\dfrac{49.8 + 0.15 • 49.8 + 0.05 • 49.8}{4}$$

$$\dfrac{49.8 + 7.47 + 2.49}{4} = \dfrac{59.76}{4} = 14.94$$

Step 4

Compare the exact value with the estimate. 14.94 is close to 15, so the answer is reasonable.

➤ Each friend will owe $14.94.

For exercises, 1–5, follow the steps to estimate and evaluate the expression

$$\frac{4.682 - (-5.123)}{\frac{1}{2}}.$$

1. Estimate $4.682 - (-5.123)$.

   My estimate is _____

2. Use your estimate from exercise 1 to estimate $\dfrac{4.682 - (-5.123)}{\frac{1}{2}}$.

   My estimate is _____

3. Circle the value below that is closest to your estimate.

   1.961   19.61   490.25   49.025

4. Find the exact value of the expression $\dfrac{4.682 - (-5.123)}{\frac{1}{2}}$. _____

5. Compare your answers to exercises 3 and 4. If your answers are not the same, go back and check your work on exercises 1–4.

Write a mathematical expression to represent the problem, estimate the answer, and solve the problem.

6. Brendan wants to buy a bicycle. The original price of the bicycle is $78, but it is on sale for 25% off. How much does Brendan pay for the bicycle if he buys it on sale and pays a 6% sales tax on the sale price?

   Expression _____

   Estimate _____

   Answer _____

☟ Think•Pair•Share

MP7 7. Without finding the exact answer, decide whether the value of the expression at the right is greater than or less than 15. Explain your reasoning.

$$\frac{10\frac{1}{5} + 20\frac{2}{9}}{6} + \frac{-19\frac{4}{5} - 3\frac{5}{8}}{-1.9}$$

Independent Practice

For exercises, 1–4, follow the steps to estimate and evaluate the expression

$$\dfrac{-19.64 + 2(-7.48)}{\frac{1}{3}}.$$

1. Estimate $-19.64 + 2(-7.48)$

   My estimate is _____

2. Use your estimate from exercise 1 to estimate $\dfrac{-19.64 + 2(-7.48)}{\frac{1}{3}}$.

   My estimate is _____

3. Find the exact value of the expression $\dfrac{-19.64 + 2(-7.48)}{\frac{1}{3}}$.

   _____

4. Compare your exact answer to your estimate. Are the two close in value?

   _____

   If your answer and your estimate are not close in value, go back and check
   your work on exercises 1–3.

**Write a mathematical expression to represent the problem, estimate the answer,
and solve the problem.**

5. A one-way train ticket to Philadelphia costs $48.50. For an extra 40%, Nandita
   can buy a round-trip ticket. There is a 5% tax. How much does Nandita pay for
   a round-trip ticket including the tax?

   Expression _____

   Estimate _____

   Answer _____

For exercises 6–11, circle the correct answer or answers.

6. Which of the following is a reasonable estimate for the value of $\dfrac{7\frac{1}{2} + \frac{1}{3}(-4.53)}{\frac{1}{7}}$?

   a. 42

   b. −42

   c. $8\frac{1}{2} \cdot 7$

   d. $6 \div \frac{1}{7}$

7. Esteban estimated a product to be about −52. Which quantity is reasonably close to Esteban's estimate?

   a. 54.41

   b. 26% of 108.4

   c. −55.73

   d. $\frac{1}{4}$ of −206.6

8. Which of the following is equivalent to 120% of 20?

   a. 1.2 • 20

   b. (100% of 20) + (20% of 20)

   c. 1.2% of 200

   d. 12% of 20

9. Which of the following is equivalent to 15 + 70% of 40?

   a. 0.7(15 + 40)

   b. 0.7 • 15 + 0.7 • 40

   c. 0.7 • 40 + 15

   d. 15 + 0.7 • 40

10. Hernan has 6.3 pounds of Yukon gold potatoes and 8.4 pounds of fingerling potatoes. He combines $\frac{2}{3}$ of the Yukon golds and $\frac{3}{4}$ of the fingerlings in a blender, and makes potato pancakes weighing $\frac{1}{2}$ pound each. Which of the following expressions can represent the number of potato pancakes Hernan makes?

   a. $\dfrac{\frac{2}{3}(6.3) + 0.75(8.4)}{0.5}$

   b. $\dfrac{\frac{2}{3}(6.3) + \frac{3}{4}(8.4)}{\frac{1}{2}}$

   c. $\dfrac{\frac{2}{3}(6.3) + 0.75(8.4)}{2}$

   d. $\frac{2}{3}(6.3) + 0.75(8.4) \cdot \frac{2}{1}$

11. Randi invests $1,000 in an account that gains 6% in value the first year. At the end of the first year, Randi re-invests the money and loses 4% of her total the second year. Which expression represents how much money in dollars Randi has at the end of the second year?

   a. 0.96[1.06(1,000)]

   b. 1.06(1,000) + 0.96(1,000)

   c. 0.96(1,060)

   d. (2.02)(1,000)

Independent Practice

MP3 **12.** Koji wants to cut a 47.6-inch wide board into slats that are each $\frac{3}{4}$ of an inch wide. He estimates that he will cut about 36 slats because 47.6 is close to 48 and $\frac{3}{4}$ of 48 is 36. Is Koji's estimate reasonable? Explain.

MP2 **13.** Anna calculates 85% of a number by finding half of the number to get 50%, adding 10% of the number to get 60%, adding another 10% to get 70%, adding one more 10% to get 80%, and adding half of 10% to get the last 5%.

   a. Use Anna's method to find 85% of 560.

       Show your work.

       Answer _____

   b. Explain why Anna's method works.

Write a mathematical expression to represent the problem, estimate the answer, and solve the problem.

MP2 **14.** Nesbo's Sport Shop is having a sale with 35% off all athletic equipment and 25% off all clothing and shoes. Suzanne buys a tennis racquet with a regular price of $89.95, 4 cans of tennis balls (regular price $3.25 per can), and 2 pairs of tennis shoes, each with a regular price of $74.50. Suzanne has 6 months to pay off her entire bill. How much will Suzanne's monthly payment be?

   Expression _____

   Estimate _____

       Show your work.

   Answer _____

Independent Practice

Solve the problems.

MP3 **15.** In October, the Rosenberg family paid $172 for heat and $114 for electricity. In November, the heating bill went up 42% and the electric bill went down 8%. Mr. Rosenberg says that the family spent more on heat and electricity per day during November than it did in the heat of the summer when the family averaged $12 per day. Is Mr. Rosenberg correct?

Answer _____

✏️ **Justify your answer.**

MP2 **16.** LaShanna picks 63.45 pounds of Bing cherries and 50.5 pounds of Queen Anne cherries. LaShanna freezes $\frac{2}{5}$ of the Bing cherries and $\frac{4}{5}$ of the Queen Anne Cherries. She puts the rest of the cherries into $\frac{1}{4}$-pound bags. How many $\frac{1}{4}$-pound bags does LaShanna use?

Answer _____

✏️ **Justify your answer.**

MP6 **17.** Five years ago Uncle Shelby had $108,000. He put $\frac{3}{8}$ of the money in the bank. He invested the rest of the money and it gained 24%. He then gave each of his 12 nephews and nieces an equal share of the invested money. How much did each niece or nephew receive?

✏️ **Show your work.**

Answer _____

19 Solve Linear Equations

Essential Question:
How can you solve equations of the form $px + q = r$ and $p(x + q) = r$, where p, q, and r are specific rational numbers?

7.EE.4a

Guided Instruction

In this lesson, you will solve equations of the form $x + p = q$ and $px = q$ where one or more of the values is negative. You will then solve equations of the form $px + q = r$ and $p(x + q) = r$, where p, q, and r are specific rational numbers.

Understand: Solving equations of the form $x + p = q$

Solve and check. $x + 7 = -2$

Solving an equation means finding the value or values for the variable that make the equation true. To solve an equation, you write equivalent equations until you have the variable on one side of the equation and a number on the other side.

Solve.

$x + 7 = -2$
$x + 7 - 7 = -2 - 7$ ◄—— Add -7 to both sides.
$x = -9$ ◄—— Simplify both sides.

Check.

$x + 7 = -2$
$-9 + 7 = -2$ ◄—— Substitute -9 for x.
$-2 = -2$ True. ◄—— The solution checks.

➡ The solution is $x = -9$.

Solve and check. $m - 3 = -6\frac{1}{2}$

Solve.

$m - 3 = -6\frac{1}{2}$
$m - 3 + 3 = -6\frac{1}{2} + 3$ ◄—— Add $+3$ to both sides.
$m = -3\frac{1}{2}$ ◄—— Simplify both sides.

Check.

$m - 3 = -6\frac{1}{2}$
$-3\frac{1}{2} - 3 = -6\frac{1}{2}$
$-6\frac{1}{2} = -6\frac{1}{2}$ True.

➡ The solution is $m = -3\frac{1}{2}$.

Solve. $n - 9 - 5 = -4 \cdot + 3$

$n - 9 - 5 = -4 \cdot + 3$
$n - 14 = -12$ ◄—— Simplify both sides of the equation by combining like terms.
$n - 14 + 14 = -12 + 14$ ◄—— Add $+14$ to both sides.
$n = +2$ ◄—— Simplify both sides.

➡ The solution is $n = 2$.

Understand: Solving equations of the form $px = q$

> Solve and check. $-5x = -35$

Solve.

$-5x = -35$

$\dfrac{-5x}{-5} = \dfrac{-35}{-5}$ ⟵ Divide both sides by -5.

$x = 7$ ⟵ Simplify both sides.

▶ The solution is $x = 7$.

Check.

$-5x = -35$

$-5 \cdot 7 = -35$ ⟵ Substitute 7 for x.

$-35 = -35$ True. ⟵ The solution checks.

> Solve and check. $\dfrac{a}{-6} = -12$

Solve.

$\dfrac{a}{-6} = -12$

$(-6)\dfrac{a}{-6} = (-6)(-12)$ ⟵ Multiply both sides by -6.

$a = 72$ ⟵ Simplify both sides.

▶ The solution is $a = 72$.

Check.

$\dfrac{a}{-6} = -12$

$\dfrac{72}{-6} = -12$

$-12 = -12$ True.

> Solve and check. $3m - 7m = -20$

Solve.

$3m - 7m = -20$

$-4m = -20$ ⟵ Simplify both sides of the equation.

$\dfrac{-4m}{-4} = \dfrac{-20}{-4}$ ⟵ Divide both sides by -4.

$m = 5$

▶ The solution is $m = 5$.

Check.

$3m - 7m = -20$

$3 \cdot 5 - 7 \cdot 5 = -20$

$15 - 35 = -20$

$-20 = -20$ True.

✏ When solving the equation $-3x = 15$, how do you decide which operation to perform on both sides of the equation?

Guided Instruction

Connect: Solving equations of the form $px + q = r$

> Solve and check. $-5m + 8 = 18$

Solve.

$$-5m + 8 = 18$$
$$-5m + 8 - 8 = 18 - 8 \longleftarrow \text{ Add } -8 \text{ to both sides.}$$
$$-5m = 10 \longleftarrow \text{ Simplify both sides.}$$
$$\frac{-5m}{-5} = \frac{10}{-5} \longleftarrow \text{ Divide both sides by } -5.$$
$$m = -2 \longleftarrow \text{ Simplify both sides.}$$

Remember!

The goal is to get the variable by itself on one side of the equation.

Check.

$$-5 \cdot -2 + 8 = 18$$
$$+10 + 8 = 18$$
$$18 = 18 \text{ True.}$$

➡ The solution is $m = -2$.

> Solve and check. $1\frac{1}{2}x - \frac{3}{4} = -4\frac{1}{4}$

Solve.

$$1\frac{1}{2}x - \frac{3}{4} = -4\frac{1}{4}$$
$$1\frac{1}{2}x - \frac{3}{4} + \frac{3}{4} = -4\frac{1}{4} + \frac{3}{4} \longleftarrow \text{ Add } +\frac{3}{4} \text{ to both sides.}$$
$$1\frac{1}{2}x = -3\frac{1}{2} \longleftarrow \text{ Simplify both sides.}$$
$$\frac{1\frac{1}{2}x}{1\frac{1}{2}} = \frac{-3\frac{1}{2}}{1\frac{1}{2}} \longleftarrow \text{ Divide both sides by } 1\frac{1}{2}.$$
$$x = -\frac{7}{3} \text{ or } -2\frac{1}{3} \longleftarrow \text{ Simplify both sides.}$$

➡ The solution is $x = -2\frac{1}{3}$.

Check.

$$1\frac{1}{2}x - \frac{3}{4} = -4\frac{1}{4}$$
$$1\frac{1}{2} \cdot -2\frac{1}{3} - \frac{3}{4} = -4\frac{1}{4}$$
$$-3\frac{1}{2} - \frac{3}{4} = -4\frac{1}{4}$$
$$-4\frac{1}{4} = -4\frac{1}{4} \text{ True.}$$

> Solve. $2m + 3m - 4 - 3 = 8$

$2m + 3m - 4 - 3 = 8$

$5m - 7 = 8$ ←———— Simplify both sides of the equation.

$5m - 7 + 7 = 8 + 7$ ←—— Add +7 to both sides.

$5m = 15$ ←———— Simplify both sides.

$\dfrac{5m}{5} = \dfrac{15}{5}$ ←———— Divide both sides by 5.

$m = 3$ ←———— Simplify both sides.

➡ The solution is $m = 3$.

Connect: Solving equations of the form $p(x + q) = r$

> Solve. $3(x + 4) = -9$

Method 1

$3(x + 4) = -9$

$3x + 3 \cdot 4 = -9$ ←———— Expand to eliminate the parentheses.

$3x + 12 = -9$ ←———— Simplify both sides.

$3x + 12 - 12 = -9 - 12$ ←—— Add −12 to both sides.

$3x = -21$ ←———— Simplify both sides.

$\dfrac{3x}{3} = \dfrac{-21}{3}$ ←———— Divide both sides by 3.

$x = -7$

Method 2

$3(x + 4) = -9$

$\dfrac{3(x + 4)}{3} = \dfrac{-9}{3}$ ←———— Divide both sides by 3.

$x + 4 = -3$ ←———— Simplify both sides.

$x + 4 - 4 = -3 - 4$ ←—— Add −4 to both sides.

$x = -7$ ←———— Simplify both sides.

➡ With both methods, the solution is the same, $x = -7$.

✏ How are Method 1 and Method 2 alike? How are they different?

Guided Practice

Solve each equation. Check your work on a separate sheet of paper.

1. $x + 4 = -6$

   $x =$ _____

2. $c - 4 = -2\frac{1}{2}$

   $c =$ _____

3. $m - 4 + 3 = -10 \cdot 2$

   $m =$ _____

4. $-8n = -16$

   $n =$ _____

5. $\frac{p}{-2} = -1\frac{1}{2}$

   $p =$ _____

6. $-2r - r = 24$

   $r =$ _____

7. $2x + 8 = 20$

   $x =$ _____

8. $-7q - 10 = 32$

   $q =$ _____

9. $-2r - 10 + 8 = 32$

   $r =$ _____

10. $5(x - 7) = 5$

    $x =$ _____

11. $20 = \frac{1}{2}(m - 8)$

    $m =$ _____

12. $-(g - 2) = 12$

    $g =$ _____

⍢⍣ Think•Pair•Share

MP7 **13.** Another way to solve the equation $-5m + 8 = 18$ (the first example on page 168) is to first divide and then add. Show how to solve the equation using this method. Do you get the same solution, $m = -2$? Which method do you prefer? Why?

Guided Instruction

Understand: Using equations to solve mathematical problems

> Solve this riddle:
> If you add 2 to a number and then multiply the sum by −5, the result will be 30. What is the number?

You can solve this problem, by writing and solving an equation.
Let n = the number. You can use the equation $-5(n + 2) = 30$ to represent the problem. Here are two ways to solve the equation.

Method 1
Begin by using the distributive property to eliminate the parentheses.

$$-5(n + 2) = 30$$
$$-5n - 10 = 30$$
$$-5n - 10 + 10 = 30 + 10$$
$$-5n = 40$$
$$\frac{-5n}{-5} = \frac{40}{-5}$$
$$n = -8$$

Method 2
Begin by dividing both sides of the equation by −5.

$$-5(n + 2) = 30$$
$$\frac{-5(n + 2)}{-5} = \frac{30}{-5}$$
$$n + 2 = -6$$
$$n + 2 - 2 = -6 - 2$$
$$n = -8$$

▶ Either way, the number is −8.

> Three consecutive integers have a sum of −9. What are the three integers?

You can solve this problem, by writing and solving an equation.

Consecutive integers are integers that follow each other in order with no gaps, for example, 34, 35, 36, or −2, −1, 0. Consecutive integers can be represented by $n, n + 1, n + 2, n + 3$, and so on.

So, you can use the equation $n + (n + 1) + (n + 2) = -9$ to represent the problem.

Solve the equation.
$$n + (n + 1) + (n + 2) = -9$$
$$n + n + 1 + n + 2 = -9$$
$$3n + 3 = -9$$
$$3n + 3 - 3 = -9 - 3$$
$$3n = -12$$
$$\frac{3n}{3} = -\frac{12}{3}$$
$$n = -4$$

Find the three integers.
If $n = -4$, the first integer is −4.
The second integer, $n + 1$, is −4 + 1, or −3.
The third integer, $n + 2$, is −4 + 2, or −2.

▶ The three integers are −4, −3, and −2.

Guided Instruction

Connect: Comparing algebraic solutions to arithmetic solutions

> Four friends rent bicycles and bike helmets for a day. The cost for renting each helmet is $2. The total cost for renting four bicycles and four helmets is $116. What is the cost of renting one bicycle?
>
> Compare algebraic and arithmetic solutions to the problem.

Show two ways to solve the problem using arithmetic.

Arithmetic Solution 1	**Arithmetic Solution 2**
Find the cost in dollars of renting 4 helmets. $4 \cdot 2 = 8$	Divide the total cost in dollars by 4. $116 \div 4 = 29$
Subtract the cost of renting 4 helmets from the total cost. $116 - 8 = 108$	Subtract the cost of renting 1 helmet. $29 - 2 = 27$
Divide the cost of renting 4 bicycles by 4. $108 \div 4 = 27$	

➡ The solution to the problem is the same: It costs $27 to rent one bicycle.

Show two ways to solve the problem using algebra. Let $x =$ the cost in dollars of renting 1 bicycle.

Algebraic Solution 1	**Algebraic Solution 2**
$4x + 4 \cdot 2 = 116$ $4x + 8 = 116$ $4x + 8 - 8 = 116 - 8$ $4x = 108$ $\dfrac{4x}{4} = \dfrac{108}{4}$ $x = 27$	$4(x + 2) = 116$ $\dfrac{4(x + 2)}{4} = \dfrac{116}{4}$ $x + 2 = 29$ $x + 2 - 2 = 29 - 2$ $x = 27$

➡ The solution to the problem is the same: It costs $27 to rent one bicycle.

Compare the sequence of operations in the algebraic solutions and in the arithmetic solutions.

Arithmetic and Algebraic Solution 1:	**Arithmetic and Algebraic Solution 2:**
• Multiply 2 by 4 to get 8. • Subtract 8 from 116 to get 108. • Divide 108 by 4 to get 27.	• Divide 116 by 4 to get 29. • Subtract 2 from 29 to get 27.

1. Use an equation to solve the problem below.

Damitri bought 5 packages of paper plates. He used 139 plates and had 11 plates left over. How many plates were in each package?

Answer There were _____ plates in each package.

For exercises 2–3, use the word problem below.

The perimeter of a rectangle is 38 feet. The length of the rectangle is 12 feet. What is the width of the rectangle?

2. Follow the steps to show two ways to solve the problem using arithmetic.

   a. Arithmetic Solution 1

   Multiply the length by 2 to find the total of the two lengths.

   _____

   Subtract the total of the two lengths from the perimeter to find the total of the two widths.

   _____

   Divide the total of the two widths by 2 to find the width.

   _____

   b. Arithmetic Solution 2

   Divide the perimeter by 2 to find the sum of the length and width.

   _____

   Subtract the length from the sum of the length and width to find the width.

   _____

   The solution to the problem is: The width of the rectangle is _____ feet.

Think•Pair•Share

MP7 3. Show an algebraic solution that has the same sequence of operations as Arithmetic Solution 2.

Independent Practice

Write an equation. Use *x* for the unknown number. Then solve the equation and the problem.

1. Boris buys 5 markers and a 29-cent eraser for a total of $3.24. How much does each marker cost?

   Equation _____

   Answer _____

2. Steve's Nut World increases the weight of its Big Almond Bag by 3 ounces. Seven Big Almond Bags now weigh a total of 126 ounces. How many ounces did the old Big Almond Bag weigh?

   Equation _____

   Answer _____

3. Dave sells popcorn at the ballpark. He is paid a flat rate of $40 each day, but also earns $0.45 for each box of popcorn he sells. Dave earns a total of $112 at Wednesday night's game. How many boxes of popcorn does he sell?

   Equation _____

   Answer _____

Independent Practice

For exercises 4–5, circle the equation or equations that could be used to represent the problem.

4. In the final hour that the Farmer's Market is open, Monica reduces the price of a fruit tart by $2.50. During that last hour, Monica sells 14 tarts and takes in $56. What is the regular price of one of Monica's tarts?

   a. $14t = 56$

   b. $14(t + 2.50) = 56$

   c. $14(t - 2.50) = 56$

   d. $14t - 2.50 = 56$

5. In training for the kayak race, Hannah kayaks 4 times back and forth across the river, then goes upstream 3.75 miles. In all, Hannah kayaks 15.7 miles. What is the distance from one side of the river to the other?

   a. $4(2d) + 3.75 = 15.7$

   b. $4(2d + 3.75) = 15.7$

   c. $8d + 3.75 = 15.7$

   d. $8(d + 3.75) = 15.7$

Write an equation for each problem below. Then solve the problem.

MP5 6. The perimeter of the new m-Phone is 16 inches. The phone's length is 5.25 inches. What is the width of the phone?

Equation _____

Answer _____

MP1 7. At Fish World, clownfish are on sale for $5 off with a maximum of 6 fish per customer. Rudy buys 6 clownfish on sale plus 3 more clownfish at the regular price and spends a total of $149.55. What is the regular price of a clownfish?

Equation _____

Answer _____

Independent Practice

MP2 **8.** Raoul makes a computer animation showing how to solve the equation $5(t - 1.25) = 8.75$. He now needs a word problem to go with his animation.

a. Write a word problem that matches the equation.

b. Solve the equation and write the answer for your problem.

Answer _____

MP3 **9.** Polk and Brian each solved the problem below using arithmetic.

Jake buys 4 bags of flour and 4 bags of sugar that weigh a total of 84 pounds. Each bag of sugar weighs 9 pounds. How much does each bag of flour weigh?

Polk

Find weight of 1 bag of sugar plus 1 bag of flour.
$$84 \div 4 = 21$$

Subtract weight of 1 bag of sugar.
$$21 - 9 = 12$$
Each bag of flour weighs 12 pounds.

Brian

Find the total weight of the sugar.
$$4 \cdot 9 = 36$$

Find the total weight of the flour.
$$84 - 36 = 48$$

Find the weight of 1 bag of flour.
$$48 \div 4 = 12$$
A bag of flour weighs 12 pounds.

Compare Maddie's algebraic solution at the right to Polk's and Brian's arithmetic solutions. Whose arithmetic solution has the same sequence of operations as Maddie's solution?

Maddie

Let f = weight of flour in pounds.
$$4f + 4(9) = 84$$
$$4f + 36 = 84$$
$$4f + 36 - 36 = 84 - 36$$
$$4f = 48$$
$$4f \div 4 = 48 \div 4$$
$$f = 12$$
Each bag of flour weighs 12 pounds.

Answer _____ arithmetic solution has the same sequence of operations as Maddie's algebraic solution.

> **Justify your answer.**

Solve the problems.

MP7 **10.** Four consecutive integers have a sum of −2. What are the integers?

✏ **Show your work.**

Answer _____

MP8 **11.** Three consecutive odd integers have a sum of −3. What are the integers?

✏ **Show your work.**

Answer _____

MP1 **12.** Together, Jason and Mara have $74. Jason has $6 more than $\frac{1}{3}$ as much money as Mara has. How much does each person have?

✏ **Show your work.**

Answer _____

Essential Question:
How can you solve inequalities of the form $px + q > r$ and $px + q < r$, where p, q, and r are specific rational numbers?

7.EE.4b

Guided Instruction

In this lesson, you will extend what you know about solving equations to solve inequalities.

Understand: Exploring properties of inequalities

Begin with the inequality $6 < 8$. Perform each of these operations on both sides of the inequality: add $+2$, subtract $+2$, multiply by $+2$, divide by $+2$, add -2, subtract -2, multiply by -2, and divide by -2. Which operations result in a true inequality?

Beginning Inequality	Operation Performed on Both Sides	Result	True or False?
$6 < 8$	Add $+2$	$8 < 10$	true
$6 < 8$	Subtract $+2$	$4 < 6$	true
$6 < 8$	Multiply by $+2$	$12 < 16$	true
$6 < 8$	Divide by $+2$	$3 < 4$	true
$6 < 8$	Add -2	$4 < 6$	true
$6 < 8$	Subtract -2	$8 < 10$	true
$6 < 8$	Multiply by -2	$-12 < -16$	false
$6 < 8$	Divide by -2	$-3 < -4$	false

➤ All of the operations except the last two result in a true inequality.

To make the false inequalities above into true inequalities, you must reverse the direction of the inequality symbol.

- The inequality $-12 < -16$ is false, but $-12 > -16$ is true.

- The inequality $-3 < -4$ is false, but $-3 > -4$ is true.

The examples above can be used to illustrate these properties of inequalities:

When you add (or subtract) a positive number or a negative number to (from) both sides of an inequality, you get a true inequality.

When you multiply (or divide) both sides of an inequality by a positive number, you get a true inequality.

When you multiply or divide both sides of an inequality by a negative number, you must reverse the direction of the inequality symbol to get a true inequality.

Understand: Solving inequalities of the form $px + q > r$

> Solve and graph the solution. $-3x + 2 > 17$

Solving an inequality means finding the values for the variable that make the inequality true. The steps for solving an inequality are like the steps for solving an equation. You write equivalent inequalities until you have the variable on one side of the inequality and a number, or constant term, on the other side.

$-3x + 2 > 17$
$-3x + 2 - 2 > 17 - 2$ ←——— Add -2 to both sides.
$-3x > 15$ ←——— Simplify both sides.
$\dfrac{-3x}{-3} < \dfrac{15}{-3}$ ←——— Divide both sides by -3.
    Reverse the direction of the inequality symbol.

$x < -5$ ←——— Simplify both sides.

Remember!

When you multiply or divide both sides of an inequality by a negative number, you must reverse the direction of the inequality symbol to get a true inequality.

The solution $x < -5$ means that any number that is less than -5 will make the inequality true. You can show the solution on a number line.

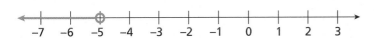

The open circle at -5 shows that the number -5 is *not* part of the solution.

➡ The solution is $x < -5$. The graph of the solution is shown above.

> Solve and graph the solution. $2n - 3 \geq 5$

$2n - 3 \geq 5$
$2n - 3 + 3 \geq 5 + 3$ ←——— Add $+3$ to both sides.
$2n \geq 8$ ←——— Simplify both sides.
$\dfrac{2n}{2} \geq \dfrac{8}{2}$ ←——— Divide both sides by 2.
$n \geq 4$ ←——— Simplify both sides.

The symbol $\geq$ means "is greater than or equal to."

The solution $n \geq 4$ means that any number that is greater than 4 or equal to 4 will make the inequality true. You can show the solution on a number line.

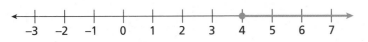

The closed circle at 4 shows that the number 4 is part of the solution.

➡ The solution is $n \geq 4$. The graph of the solution is shown above.

Guided Instruction

Connect: Checking the solution of an inequality

Check the solution and graph of the inequality $-3x + 2 > 17$.

Solution   **Graph**

$x < -5$

-7 -6 -5 -4 -3 -2 -1 0 1 2 3

Step 1

Check that the constant term in the solution is correct. Substitute the constant term for the variable in the equation that is related to the inequality.

In the solution $x < -5$, the constant term is -5.

Check

$$-3x + 2 = 17$$
$$-3 \cdot -5 + 2 = 17$$
$$15 + 2 = 17$$
$$17 = 17 \text{ True.}$$

Step 2

Check that the inequality sign is correct. Choose a number that is close to the constant, is easy to compute with, and that should make the inequality true. Substitute that number in the inequality and check that it is true.

Since the solution is $x < -5$, -6 should make the inequality true.

Check

$$-3x + 2 > 17$$
$$-3 \cdot -6 + 2 > 17$$
$$18 + 2 > 17$$
$$20 > 17 \text{ True.}$$

Do a second check to be sure that the inequality sign is correct. Choose a number that is close to the constant, is easy to compute with, and that should make the inequality *false*. Substitute that number in the inequality and check that it is *false*.

Since the solution is $x < -5$, -4 should make the inequality *false*.

Check

$$-3x + 2 > 17$$
$$-3 \cdot -4 + 2 > 17$$
$$12 + 2 > 17$$
$$14 > 17 \text{ False.}$$

Step 3

Check the graph.

-7 -6 -5 -4 -3 -2 -1 0 1 2 3

- If $\leq$ or $\geq$ is involved, is the circle closed?
  If $<$ or $>$ is involved, is the circle open?

Since the solution is $x < -5$, the circle should be open. It is. It checks.

- Find the location of the point representing your first number in Step 2. Be sure this location has a solid line. The point for -6 is part of the solid line. It checks.

- Find the location of the point for your second number in Step 2. Be sure this location does *not* have a solid line. The point for -4 is not part of the solid line. It checks.

➡ The solution $x < -5$ is correct and the graph is correct.

184   Unit 3 ▪ Focus on Expressions and Equations

Guided Practice

Complete the sentence.

1. When solving an inequality, you must reverse the direction of the inequality

   symbol if you _____ or _____ both sides of the inequality by

   a _____ number.

Draw lines to match.

2. $x > 2$

3. $x \geq 2$

4. $x < 2$

5. $x \leq 2$

a. ← | | | | | | | ○ | | →
   -4 -3 -2 -1 0 1 2 3 4

b. ← | | | | | | ● | | | →
   -4 -3 -2 -1 0 1 2 3 4

c. ← | | | | | | ● | | | →
   -4 -3 -2 -1 0 1 2 3 4

d. ← | | | | | | ○ | | | →
   -4 -3 -2 -1 0 1 2 3 4

Solve each inequality. Graph the solution.

6. $x + 8 > 2$

7. $-2c \leq 8$

8. $6m - 4 \leq -10$

_____

_____

_____

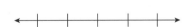

9. $-\frac{1}{2}n + \frac{3}{4} \geq 2$

10. $\frac{p}{-2} - 3 < 4$

11. $-r - 7.2 > 21.3$

_____

_____

_____

Think•Pair•Share

MP8 **12.** Predict the symbol in the solution for the inequality $-6x - 4 < 8$. Explain how
you made your prediction. Then solve the inequality and check your prediction.

Independent Practice

Draw lines to match.

1. $x < -1$

a.
```
  -6 -5 -4 -3 -2 -1  0  1  2  3  4  5  6
```

2. $x \geq -1$

b.
```
  -6 -5 -4 -3 -2 -1  0  1  2  3  4  5  6
```

3. $x \leq -1$

c.
```
  -6 -5 -4 -3 -2 -1  0  1  2  3  4  5  6
```

4. $x > -1$

d.
```
  -6 -5 -4 -3 -2 -1  0  1  2  3  4  5  6
```

For each inequality, write the letters that identify points that belong to the solution set.

a. $x = 2$　　　　**b.** $x = 0$　　　　**c.** $x = -4$　　　　**d.** $x = -8$

5. $x > -3$ _____

6. $x \leq 1$ _____

7. $x \geq 7$ _____

8. $x < -5$ _____

Solve each inequality. Graph the solution.

9. $x - 5 \geq -3$

10. $5k > -45$

_____

_____

11. $j - 13 < -13$

12. $\dfrac{i}{25} \geq -\dfrac{3}{5}$

_____

_____

13. $5m \geq -105$

_____

14. $2r + 5 \leq -11$

_____

15. $7b + 1 < -125$

_____

16. $6(c - 4) > 18$

_____

17. $-x \leq 45$

_____

18. $-z + 28 < -5$

_____

19. $17 - p \leq -53$

_____

20. $-12j \geq 156$

_____

21. $n + 4 + 2n < -20$

_____

22. $-\frac{1}{2}k - 14 < 11$

_____

Independent Practice

For exercises 23–28, circle the correct answer or answers.

23. Which of the following shows the solution of $7x - 5 > 16$?

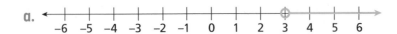

a.

b.

c.

d.

24. Which inequality's solution is shown on the graph?

a. $-2d + 1 < -7$ b. $-2d - 1 < -7$

c. $-2d + 1 > 7$ d. $3(d + 3) > -3$

25. Which number makes the inequality $5 - 5x \leq -35$ true?

a. 8   b. -8

c. 0   d. 100

26. Which number is a solution for $-8x < 48$?

a. -7 b. -6

c. -5 d. 12

27. Which number makes the inequality $-3n + 2 > -4$ true?

a. 0   b. 2

c. 4   d. 7

28. Which number is a solution for $9r - 4 < -40$?

a. -8 b. -4

c. 0   d. 4

MP3 **29.** Baxter's solution for $9x - 3(4x - 5) > 6$ is $x > -3$.
Is Baxter's solution correct? Explain.

$$9x - 3(4x - 5) > 6$$
$$9x - 12x + 15 > 6$$
$$-3x + 15 > 6$$
$$-3x + 15 - 15 > 6 - 15$$
$$-3x > -9$$
$$-3x \div -3 > -9 \div -3$$
$$x > -3$$

MP3 **30.** Kyanna wrote this statement: If $a > b$ then $a + c > b + c$. Is the statement always true? Can you write a similar statement for subtracting, multiplying, and dividing both sides of the inequality by c? Explain.

MP7 **31.** Jeffrey created an app to solve any algebraic equation. Jeffrey wants to modify the app so it will also solve any inequality. What kinds of changes does he need to make? Explain.

Problem Solving:
Linear Inequalities

Essential Question:
How can you construct inequalities of the form $px + q > r$ and $px + q < r$ to solve problems?

7.EE.4b

Guided Instruction

In this lesson, you will use inequalities to solve word problems.

Understand: Using an inequality to solve a real-world problem

> Mr. Lin is a telemarketer for a carpet-cleaning service. He is paid $100 per week plus $5 for every customer he brings in. If he wants to make $300 or more this week, how many customers does he need to bring in?

Step 1

Write an inequality to represent the problem.

You know that Mr. Lin is paid $100 per week plus $5 for every customer he brings in, and that he wants to make $300 or more.

Use a variable to represent the unknown. Use x to represent the unknown, the number of customers Mr. Lin needs to bring in.

$100 + 5x \geq 300$

Step 2

Solve the inequality.

$$100 + 5x \geq 300$$
$$100 - 100 + 5x \geq 300 - 100$$
$$5x \geq 200$$
$$\frac{5x}{5} \geq \frac{200}{5}$$
$$x \geq 40$$

Step 3

Use the solution to the inequality to answer the question posed in the problem.

The solution $x \geq 40$ tells us that Mr. Lin must bring in 40 customers or more to make $300 or more. This makes sense because Mr. Lin's weekly earnings will increase as the number of customers increases.

While the solution to the inequality includes all numbers greater than or equal to 40, only whole numbers will be solutions to this problem because, for example, it does not make sense that Mr. Lin bring in $40\frac{1}{2}$ customers.

➡ Mr. Lin must bring in 40 customers or more to make $300 or more.

✏ How would a graph of the inequality $x \geq 40$ be different from a graph representing the solutions to the word problem?

Guided Instruction

Understand: Solving a real-world problem in which the solution requires reversing the inequality symbol

> A game show contestant is given $1,000 and then asked 15 trivia questions. For every incorrect answer, the contestant loses $50. How many questions can the contestant get wrong and still take home $700 or more?

Step 1

Write an inequality to represent the problem.

You know that the contestant begins with $1,000 and loses $50 for each incorrect answer.

Use q to represent the unknown, the number of questions the contestant can get wrong and still take home $700 or more.

$1,000 - 50q \geq 700$

Step 2

Solve the inequality.

$$1,000 - 50q \geq 700$$

$$1,000 - 1,000 - 50q \geq 700 - 1,000$$

$$-50q \geq -300$$

$$\frac{-50q}{-50} \leq \frac{-300}{-50}$$ ← Divide both sides by -50. So, you must reverse the direction of the inequality symbol.

$$q \leq 6$$ ← Simplify both sides.

Step 3

Use the solution to the inequality to answer the question posed in the problem.

The solution $q \leq 6$ tells us that the contestant can get 6 or fewer questions wrong and take home $700 or more. This makes sense because the fewer questions the contestant gets wrong, the more money he takes home. This problem shows in a real-world situation why the inequality symbol is reversed.

While the solution to the inequality includes all numbers less than or equal to 6, only whole numbers will be solutions to this problem because, for example, it does not make sense that the contestant get -6 or $5\frac{1}{2}$ questions wrong. So, the only solutions to the problem are 0, 1, 2, 3, 4, 5, and 6 questions.

▷ The contestant must get 6 or fewer questions wrong.

✏ Draw a graph of the inequality $q \leq 6$. Draw a graph of the solution to the word problem.

Guided Instruction

Connect: Translating real-world phrases into inequality symbols

> How do you know which inequality symbol to use when writing an inequality?

You need to read carefully and think about what the words mean before writing the inequality symbol.

Let x = the cost in dollars of one concert ticket. We can look at how different phrases translate into inequality symbols.

- **The cost of 4 tickets *is greater than or equal to* $20.**
  The translation is $4x \geq 20$. When the phrase *is greater than*, *is less than*, *is greater than or equal to*, or *is less than or equal to* are used, the translation is straightforward.

- **The cost of 4 tickets *is at least* $20.**
  The translation is $4x \geq 20$. In this case you need to think about the situation. If the cost is at least $20, the cost may be $20 or it may be more than $20.

- **The cost of 4 tickets *is at most* $20.**
  The translation is $4x \leq 20$. In this case you again need to think about the situation. If the cost is at most $20, the cost may be $20 or it may be less than $20.

- **The *minimum* cost of 4 tickets *is* $20.**
  The translation is $4x \geq 20$. Again, think about the situation. If the minimum cost is $20, the least the cost may be is $20, so the cost is greater than or equal to $20.

- **The *maximum* cost of 4 tickets *is* $20.**
  The translation is $4x \leq 20$. The maximum is the opposite of the minimum. If the maximum cost is $20, the most the cost may be is $20, so the cost is less than or equal to $20.

- **The cost of 4 tickets *is no more than* $20.**
  The translation is $4x \leq 20$. In this case you again need to think about the situation. If the cost is no more than $20, the most the cost can be is $20, so the cost is $20 or less.

✎ Write an inequality for this word problem. Solve the problem. Does your answer make sense?

Four tickets cost no less than $20. What could be the cost of one ticket?

Draw lines to match the inequality with the words.

Nikki wants to buy a sandwich and a bottle of water. The water costs $2.
Let s = the amount in dollars that the sandwich can cost.

1. $s + 2 \leq 6$ **a.** The water and sandwich cost at least $6.

2. $s + 2 \geq 6$ **b.** The maximum cost of the water and sandwich is $6.

3. Follow the steps to solve the problem.

Two hikers begin their hike at the base of a mountain. The altitude
is 1,500 feet above sea level and the temperature is 9°C. For every 1,000 feet
rise in altitude, the temperature drops 3°C. They want to turn around and go
back down before the temperature reaches −6°C. At what altitude should they
turn back?

a. Write an inequality to find x, the number of thousands of feet in altitude that
the hikers can go up.

• The temperature at the base is _____°C.

• For every 1,000 feet rise in altitude, the temperature drops _____°C.

• They hikers want to go back down before the temperature reaches _____°C.

Inequality _____

b. Solve the inequality. How many feet can the hikers go up?

c. Find this information in the problem and then solve the problem.

• The altitude at the base is _____ feet above sea level.

Answer _____

 **Think•Pair•Share**

MP2 4. Use your answers from exercise 3. Draw a graph of your inequality from part b.
Draw a graph that represents the solution to the problem.

Independent Practice

Draw lines to match.

The city of New Rochelle declares snow warnings and snow emergencies during snow storms. In each inequality below, *s* represents the total amount of snow in inches. Match the sentence to the inequality. Some inequalities may be used more than once.

1. Snow total must exceed 2 inches to qualify as a snow emergency.

2. Snow total must be at least 2 inches to qualify as a snow emergency.

3. Snow total must be no more than 2 inches to qualify as a snow warning.

4. Snow total must be a minimum of 2 inches to qualify as a snow emergency.

5. Snow total must be less than 2 inches to qualify as a snow warning.

a. $s < 2$

b. $s > 2$

c. $s \leq 2$

d. $s \geq 2$

For exercises 6–11, circle the inequality or graph that matches the word problem.

6. Each of the 10 essay questions on the history exam counts for 6 points. Each true-false item counts for 4 points. Nancy scores 56 points on the essay section of the test. How many true-false items, *x*, can Nancy get correct to score more than 80 out of 100 points on the test?

   a. $4 + 56x > 80$

   b. $56 + 4x \geq 80$

   c. $56 + 4x \leq 80$

   d. $56 + 4x > 80$

7. Which graph shows the correct solution set for the problem in exercise 6?

a.

b.

c.

d.

8. The floor plan for Jenna's new kitchen shows an increase in the width of the original room by 3 feet but no change in the original length of the room, 16 feet. What is w, the width in feet of the original room, if the perimeter of the new room is no more than 58 feet?

   a. $2(16) + 2(w + 3) \leq 58$

   b. $2(16) + 2(w + 3) < 58$

   c. $32 + 2w + 6 < 58$

   d. $2(16) + 2w + 3 \geq 58$

9. Which graph shows the correct solution set for the problem in exercise 8?

   a.

   b.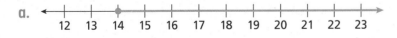

   c.

   d.

10. At Rye Indoor Tennis Club, court time is $\frac{1}{2}$ off the regular hourly rate after 10:00 P.M. On Saturday, Franco had \$35 in cash, played from 8:30 P.M. until midnight and did not have enough money to pay the total bill. How much is the regular hourly rate, r?

   a. $\frac{2}{3}r + \frac{1}{2}(2r) > 35$

   b. $\frac{3}{2}r + \frac{1}{2}r \geq 35$

   c. $\frac{3}{2}r + r > 35$

   d. $\frac{3}{2}r + 2(r - \frac{1}{2}r) \geq 35$

11. Which graph shows the correct solution set for the problem in exercise 10?

   a.

   b.

   c.

   d.

Independent Practice

MP7 **12.** At the start of each day, the cash drawer at Colossal National Bank has $10,000 in $20 bills. An electronic warning text is sent to the manager when the $20-bill drawer has $1,000 or less. The manager writes the inequality below to show b, the number of $20 bills that have been removed from the drawer when the message is sent.

$10{,}000 - 20b \leq 1{,}000$

a. Solve the inequality.

b. Explain in words what your solution means.

c. In the solution of the inequality, did the inequality sign reverse direction? If so, explain why this reversal makes sense. If not, explain why the inequality sign did not reverse direction.

d. What would the graph of the solution set of this problem look like? Would it show only whole-number points? Explain.

Write an inequality to represent the problem. Then solve the problem.

MP7 **13.** A 24-gallon fish tank is completely filled. Water is then continually added to the tank at a rate of $2\frac{3}{8}$ gallons per hour, and water is removed at a rate of $2\frac{5}{8}$ gallons per hour. The tank now has less than 20 gallons of water. How many hours (h) has it been since the tank was completely full?

Inequality _____

✏ **Show your work.**

Answer _____

MP1 **14.** The EYE Company spends $4,000,000 to refurbish its prescription-sunglass factory. Each pair of sunglasses sells for $99. Labor and materials cost $30 per pair and marketing costs another $19 per pair. How many pairs of sunglasses, s, will the company need to sell so that it makes a profit?

Inequality _____

✏️ **Show your work.**

Answer _____

MP2 **15.** In a skate-boarding competition, contestants start with a perfect 10.0 score and points are deducted. Contestants lose 0.1 point for a minor deduction and 0.3 point for a major deduction. Jara usually has twice as many minor deductions as major deductions in her routine. If Jara follows her normal minor/major ratio, how many major deductions, d, can she get and still obtain a total score of 8.0 or better?

Inequality _____

✏️ **Show your work.**

Answer _____

MP8 **16.** Look back at the problem in exercise 15. Explain how the graph of the solution to the inequality would be different from the graph of the solution to the problem.

Simplify each expression.

1. $-5(a - 9)$

2. $\dfrac{-8.3 - (+2.7)}{\frac{1}{5}}$

3. $13p + 13 - p$

_____

4. $-11b - 3(-4b + 1)$

5. $-2n + \dfrac{1}{6} - 4\dfrac{1}{2}n$

6. $3.75q - 0.6 - (-2.25q)$

_____

7. $-\dfrac{3}{5}(20r - 5) - (-6r)$

8. $-\dfrac{5}{6}x + \dfrac{4}{9} + \dfrac{2}{3}x + \dfrac{1}{3}$

9. $\dfrac{\frac{5}{6} - 2(-1\frac{3}{4})}{5\frac{1}{5}}$

_____

Solve each equation.

10. $v - 5 = 7$

11. $-4s - 2 = -14$

12. $-10(h - 2) - 4 = 36$

_____

Solve each inequality. Graph the solution.

13. $z + 5 < 5$

14. $9r + 3 \leq -15$

15. $-\dfrac{2}{5}k + 20 < -8$

_____

For exercises 16–21, circle the correct answer or answers.

16. On Tuesday at noon there were 4 inches of snow on the ground. Then it snowed at a rate of i inches per hour for 7 hours. By Tuesday at 7:00 P.M. there were 25 inches of snow on the ground. Which equation represents this situation?

   a. $7(i + 4) = 25$

   b. $4 + 7i = 25$

   c. $7i = 25 - 4$

   d. $7i - 4 = 25$

17. Rona receives a $70 gift card to use at the Bootery. She buys a pair of boots for $36 and 8 pairs of socks. She does not use the entire amount on the gift card. Which inequality can be used to find s, the price in dollars of each pair of socks?

   a. $70 + 8s < 36$ **b.** $36 + 8s < 70$

   c. $70 - 8s < 36$ **d.** $36 - 8s < 70$

18. A house valued at $100,000 gains 6 percent in value. Which expression shows the current value of the house in dollars?

   a. $\frac{6}{100} \cdot 100{,}000$ **b.** $1.06 \cdot 100{,}000$

   c. $(1 + 0.06)100{,}000$ **d.** $1.06(1 + 100{,}000)$

19. Which of the following is equivalent to $-22m - 33 - 44m$?

   a. $11(-2m - 3 - 4m)$ **b.** $-11(-2m - 3 - 4m)$

   c. $-11(2m + 3 + 4m)$ **d.** $-11(2m - 3 - 4m)$

20. Which equation has the same solution as $-3(2x - 4) = 30$?

   a. $2x - 4 = -10$ **b.** $2x - 4 = 10$

   c. $2x = -6$ **d.** $x = -3$

21. Which of the following is equivalent to $\dfrac{-\frac{1}{4}(16.4) + \frac{5}{8} \div 1\frac{1}{4}}{\frac{1}{3}}$?

   a. -10.8 **b.** $(-4.1 + 0.5) \cdot 3$

   c. $(-4.1 + 0.5) \div 3$ **d.** -3.6

Solve the problems.

MP2 **22.** In Week 1, Boris works 30 hours and earns r dollars per hour. In Week 2, Boris gets a raise of $2.75 per hour. He works 32 hours at this new rate. During the two weeks, he earns a total of $723.50. What was his original rate per hour?

   Show your work.

Answer _____

MP7 **23.** Zero-G Space Exploration Park has a $14.50 admission price and individual activities regularly cost $4.50 each. On Tuesdays, each activity is discounted $1.25. Expressions A and B show the cost of visiting Zero-G and participating in a activities on a Tuesday.

Expression A: $(14.50 + 4.50a) - 1.25a$ **Expression B:** $14.50 + a(4.50 - 1.25)$

How does each expression show a different way to find the cost?

MP2 **24.** Romita gets the sushi lunch special at Yoshi's. By using a coupon, she receives $2 off the regular price, p. Her total cost, including 20% for tax and tip, is $9. What is p, the regular price of the lunch special?

✎▸ **Show your work.**

Answer _____

MP2 **25.** The city treasury began with $1,100,000 at the beginning of the year. Each day since, tax revenues have come in at a rate of $12,500 per day. Expenditures each day average $15,000 per day. The treasury now has less than $1,000,000. How many days, d, has it been since the beginning of the year?

✎▸ **Show your work.**

Answer _____

Progress Check

UNIT 4

Look at how the Common Core standards you have learned and will learn connect.

It is very important for you to understand the standards from the prior grade level so that you will be able to develop an understanding of geometry in this unit and be prepared for next year. To practice your skills, go to sadlierconnect.com.

GRADE 6	GRADE 7	GRADE 8
I Can...	Before Unit 4 / **Can I ?** / After Unit 4	**I Will...**
	☐ **7.G.1** Solve problems involving scale drawings of geometric figures ☐	**8.G.4** Understand and demonstrate similarity of two-dimensional figures
	☐ **7.G.2** Draw geometric shapes for given conditions ☐	
	☐ **7.G.3** Describe two-dimensional figures that result from slicing three-dimensional figures ☐	
6.G.1 Find the area of triangles, quadrilaterals, and polygons composed of rectangles, triangles, and other shapes	☐ **7.G.4** Apply the formulas for the area and circumference of a circle ☐	
	☐ **7.G.5** Use facts about angles to write and solve simple equations for unknown angles in figures ☐	**8.G.5** Establish facts about angles formed when parallel lines are cut by a transversal and facts about angle relationships involving triangles
6.G.1 Find the area of triangles, quadrilaterals, and polygons composed of rectangles, triangles, and other shapes **6.G.2** Find the volume of rectangular prisms using formulas **6.G.4** Use nets to find the surface area	☐ **7.G.6** Solve problems involving the area of two-dimensional objects composed of triangles, quadrilaterals, and polygons ☐ Solve problems involving the surface area or volume of three-dimensional objects composed of cubes and right prisms	**8.G.9** Apply the volume formulas for cones, cylinders, and spheres

HOME◆CONNECT...

In this unit your child will:

- Work with scale drawings

- Construct various shapes, including triangles

- Slice three-dimensional figures to observe the cross-sections

- Develop and use formulas for area and circumference of circles

- Use equations to find unknown angle measures

- Solve problems involving area, volume, and surface area

NOTE: All of these learning goals for your child are based on the Grade 7 Common Core State Standards for Mathematics.

In this unit your child will be studying scale drawings, constructions, cross-sections, circles, surface area, volume, and finding unknown angle measures. The work with scale drawings uses ratio concepts and the work with unknown angle measures uses equations, so this unit demonstrates connections between different parts of mathematics.

Your child will combine previously learned area formulas for polygons to find the total surface area of a solid.

Ways to Help Your Child

Encourage your child to explain his or her mathematics homework to you, even if it is a topic that is not familiar to you. If a part of the explanation seems unclear, ask your child to go over it again, breaking it into smaller steps that you can follow. Do not be concerned that you are not familiar with a topic—much of the mathematics your child is learning goes beyond the topics that were taught 20 to 30 years ago. Playing the role of teacher, which is what your child will be doing, is an effective way for him or her to develop even better and deeper understanding of a topic.

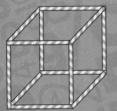 **Activity:** The strong shape of a triangle makes it useful in construction because it does not easily become deformed. As an experiment, you and your child can build two cubes—one with faces that are squares and one with diagonals that form two triangles in each face. You will need 24 straws about 5 inches long and 4 straws a little over 7 inches long. Use tape or staples to hold the straws together.

Place a paper plate on top of each cube and then start adding the same objects, such as coins or marbles, to both plates. The cube without the diagonal supports should collapse first, showing that triangles are a strong shape.

Focus on Geometry

Essential Question:
How do geometric concepts help you represent and solve real-world problem situations?

Use Scale Drawings to Solve Problems

Essential Question:
How can you solve problems about scale drawings and how do you make a scale drawing?

7.G.1

Words to Know:
scale drawing
scale
scale factor

Guided Instruction

In this lesson, you will learn how to use scale drawings and how to make scale drawings.

Understand: Solving problems about scale drawings

Fran makes this scale drawing of her rectangular bedroom floor. She uses inch grid paper. In her drawing, the width is 2 inches and the length is 3 inches. If the actual width of Fran's room is 8 feet, what is the actual length?

8 ft

? ft

Here are three ways to find the actual length of Fran's room.

Method 1 A scale drawing is a drawing of a two-dimensional figure. A scale drawing is smaller than the actual figure. In a scale drawing, there is a proportional relationship between the lengths in the scale drawing and the corresponding lengths in the actual figure.

To find the length of Fran's room, you can find the unknown quantity in this proportional relationship.

Let f = the length of the room in feet.

width in scale drawing ⟶ $\dfrac{2 \text{ in.}}{8 \text{ ft}} = \dfrac{3 \text{ in.}}{f \text{ ft}}$ ⟵ length in scale drawing
width of actual room ⟶ ⟵ length of actual room

Using cross products:
$2f = 8 \cdot 3$
$2f = 24$
$\dfrac{2f}{2} = \dfrac{24}{2}$
$f = 12$ ⟵ The length of Fran's room is 12 feet.

The next two methods will each give you the same answer.

Remember!

Using cross products is one way to find the unknown quantity in a proportional relationship.

Method 2 The scale is the ratio of the length of a side in the scale drawing to the corresponding length in the actual figure. The ratio is usually written using a colon, but may also be written using an equal sign. In this example, the scale is 2 inches : 8 feet or 1 inch : 4 feet.

The scale factor is the ratio of the lengths of the corresponding sides *when both lengths are in the same units*. So, in this scale drawing, 2 inches and 8 feet are corresponding lengths. Since 8 feet = 8 • 12, or 96 inches, the corresponding lengths with same units are 2 inches and 96 inches.

There are two possible scale factors for any scale drawing. The ratio of length in the scale drawing to the corresponding length in the actual figure and the ratio of length in the actual figure to the corresponding length in the scale drawing.

The scale factors for this scale drawing are $\frac{2 \text{ inches}}{96 \text{ inches}} = \frac{1}{48}$ and $\frac{96 \text{ inches}}{2 \text{ inches}} = 48$. The first scale factor indicates that each length in the drawing is $\frac{1}{48}$ of the corresponding length in Fran's room. The second scale factor indicates that each length in Fran's room is 48 times the corresponding length in the scale drawing. The two scale factors are always reciprocals of each other.

You can use either scale factor to find an unknown length. In this example, we use 48 because the known length is in the scale drawing.

Multiply 3 inches (the length in the scale drawing) by 48 (the scale factor) to find the length of Fran's room in inches.

3 • 48 = 144 inches

To convert 144 inches to feet, divide by 12.
144 ÷ 12 = 12 ⟵ The length of Fran's room is 12 feet.

Method 3 There is another relationship that exists in scale drawings.

The ratio of any two lengths in the scale drawing is equal to the ratio of the corresponding lengths in the actual figure.

So, the ratio of length to width in the scale drawing is equal to the ratio of length to width in Fran's room.

Let x = the length in feet of Fran's room.

length in scale drawing ⟶ $\frac{3 \text{ in.}}{2 \text{ in.}} = \frac{x \text{ ft.}}{8 \text{ ft.}}$ ⟵ length of actual room
width in scale drawing ⟶   ⟵ width of actual room

Again, using cross products:
$2x = 3 • 8$
$2x = 24$
$\frac{2x}{2} = \frac{24}{2}$
$x = 12$ ⟵ The length of Fran's room is 12 feet.

Guided Instruction

Understand: Reproducing a scale drawing at a different scale

In this scale drawing of a play space, the scale is 1 centimeter : 6 meters. Redo the scale drawing so that the scale is 1 centimeter : 12 meters.

You can use what you know about proportional relationships to find the length and width to use in *your* scale drawing.

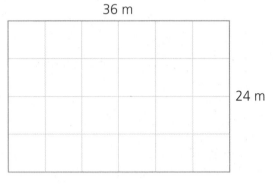

36 m

24 m

Scale 1 cm : 6 m

Step 1

Find the length of the rectangle in *your* scale drawing.

ℓ = the length of the rectangle in your scale drawing
Use the scale of your drawing for the first ratio.

$\dfrac{1\ \text{cm}}{12\ \text{m}} = \dfrac{\ell\ \text{cm}}{36\ \text{m}}$ ← length in scale drawing
← actual length

You can use multiplicative comparisons to find the unknown quantity.

×3
$\dfrac{1\ \text{cm}}{12\ \text{m}} = \dfrac{\ell\ \text{cm}}{36\ \text{m}}$
×3

$1 \times 3 = 3$
$\ell = 3$

The length of the rectangle in your scale drawing will be 3 centimeters.

Remember!
Using multiplicative comparisons is another way to find the unknown quantity in a proportional relationship.

Step 2

Find the width of the rectangle in *your* scale drawing.

w = the width of the rectangle in your scale drawing
Again, use the scale of your drawing for the first ratio.

$\dfrac{1\ \text{cm}}{12\ \text{m}} = \dfrac{w\ \text{cm}}{24\ \text{m}}$ ← width in scale drawing
← actual width

Again, use multiplicative comparisons to find the unknown quantity.

×2
$\dfrac{1\ \text{cm}}{12\ \text{m}} = \dfrac{w\ \text{cm}}{24\ \text{m}}$
×2

$1 \times 2 = 2$
$w = 2$

The width of the rectangle in your scale drawing will be 2 centimeters.

Step 3

Make the scale drawing. Use centimeter grid paper. Draw a rectangle that is 3 cm × 2 cm. Label the sides using the length and width of the actual play space. Write the scale.

➡ The scale drawing is shown in Step 3.

36 m

24 m

Scale 1 cm : 12 m

Guided Instruction

Connect: Comparing the scale factor for length to the scale factor for area

A greeting card catalog includes scale drawings of their cards. A scale drawing of a Thank You card is 5 cm long and 4 cm wide. The actual card is 15 cm long and 12 cm wide. What is a scale factor for the lengths? What is a scale factor for the areas? How are the two scale factors related?

Step 1

Find a scale factor for the lengths.

In this example, we will choose to use the ratio of the lengths on the *card* to the ratio of the lengths on the *scale drawing*.

You can use the two lengths or you can use the two widths.

Using the two lengths:

length on card ⟶ 15 cm
length in drawing ⟶ 5 cm

$\frac{15 \text{ cm}}{5 \text{ cm}} = 3$

Using the two widths:

width on card ⟶ 12 cm
width in drawing ⟶ 4 cm

$\frac{12 \text{ cm}}{4 \text{ cm}} = 3$

Either way, the scale factor for the lengths is 3.

Step 2

Find the scale factor for the areas.
Since we chose to use the ratio of the lengths on the *card* to the ratio of the lengths in the *scale drawing*, we must use the *same order* for the ratio of the areas.

Area of card:

Area = length • width

Area = 15 cm • 12 cm

Area = 180 cm²

Area of scale drawing:

Area = length • width

Area = 5 cm • 4 cm

Area = 20 cm²

Scale factor:

area of card ⟶ 180 cm²
area of drawing ⟶ 20 cm²

$\frac{180 \text{ cm}^2}{20 \text{ cm}^2} = 9$

The scale factor for the areas is 9.

Now compare the two scale factors.

9 is 3 • 3 or 3 squared or 3^2.

Remember!
You can write "square centimeters" as cm².

The scale factor for the areas is the square of the scale factor for the lengths. This is true for any scale drawing.

➡ A scale factor for the lengths is 3. The corresponding scale factor for the areas is 9. The scale factor for the areas is the square of the scale factor for the lengths.

Guided Practice

Use the information below for exercises 1–3.

Liam used centimeter grid paper to make this scale drawing. The length of the actual rectangle is 21 m. The width of the actual rectangle is the unknown.

1. The scale in the drawing is

   7 cm : _____ m or 1 cm: _____ m.

2. Let x = the length of the unknown side in meters. Complete this proportional relationship.

   $$\frac{7 \text{ cm}}{21 \text{ m}} = \frac{\underline{} \text{ cm}}{x \text{ m}}$$

3. The value of x in exercise 2 is _____. The length of the unknown side is

   _____ meters.

Make a scale drawing.

4. Using the centimeter grid, draw a scale drawing of a rectangle 60 cm by 40 cm. Use the scale 1 cm : 10 cm.

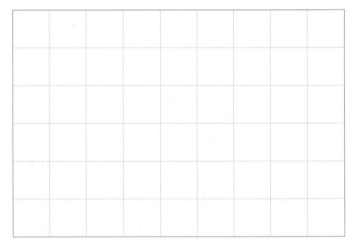

☂ Think•Pair•Share

MP2   5. In the scale drawing you drew in exercise 4, what are the two scale factors for length? Predict the scale factors for area. Then find the area of your scale drawing and the area of the actual rectangle and check your predictions.

Independent Practice

For exercises 1–4, match the scale to the drawing. Each drawing is on centimeter grid paper.

1. 1 cm : 17.5 m

2. 1 cm : 0.75 m

3. 1 cm : 8 m

4. 1 cm : 60 m

a.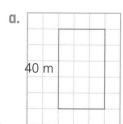
40 m

b.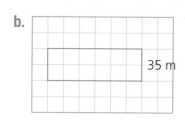
35 m

c.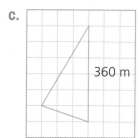
360 m

d.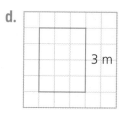
3 m

5. The figure at the right is on centimeter grid paper.

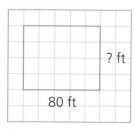
? ft

80 ft

   a. Find the scale of the drawing.

     Answer _____

   b. Write a proportion for finding the unknown length. Find the unknown length.

     Answer _____

6. A scale drawing of the floor of a theater has a scale factor of 18. Mark says that he can use this information and any length on the scale drawing to find the corresponding length in the actual theater. He says that he can also use this information and any length in the actual theater to find the corresponding length on the scale drawing. Do you agree with Mark? Explain.

Independent Practice

7. On the centimeter grid below, draw a scale drawing of a rectangular lawn that measures 66 feet by 30 feet. Use the scale 1 cm : 6 ft.

For exercises 8–10, circle the correct answer or answers.

8. The figure is shown on centimeter grid paper. Which of the following is true?

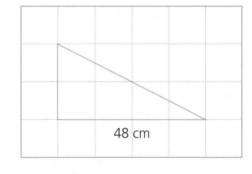

a. The scale is 1 cm : 12 cm.

b. A scale factor is $\frac{1}{12}$.

c. A scale factor is $\frac{2}{48}$.

d. A scale factor is $\frac{12}{1}$.

48 cm

9. A scale factor for a house floor plan is 24. On the drawing, the living room measures 8 inches. What will be the length of the actual living room?

a. 24 feet   b. 192 inches   c. 16 feet   d. 16 inches

10. The scale drawing at the right is on centimeter grid paper. Which of the following is true for this drawing?

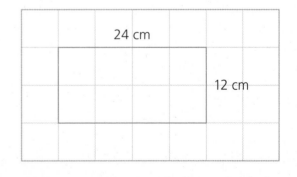

24 cm

12 cm

a. A scale factor for lengths is 6.

b. A scale factor for areas is 6.

c. A scale factor for lengths is 36.

d. A scale factor for areas is 36.

Independent Practice

Solve the problems.

MP6 **11.** Tamisha works as an intern in an architect's office. A designer drew a scale drawing of a kitchen without using grid paper. In the drawing, 1 inch represents $2\frac{1}{2}$ feet. Tamisha's supervisor wants her to determine the scale factors for the lengths and the scale factors for the areas.

a. Find the scale factors for the lengths.

✏️ **Show your work.**

Answer _____

b. Find the scale factors for the areas.

✏️ **Show your work.**

Answer _____

MP2 **12.** The scale drawing on the left shows Leanna's plan for a picture window. The scale drawing on the right is from a store catalog. Both scale drawings are shown on inch-grid paper. Will the window fit?

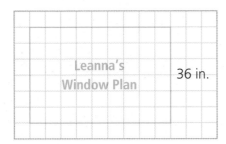

Leanna's Window Plan   36 in.   54 in.   Clear View Window Company

Answer _____

✏️ **Justify your answer.**

24 Draw Shapes that Meet Given Conditions

Essential Question:
How can you construct geometric shapes with given conditions?
7.G.2

Guided Instruction

In this lesson, you will learn how to draw shapes that meet given conditions. You will learn how to tell if three side lengths or three angle measures can be used to draw *exactly one triangle*, *more than one triangle*, or *no triangle*.

Understand: Drawing a geometric shape to meet given conditions

> Lamar is asked to draw a quadrilateral that has exactly one pair of parallel sides and one angle that measures 40°. What might this quadrilateral look like?

Lamar follows these steps to draw his shape.

Lamar uses a protractor to draw the 40° angle. The sides of the angle become two sides of the quadrilateral.

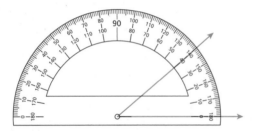

Lamar uses a ruler to draw a third side parallel to one of the sides of the angle.

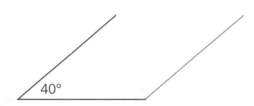

Lamar draws the fourth side of the quadrilateral.

Lamar first draws this line segment as the fourth side. Then he realizes that his shape now has two sets of parallel sides instead of just one set.

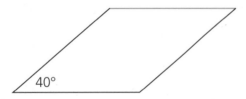

Lamar revises his drawing.

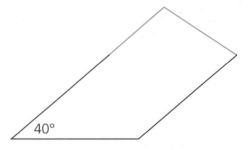

▶ The second figure at the right shows the drawing that Lamar made to meet the given conditions.

▭▶ Draw a figure that is different from Lamar's, but still meets the given conditions. Use a ruler and a protractor or technology. What is the best name for the shape?

Understand: Drawing a triangle when given three side lengths

> Stan has three straws that are 4 inches, 8 inches, and 6 inches long. Can he make a triangle using the straws? Can he make *more than one triangle*?

Stan tries to make a triangle. He lays out the straws side by side.

4 in.   8 in.   6 in.

Stan makes a triangle by moving the red and purple straws so that they meet at a point.

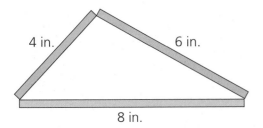

4 in.   6 in.

8 in.

This is the only triangle that Stan can make using the three straws. If Stan makes a triangle that looks different, he can turn it or flip it so that it exactly fits onto this triangle.

We say that the three sides make *exactly one triangle* or that the three sides determine *one unique triangle*.

▶ Stan can make *exactly one triangle* using straws with lengths 4 in., 8 in., and 6 in.

> Stan has three more straws that are 3 centimeters, 9 centimeters, and 4 centimeters long. Can he make a triangle using those straws?

Stan tries to make a triangle. He lays out the straws side by side.

3 cm   9 cm   4 cm

Stan tries to connect the teal and green straws but they are too short. He cannot make a triangle.

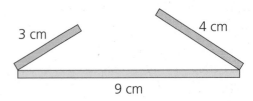

3 cm   4 cm

9 cm

▶ Stan can make *no triangle* using straws with lengths 3 cm, 9 cm, and 4 cm.

These examples help illustrate a property of triangles.

Property of Triangles: Given 3 side lengths, if each side length is less than the sum of the other two side lengths, *exactly one triangle* can be constructed. If any one side length is greater than or equal to the sum of the other two side lengths, *no triangle* can be constructed.

Guided Instruction

Understand: Drawing a triangle when given three angle measures

> Can Jeff make a triangle with these three angle measures: 40°, 60°, and 80°?
> Can he make *more than one triangle*?

Here are the steps Jeff uses to try to make a triangle.

Jeff uses a protractor to draw a 40° angle.

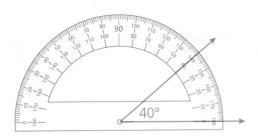

Jeff moves the protractor and draws a 60° angle that shares a ray with the 40° angle.

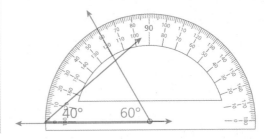

The rays intersect to form a triangle with a 40° angle and a 60° angle. Jeff measures the third angle. It measures 80°.

Jeff has made a triangle with angle measures 40°, 60°, and 80°.

Jeff realizes that he can make a different triangle by keeping the angles the same measure and increasing the lengths of the sides. He sees that there is no limit to the number of triangles he can make. We can say that *more than one triangle* can be made. We can also say that *an infinite number of triangles* can be made.

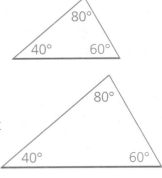

➡ Jeff can make *more than one triangle*.

> Can Jeff make a triangle with these three angle measures: 30°, 50°, and 25°?

Jeff uses the same method as in the first example. But he finds that the third angle has a measure of 100°, not 25°. Jeff cannot make a triangle with angle measures 30°, 50°, and 25°.

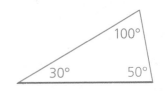

➡ Jeff can make *no triangle*.

The above examples help to illustrate this property of triangles.

> **Property of Triangles:** If the sum of three angle measures is exactly 180°, *an infinite number of triangles* can be constructed. If the sum is less than or greater than 180°, *no triangle* can be constructed.

Connect: **Constructing triangles when given 3 side lengths or 3 angle measures**

> When given 3 side lengths or 3 angle measures, how do you predict if you can construct *exactly one triangle*, *more than one triangle*, or *no triangle* for each set of conditions?

➡ Under certain conditions you can make general statements about constructing triangles.

The examples on pages 213 and 214 illustrate these four **Properties of Triangles:**

Given 3 side lengths:

1. If each side length is less than the sum of the other two side lengths, *exactly one triangle* can be constructed.
2. If any one side length is greater than or equal to the sum of the other two side lengths, *no triangle* can be constructed.

Given 3 angle measures:

3. If the sum of the angle measures is exactly 180°, *more than one triangle* can be constructed. In fact, an infinite number of triangles can be constructed.
4. If the sum of the angle measures is greater than or less than 180°, *no triangle* can be constructed.

✏ Use the properties of triangles to predict whether you can draw *exactly one triangle*, *more than one triangle*, or *no triangle* for each set of conditions. Then try to draw the triangle to check your prediction.

a. side lengths: 3 cm, 4 cm, 5 cm

Predict

_____

Property used: _____

Draw

Was your prediction correct? _____

b. angle measures: 75°, 25°, 30°

Predict

_____

Property used: _____

Draw

Was your prediction correct? _____

Guided Practice

Draw one shape that meets the given conditions. Use a ruler and a protractor.

1. a parallelogram (a quadrilateral with two sets of parallel sides) with no right angles

2. a pentagon with exactly three of its sides measuring 2 cm

3. a triangle with side lengths 3 cm, 3 cm, and 5 cm

4. an isosceles triangle (a triangle with at least two sides the same length) with one angle that measures 100°

Tell whether *exactly one triangle, more than one triangle,* or *no triangle* can be constructed given the side lengths or angle measures.

5. side lengths: 3 cm, 6 cm, 9 cm

____

6. side lengths: 2 in., 5 in., 5 in.

____

7. angle measures: 50°, 50°, and 80°

____

8. angle measures: 20°, 30°, and 50°

____

Think•Pair•Share

MP3 9. Can you draw a triangle with more than one right angle? Explain.

Draw one shape that meets the given conditions. Use a ruler and a protractor.

1. a trapezoid with two pairs of equal angles

2. a pentagon with two right angles

3. a triangle with one right angle and two equal sides of 2 cm each

4. a quadrilateral with sides 3 cm, 4 cm, 5 cm, and 6 cm

5. a triangle with angle measures 85°, 35°, and 60°

6. a rhombus that is not a square with sides that each measure 3 cm

Independent Practice

Tell whether *exactly one triangle*, *more than one triangle*, or *no triangle* can be constructed given the side lengths or angle measures.

7. angle measures: 32°, 48°, and 100°

   _____

8. side lengths: 12 cm, 8 cm, 3 cm

   _____

9. side lengths: 13 in., 9 in., 8 in.

   _____

10. angle measures: 60°, 60°, and 100°

   _____

For exercises 11–15, circle each correct answer. Use a ruler and a protractor if necessary.

11. Which figure has all sides equal in length and all angles equal in measure?

   a.   b.    c.   d.

12. Which figure has two obtuse angles?

   a.   b.   c.    d.

13. For which of the following conditions can you draw *exactly one triangle*?

   a. Each side of the triangle is 6.25 feet long.

   b. One angle of the triangle has a measure of 45°.

   c. The triangle has angle measures of 70°, 80°, and 30°.

   d. For *n* = 8, the sides of the triangle measure *n*, *n* + 1, and *n* + 2 units.

14. For which of the following conditions is *no triangle* possible?

   a. The sides of the triangle measure 3 ft, 4 ft, and 5 ft.

   b. The triangle has angles that measure 40°, 80°, 40°.

   c. The triangle has two obtuse angles.

   d. For any value of *n*, the sides of the triangle measure *n*, *n* + 1, and *n* + 2 units.

15. For which of the following conditions can *more than one triangle* be drawn?

    a. The triangle has angles that measure 40°, 90°, and 40°.

    b. The triangle has two equal angles.

    c. The triangle has three equal angles.

    d. The triangle has no equal angles.

MP3 **16.** Julio claims that he can draw a triangle that has three acute angles. Geulia says that she can draw a triangle that has no acute angles. Is either student correct, or are both students correct? Explain.

MP4 **17.** Freida says that she can draw a triangle that has three angles with equal measure, but the sides are not of equal length. Is Freida is correct? Explain. Use a drawing in your explanation.

Solve the problem.

MP2 **18.** An isosceles triangle has two angles with equal measure, 25°. Todd says that the third angle must have a measure of 130°. Is Todd correct?

    Answer _____

    ✏ **Justify your answer.**

Construct Triangles Using Both Side Lengths and Angle Measures

Essential Question:
Given two side lengths and one angle measure, or two angle measures and one side length, can you construct *exactly one triangle, more than one triangle,* or *no triangle?*

7.G.2

Guided Instruction

In this lesson, you will learn how to tell if two side lengths and one angle measure, or two angle measures and one side length, can be used to draw *exactly one triangle, more than one triangle,* or *no triangle.*

Understand: Drawing a triangle when given two side lengths and the measure of the angle between them

> Can Selina draw a triangle with a 4 cm side, a 3 cm side, and a 50° angle between those two sides? Can she draw *more than one triangle?*

Selena follows these steps to draw a triangle.

Selena uses a protractor to draw a 50° angle.

She uses a ruler to mark end points of the two sides so that one side is 4 cm long and the other side is 3 cm long.

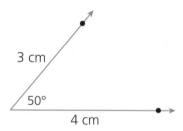

Selena connects the two endpoints to draw the third side of the triangle.

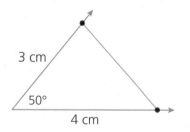

This is the only triangle that Selena can draw. If she draws a triangle that looks different, she can turn it and/or flip it so that it exactly fits onto this triangle.

Property of Triangles: Any time you are given 2 side lengths and the measure of the angle (less than 180°) between them, you can draw *exactly one triangle.*

➡ Selena can draw exactly one triangle, not more than one triangle.

✏️ Use a protractor and a ruler. Draw a triangle that has sides 3 cm and 4 cm and a 50° angle between them. Did you or anyone in your class draw a triangle that is different from Selena's?

Guided Instruction

Understand: Drawing a triangle when given two side lengths and the measure of an angle not between them

> Can Selina draw a triangle with a 4 cm side, a 5 cm side, and a 50° angle that is *not* between those two sides? Can she draw more than one triangle?

Selena draws a 50° angle. She finds that she can draw three different triangles in which the 50° angle is not between the 4 cm side and the 5 cm side.

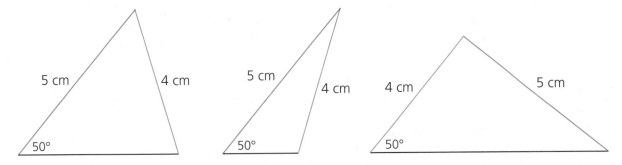

➡ Selena can draw more than one triangle.

For the particular conditions above, Selena can draw more than one triangle. However, this is *not* the case for any two given side lengths and an angle not between them. **You cannot generalize in this case. You have to try different options for each set of measurements you may be given.**
Here are two examples:

For side lengths 2 cm, 2 cm, and a 40° angle not between them, exactly one triangle can be drawn.

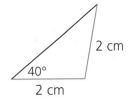

For side lengths 3 cm, 3 cm, and a 160° angle not between them, no triangle can be drawn.

Property of Triangles: If given two sides that do not make up the given angle, *sometimes no triangle, sometimes exactly one triangle,* and *sometimes more than one triangle* can be constructed.

✏ Use a protractor and a ruler or technology software to draw a triangle that has two sides 4 cm and 5 cm and a 50° angle *not* between them. Did you or any of your classmates draw a triangle that is different from the three triangles Selena drew?

Guided Instruction

Understand: Drawing a triangle when given two angle measures and the length of one side

> Can Selina draw a triangle with a 30° angle, a 110° angle, and a 5 cm side that is between the two angles? Can she draw *more than one triangle*?

Step 1

Selena draws the 5 cm segment.

_____
5 cm

Step 2

She draws a 30° angle at one end of the segment and a 110° angle at the other end.

30°   110°
5 cm

Step 3

Selena extends the sides of each angle to make the only possible triangle.

▶ Selena can draw *exactly one triangle*, not more than one triangle.

This is the only triangle that Selena can draw.

Property of Triangles: Any time you are given 2 angle measures (sum less than 180°) and the measure of the side between them, you can draw *exactly one triangle*.

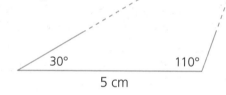
30°   110°
5 cm

> Can Selina draw a triangle with a 30° angle, a 45° angle and a 3 cm side that is *not* between the two given angles? Can she draw *more than one triangle*?

Selena uses a ruler and a protractor to explore different options and she finds that she can draw two different triangles.

She can draw *exactly one triangle* that has the 3 cm side opposite the 30° angle.

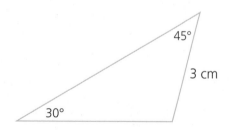
45°
3 cm
30°

She can draw *exactly one triangle* that has the 3 cm side opposite the 45° angle.

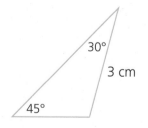
30°
3 cm
45°

▶ Selena can draw *more than one triangle*: *exactly one triangle* with the given side opposite the 30° angle and *exactly one triangle* with the given side opposite the 45° angle.

> **Property of Triangles:** If the two given angle measures are different (sum less than 180°), you can always draw two different triangles. If the two given angles have the same measure (sum less than 180°), you can only draw one triangle.

Connect: Constructing triangles when given two side lengths and one angle measure or two angle measures and one side length

> When given two side lengths and one angle measure or two angle measures and one side length, how can you predict whether *exactly one triangle*, *more than one triangle*, or *no triangle* can be constructed?

▶ Under certain conditions, you can make general statements about constructing triangles.

The examples on pages 220 and 221 illustrate these four **Properties of Triangles:**

Given two side lengths and one angle measure (less than 180°):

1. If the two given sides make up the given angle, *exactly one triangle* can be constructed.

2. If the two given sides do not make up the given angle, *sometimes exactly one triangle*, *sometimes more than one triangle, and sometimes no triangle* can be constructed.

Given two angle measures (sum less than 180°) and one side length:

3. If the side given is between the two given angles, *exactly one triangle* can be constructed.

4. If the side given is not between the two angles there will be exactly two triangles: *exactly one triangle* in which the given side is opposite the larger angle and *exactly one triangle* in which the given side is opposite the smaller angle. (If the given angles have the same measure, there will be exactly one triangle.)

✏️ Use a ruler and a protractor, or technology software. Draw a triangle with sides 3 cm and 6 cm and a 120° angle that is not between the given sides. Predict whether all of your classmates will draw the same triangle. Check your prediction.

Guided Practice

Use a ruler and a protractor (and a separate sheet of paper) or technology software.

Draw a triangle that meets the given conditions. If more than one triangle meets the given conditions, draw two different triangles. Then write *exactly one triangle* or *more than one triangle*.

1. sides measuring 2 cm and 3 cm with a 90° angle between these two sides
   (*Hint:* Draw the 90° angle first. Then mark off the given side lengths.)

   _____

2. sides measuring 4 cm and 5 cm with a 40° angle that is *not* between these two sides
   (*Hint:* Draw the 40° angle first. Mark one side of the angle to be 4 inches or 5 inches. Use the other given length to draw the third side of the triangle so that it intersects the unmarked side of the angle.)

   _____

3. a 120° angle and a 20° angle with a 3 in. side between these two angles
   (*Hint:* Draw the 3 in. side first. Then draw the two angles on each end.)

   _____

4. a 50° angle and a 30° angle with a side 5 cm *not* between these two angles
   (*Hint:* The 5 cm side may be opposite the 30° angle or it may be opposite the 50° angle.)

   _____

ᐱᐱ Think•Pair•Share

MP3 5. Deb and Santiago were each asked to draw a triangle with a 30° angle, a 60° angle, and a 5 cm side between the two angles. They drew the figures at the right. Does each triangle meet the conditions? Did Deb and Santiago draw the same triangle or different triangles? Explain.

Deb

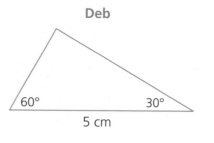

Santiago

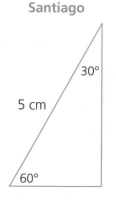

Use a ruler and a protractor or technology software.

Draw a triangle that meets the given conditions. If more than one triangle meets the given conditions, draw two different triangles. Then write *exactly one triangle* or *more than one triangle*.

1. a 40° angle and a 50° angle with a 5 cm side between these two angles

   _____

2. sides measuring 2.5 cm and 4.5 cm with a 65° angle between these two sides

   _____

3. sides measuring 1 in. and 1.5 in. with a 35° angle that is *not* between these two sides

   _____

Independent Practice

4. a 20° angle and a 55° angle with a side 1 in. *not* between these two angles

_____

5. Which of the triangles below meet these conditions: a 30° angle, a 60° angle and a side of length 1 inch that is not between the two given angles?

a.

b.

c.

d. No triangle will meet the conditions.

6. Sean is asked to draw a triangle with sides $\frac{3}{4}$ in. and $1\frac{1}{2}$ in. and a 60° angle between those two sides. Sean draws the two triangles shown below. Cassandra says that one of the triangles must be drawn incorrectly because there is only one triangle that meets the conditions. Is Cassandra correct? Explain.

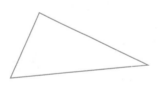

7. Diane and Dakota are asked to draw a triangle with an 80° angle, a 110° degree angle and a side of length 3 cm between them. Before even starting to draw, Dakota says that she is sure that no triangle will meet these conditions. How does Dakota know this?

Independent Practice

For exercises 8–10, use the information below. Use a ruler.

From: Carl
Subject: Let's meet after school.
To: Al and Ben

Follow these directions to draw a triangle on the map.

- Begin at the 60° angle at the point for school.

- Use the scale. Draw the two sides of the triangle that form the 60° angle. One side is 400 feet and the other side is 700 feet.

- Complete the triangle.

Meet at the north-most point of the triangle at 3:00.

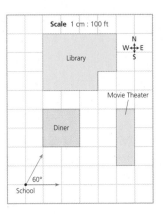

MP4 **8.** Both Al and Ben follow the directions correctly. But, at 3:00, Al is at the library and Ben and Carl are at the diner. Draw Al's triangle. Draw Ben's triangle.

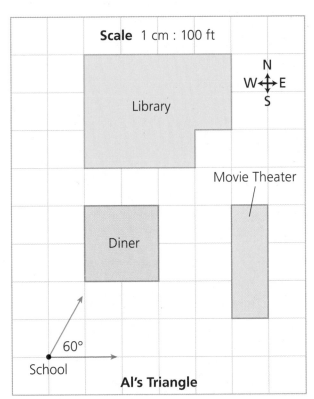

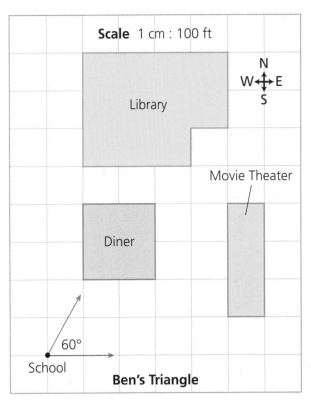

9. Are Al's and Ben's triangles the same triangle or different triangles? Explain.

MP6 **10.** Rewrite the directions so that it is clear that the diner was the meeting place.

26 Slice Three-Dimensional Figures

Guided Instruction

Essential Question:
How can you describe the two-dimensional figures that result from slicing three-dimensional figures?

7.G.3

Words to Know:
right rectangular prism
plane
plane section
cross section
parallel planes
perpendicular planes
right rectangular
  pyramid
vertex

In this lesson, you will learn how to describe a two-dimensional figure that results from slicing a three-dimensional figure.

A right rectangular prism is a three-dimensional shape that has six faces that are rectangles.

Understand: Describing cross sections that result from slicing a right rectangular prism using a geometric plane

> What cross sections can result from using a geometric plane to slice a right rectangular prism?

A geometric plane is a two-dimensional figure that goes on and on in both directions without end. Think of it as a sheet of paper that never ends. The two-dimensional shape that is made by slicing through a three-dimensional figure using a plane is called a plane section or a cross section.

▶ The examples below show some of the plane sections that can be made by slicing a right rectangular prism with a plane.

Example 1
Parallel planes are planes that do not intersect. Think of the floor and the ceiling of a room as parallel planes

When a geometric plane slices a prism so that the cut is parallel to the plane of the base, the cross section will have the shape of the base. So, in the case of a right rectangular prism, the cross section is a rectangle.

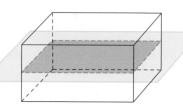

Example 2
Perpendicular planes are planes that meet at right angles. Think of the floor and a wall of a room as perpendicular planes.

If the cut is perpendicular to the base and parallel to one pair of lateral (side) faces, the cross section will be a rectangle that has the same shape as the lateral face.

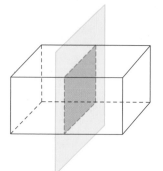

Example 3

In this case, the cut is not parallel or perpendicular to either base, but the cross section is still a rectangle. However, the cross-section rectangle is not the same as the rectangle that is the base of the rectangular prism.

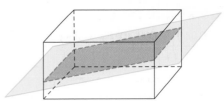

Example 4

In this case, the sides of the cross section are not parallel or perpendicular to any edge of the prism. The cross section is a parallelogram.

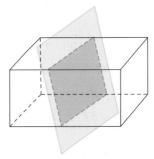

Example 5

This cut slices through three faces. The cross section is a triangle.

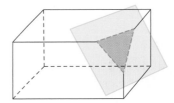

→ If the right rectangular prism is a cube, would the cross sections in Examples 1 and 2 be the same? If they would be different, how would they be different?

Guided Instruction

Understand: Describing cross sections that result from slicing a right rectangular pyramid using a geometric plane

> What plane sections (or cross sections) can result from using a geometric plane to slice a right rectangular pyramid?

A right rectangular pyramid is a three-dimensional figure that has a rectangular base and three triangular faces that meet at a point called the vertex. The vertex is positioned exactly above the center of the base.

The examples below show some of the cross sections that can be made by slicing a right rectangular pyramid with a plane.

Example 1
When a geometric plane slices any right pyramid so that the cut is parallel to the plane of the base, the cross section will have the same shape (but not the same size) as the base. So, in the case of a right rectangular pyramid, the cross section is a rectangle.

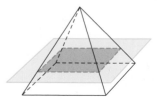

Example 2
If the cut is perpendicular to the base and passes through the vertex, the cross section will be an isosceles triangle.

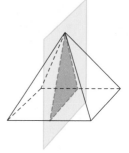

Example 3
If the cut is perpendicular to the base but does not pass through the vertex, the cross section will be a trapezoid.

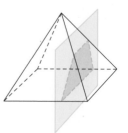

✏️ Dan sliced a right rectangular pyramid using a cut parallel to the base. The cross section was a square. What does that tell you about Dan's pyramid?

Guided Instruction

Connect: Solving a problem using what you know about cross sections

Victor cuts this stick of margarine in half to make two right rectangular prisms that are the same shape and size. What are the dimensions (the length, width, and height) of each half of the stick of margarine?

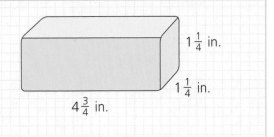

$1\frac{1}{4}$ in.

$1\frac{1}{4}$ in.

$4\frac{3}{4}$ in.

This problem has two solutions. Think about the different ways that Victor can slice the margarine into two right rectangular prisms that have the same size and shape.

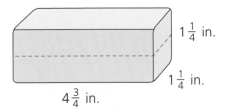

$1\frac{1}{4}$ in.

$1\frac{1}{4}$ in.

$4\frac{3}{4}$ in.

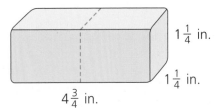

$1\frac{1}{4}$ in.

$1\frac{1}{4}$ in.

$4\frac{3}{4}$ in.

Solution 1

Victor can cut the margarine with a cut that is parallel to the base. The cut must be exactly between the two bases. The red dashed line shows the cut.

Each right rectangular prism will have the same length and width as the whole stick of margarine. The height will be $\frac{1}{2}$ the height of the whole stick.

Length: $4\frac{3}{4}$ in.

Width: $1\frac{1}{4}$ in.

Height $\frac{1}{2} \cdot 1\frac{1}{4}$ in. $= \frac{5}{8}$ in.

Solution 2

Victor can cut the margarine with a cut that is perpendicular to the base and parallel to the square lateral faces. The cut must be exactly between the two square faces. The red dashed line shows the cut.

Each right rectangular prism will have a length $\frac{1}{2}$ the length of the whole stick of margarine. The width and height will be the same.

Length: $\frac{1}{2} \cdot 4\frac{3}{4}$ in. $= 2\frac{3}{8}$ in.

Width: $1\frac{1}{4}$ in.

Height $1\frac{1}{4}$ in.

➡ The dimensions could be $4\frac{3}{4}$ in. by $1\frac{1}{4}$ by $\frac{5}{8}$ in. or they could be $2\frac{3}{8}$ in. by $1\frac{1}{4}$ in. by $1\frac{1}{4}$ in.

✏ Do each of the halves of the stick of margarine have the same volume?

Guided Practice

For exercises 1–9, write the best name for the plane section (or cross section).

1. right rectangular prism

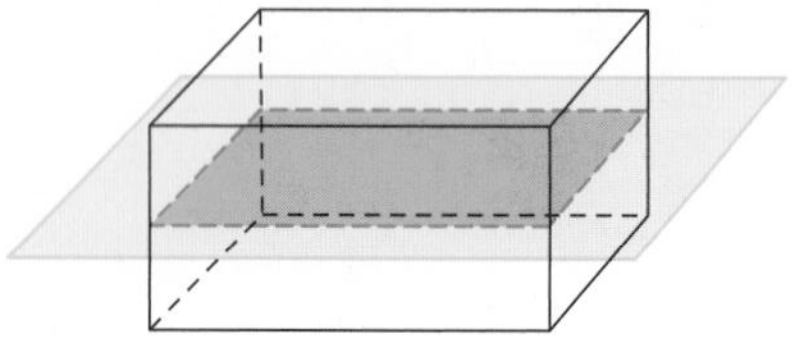

____

2. right rectangular prism

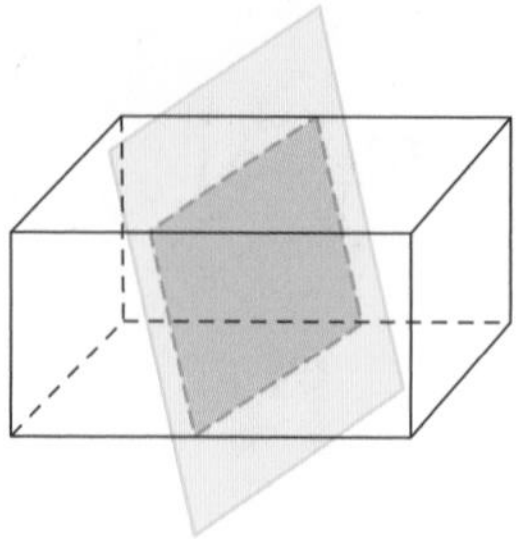

____

3. right rectangular prism

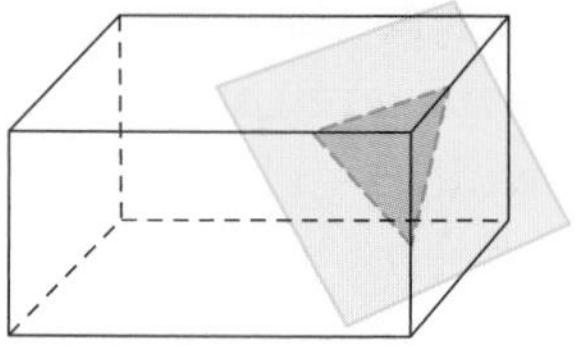

____

4. right rectangular pyramid

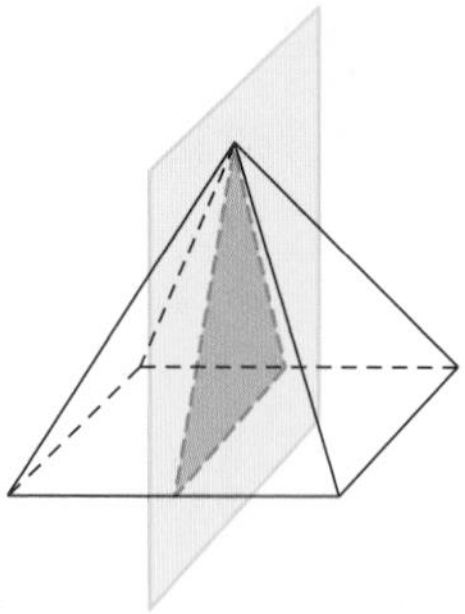

____

5. right rectangular pyramid

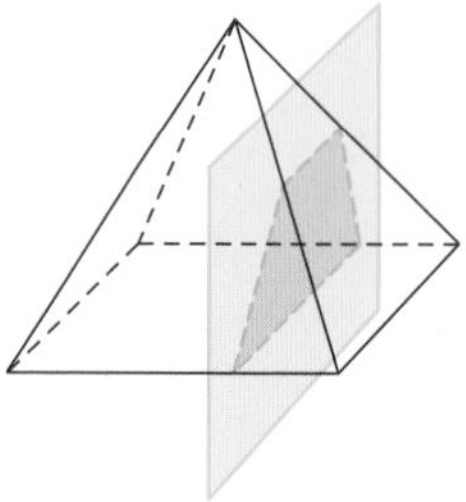

____

6. cube

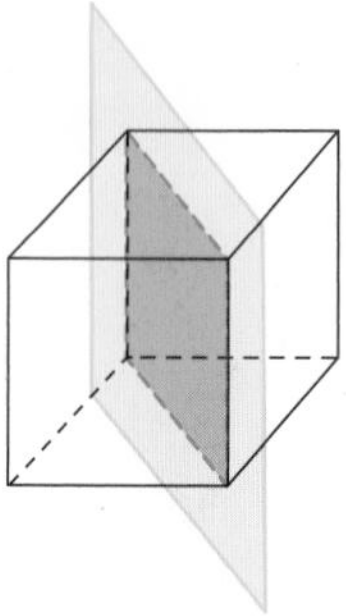

____

7. A cylinder is cut parallel to its base. ______________________

8. A cone is cut through the vertex perpendicular to its base. ______________________

9. A cylinder is cut perpendicular to its base. ______________________

Think•Pair•Share

MP4 **10.** Brendan has a block of cheese 9 in. by 2 in. by 2 in. He wants to cut it into thirds by making two slices. He wants both of the cross sections to be squares. On the drawing at the right, show the two cuts Brendan can make. What will be the dimensions of each third of the block of cheese? Is there more than one solution to this problem?

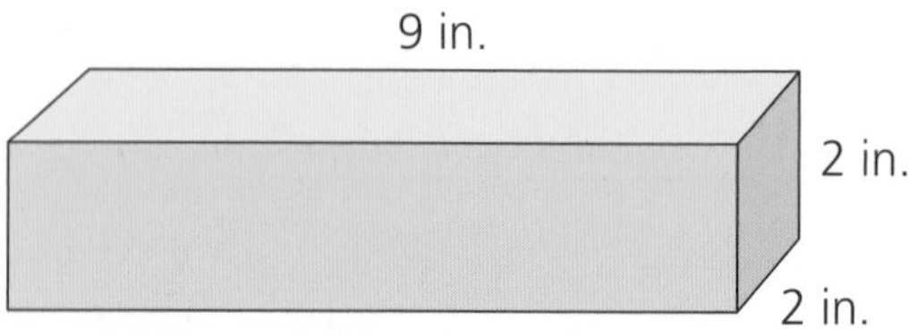

For exercises 1–9, write the best name for the plane section (or cross section).

1. right rectangular prism with square base

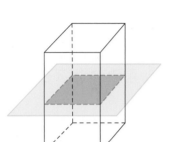

_____

2. right square pyramid

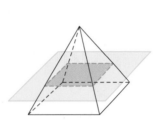

_____

3. cone

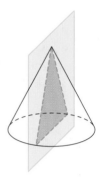

_____

4. right rectangular prism

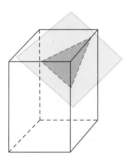

_____

5. right rectangular prism

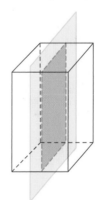

_____

6. cylinder

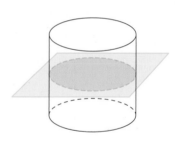

_____

7. A right rectangular prism in the shape of a shoebox is cut parallel to its bottom face.

_____

8. A slice is perpendicular to the base of a right square pyramid but does not pass through the vertex.

_____

9. A cone is cut parallel to its base.

_____

Independent Practice

For exercises 10–15, circle each correct solution.

10. Which slice will result in a triangle for a cross section?

    a. a slice parallel to the base of a right square pyramid

    b. a corner slice from a right rectangular prism

    c. a slice parallel to the base of a cone

    d. a slice perpendicular to the base of a right square pyramid and passing through the vertex

11. Which slice will result in a square for a cross section?

    a. a slice parallel to the base of a right square pyramid

    b. a slice parallel to any face of a cube

    c. a slice parallel to the base of a cylinder

    d. a slice perpendicular to the base of a right square pyramid

12. Which slice will result in a trapezoid (not a parallelogram) for a cross section?

    a. a slice parallel to one of the sides of a right rectangular prism

    b. a slice perpendicular to the base of a right square pyramid and passing through the vertex

    c. a slice perpendicular to the base of a right square pyramid but not passing through the vertex

    d. a slice parallel to the base of a right square pyramid

13. Which could be a cross section resulting from a slice perpendicular to the base of a right square pyramid?

    a. a square

    b. a rectangle

    c. a trapezoid

    d. a triangle

14. Which could be a cross section of a right rectangular prism with a square base?

    a. a square

    b. a rectangle (not a square)

    c. a parallelogram (not a rectangle)

    d. a triangle

15. A right rectangular prism that measures 6 cm by 2 cm by 3 cm is cut in half. What is the volume of each half?

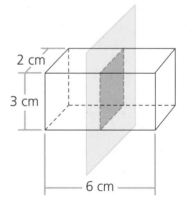

    a. 36 cm³

    b. 36 cm²

    c. 18 cm³

    d. 72 cm³

MP1 **16.** Rodney cuts a slice parallel to the base of a right square pyramid. Romina cuts a slice from the same pyramid. Romina's slice is also parallel to the base but her slice has a greater area than Rodney's slice.

    a. Rodney claims that Romina must have cut her slice from a different pyramid than the pyramid he used. Romina disagrees. Is it possible that both students sliced the same pyramid? Explain.

    b. Sidney wants to cut a slice from the same pyramid that will be larger than Rodney's slice but smaller than Romina's slice. What should she do?

MP4 **17.** What would the cross section of this figure look like? Draw the slice.

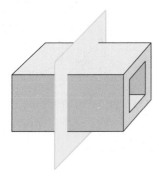

MP2 **18.** Eli says that the cross section of a sphere is a circle if and only if the cut passes through the center of the sphere. Do you agree or disagree? Explain.

MP4 **19.** An architect wants to design a building in the shape shown. How can she use shapes from this lesson to create the building?

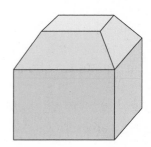

MP2 **20.** Hadley cuts slices near each of the five corners of a right square pyramid. Four of the slices are triangles, but the top slice is a quadrilateral. Can you explain why the slices would be different?

Lesson 27

Use Formulas for Area and Circumference of Circles

Essential Question:
How can you use formulas to solve problems about the circumference and area of circles?

7.G.4

Words to Know:
diameter
circumference
pi (π)
irrational number
radius
semicircle

Guided Instruction

In this lesson, you will learn to solve problems about the circumference and area of circles.

Understand: Relating the diameter of a circle to its circumference

> For all circles, there is a proportional relationship between the circumference of a circle and its diameter. What is the constant of proportionality? What equation can be used to show this proportional relationship?

The diameter of a circle is the distance across a circle through the center. The circumference of a circle is the distance around the circle.

For any circle, the ratio of the circumference of the circle to the diameter of the circle is a number called pi. Pi is the constant of proportionality for the ratio of the circumference of any circle to its diameter.

Pi is represented by the symbol π. Pi is not a rational number. It cannot be represented by any decimal that terminates or any decimal that repeats. Thus, it is an irrational number.

Because π cannot be represented by a terminating or repeating decimal, we use *approximations* for π. We can use the decimal 3.14 or the fraction $3\frac{1}{7}$ ($\frac{22}{7}$) as an approximation for π.

Since π is the constant of proportionality for the ratio of C (the circumference of a circle) to d (the diameter of a circle), $\frac{C}{d} = \pi$.

The equation $C = \pi d$ also shows this relationship. This equation is used as a formula for finding the circumference of a circle.

Remember!
The unit rate or the constant of proportionality for a ratio $A : B$ is $\frac{A}{B}$.

▶ The constant of proportionality for the ratio of the circumference of a circle to the diameter of a circle is π. An equation that can be used to show the relationship is $\frac{C}{d} = \pi$ or $C = \pi d$.

✏️▶ Use the formula to approximate the circumference of a circle with a diameter of 6 inches.

Understand: Using the formula for the circumference of a circle

> The figure shows the diameter of a circular swimming pool.
> What is the approximate distance around the pool?

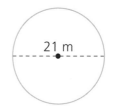
21 m

The distance around the pool is the circumference of the circle. You can use the formula $C = \pi d$. Here are three methods for using the formula.

The symbol $\approx$ means *is approximately equal to*.

Method 1
Use 3.14 for π.

$C = \pi d$
$C \approx 3.14 \cdot 21 \text{ m}$
$C \approx 65.94 \text{ m}$

Method 2
Use $\frac{22}{7}$ for π.

$C = \pi d$
$C \approx \frac{22}{7} \cdot 21 \text{ m}$
$C \approx 66 \text{ m}$

Method 3
Use π in your answer.

$C = \pi d$
$C = \pi (21 \text{ m})$
$C = 21\pi \text{ m}$

When a measurement is written using π, we say that the measurement is written "in terms of pi." That measurement is an exact measurement, not an approximate measurement.

When writing a measurement in terms of pi, the number comes first, then π, and then the measurement unit.

▶ The distance around the pool is approximately 65.94 meters, approximately 66 meters, or exactly 21π meters.

▪▬▸ Which of the above methods give an approximation for the distance around the pool?

Understand: Relating the circumference of a circle to the area of a circle

> How can you use what you know about the circumference of a circle and the area of a rectangle to develop the formula for the area of a circle?

radius
diameter

The figure at the right shows how the diameter and the radius of a circle are related. The length of the radius is $\frac{1}{2}$ the length of the diameter.

Continued»

Guided Instruction

A circle can be cut into slices and the slices can be rearranged to make a figure that is close to a parallelogram. Half of one slice can then be moved so that the figure is close to a rectangle.

Circle   Parallelogram   Rectangle
$\vdash \frac{1}{2}\pi d$ or $\pi r \dashv$

The circumference of the circle is πd. Since the measure of the length of the rectangle is $\frac{1}{2}$ of the circumference of the circle, it is $\frac{1}{2}\pi d$. Since we know that the radius of a circle (r) is $\frac{1}{2}d$, the length can be written as πr.

The width of the rectangle is r.

$A = \ell w$
$\quad = (\pi r)r = \pi \cdot r \cdot r$
$\quad = \pi r^2$

> **Remember!**
> The formula for the area of a rectangle is Area = length • width ($A = \ell w$)

So the area of the rectangle is $(\pi r)r$ or πr^2.

▶ A formula for the area (A) of a circle is $A = \pi r^2$.

✏️ A pizza has a circumference of 14π inches. What is the area of the pizza in square inches? Give the answer in terms of π.

Understand: Using the formula for the area of a circle

A circular rug has a radius of 3 feet. What is the area of the rug?

> **Remember!**
> Follow the Order of Operations. Evaluate r^2 first and then multiply by π.

You can use the formula $A = \pi r^2$.

Here are three methods for finding the area.

Method 1
Use 3.14 for π.

$A = \pi r^2$
$A \approx 3.14 \cdot 3 \text{ feet} \cdot 3 \text{ feet}$
$A \approx 28.26 \text{ ft}^2$

Method 2
Use $\frac{22}{7}$ for π.

$A = \pi r^2$
$A \approx \frac{22}{7} \cdot 3 \text{ feet} \cdot 3 \text{ feet}$
$A \approx 28\frac{2}{7} \text{ ft}^2$

Method 3
Use π in your answer.

$A = \pi r^2$
$A = \pi \cdot 3 \text{ feet} \cdot 3 \text{ feet}$
$A = 9\pi \text{ ft}^2$

▶ The area may be given as approximately 28.26 ft², approximately $28\frac{2}{7}$ ft², or exactly 9π ft².

Guided Instruction

Connect: Solving real world problems involving circles

> The extra large pizza at Pete's Pizza Place has a diameter of 16 in. The small pizza has a diameter of 10 in. How many small pizzas would you have to buy to get at least as much pizza as one extra large pizza?

To solve the problem, divide the area of the extra large pizza by the area of the small pizza. Round your answer up to the next whole pizza.

Find the area of the extra large pizza.
$A = \pi r^2$
$A = \pi \cdot 16 \text{ in.} \cdot 16 \text{ in.}$
$A = 256\pi$ square inches

> Since you will be dividing areas to find the number of small pizzas, it makes sense to write both areas in terms of π.

Find the area of the small pizza.
$A = \pi r^2$
$A = \pi \cdot 10 \text{ in.} \cdot 10 \text{ in.}$
$A = 100\pi$ square inches

Divide the area of the large pizza by the area of the small pizza.

$\frac{256\pi \text{ square inches}}{100\pi \text{ square inches}} = 2.56$ Round 2.56 to 3.

➡ You would need to buy 3 small pizzas to get at least as much as one extra large one.

> The figure at the right shows the top of a kitchen counter. How much countertop trim is needed to go around the edge?
>
> Use 3.14 for π.

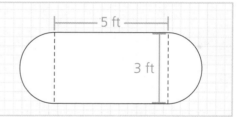

Find the distance around the top of the countertop. The countertop is made up of a rectangle and a circle. The rectangle has $\frac{1}{2}$ of the circle (a semicircle) on one side and the other half of the circle on the other side.

Find the circumference of the circle.
$C = \pi d$
$C \approx 3.14 \cdot 3$ feet
$C \approx 9.42$ feet

> The diameter of the circle is the same as the width of the rectangle, 3 feet.

Add the circumference of the circle to the lengths of sides of the rectangle that make up the edge of the counter.

$9.42 \text{ ft} + 5 \text{ ft} + 5 \text{ ft} = 19.42 \text{ feet}$

➡ About 19.42 feet of countertop trim is needed.

✏ Why is the answer to the second example an approximation and not the exact answer?

Guided Practice

For exercises 1–3, complete the statements.

1. The length of the _____ of a circle is twice the length

   of the _____ of the circle.

2. The distance around a circle is called its _____.

3. The ratio of the circumference of a circle to its _____ is π.

4. A circle with a radius of 5 meters has been
   cut into slices that have been put together
   to form a shape that is close to a rectangle
   as shown at the right. Label the length
   and width of the rectangle in meters.
   Find the area of the rectangle. Write each
   measurement using a whole number or a
   number in terms of π.

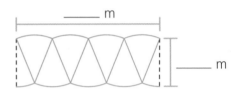

_____ m

_____ m

$A = $ _____

Find the circumference and area of each circle. Use 3.14 for π.

5.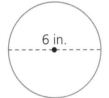

   6 in.

   $C \approx$ _____

   $A \approx$ _____

6.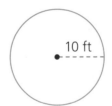

   10 ft

   $C \approx$ _____

   $A \approx$ _____

Think•Pair•Share

MP4 7. Sheldon cuts a circle with a diameter of 14 centimeters from a square piece of
   felt 15 inches on each side. How much felt is left over? Use $\frac{22}{7}$ for π.

Answer _____

Independent Practice

Match each circle to its approximate circumference (C) and area (A). Draw lines to match.

1.

2.

3.

a. $C \approx 69.08$ ft

b. $C \approx 66$ ft

c. $C \approx 62.8$ ft

d. $A \approx 346.19$ ft²

e. $A \approx 379.9$ ft²

f. $A \approx 314$ ft²

For exercises 4–6, circle each correct answer. (Let d = the diameter of the circle, r = the radius of the circle, C = the circumference of the circle, and A = the area of the circle.)

4. Which of the following is true for a circle with radius of 14 cm?

   a. $d \le 28$ cm

   b. $C \approx 88$ cm

   c. $A \approx 88$ cm²

   d. $A \approx 616$ cm²

5. Which of the following is true for a circle with a circumference of about 110 meters?

   a. $r \approx 35$ m

   b. $d \approx 35$ m

   c. $A \approx 44$ cm²

   d. $A \approx (17.5)^2 \cdot 3.14$ m²

6. Which of the following is true for a circle with a diameter of 1.4 inches?

   a. $A \approx 1.54$ in.²

   b. $C \approx 1.54$ in.

   c. $C \approx 4.4$ in.

   d. $r = \frac{7}{10}$ in.

Independent Practice

For exercises 7–9, circle the best answer.

7. George runs $3\frac{1}{2}$ laps around a circular track with a diameter of $\frac{1}{2}$ mile. About how far does George run?

   a. $\frac{11}{14}$ mile

   b. 5.5 miles

   c. 11 miles

   d. 22 miles

8. A circle has an approximate circumference of 44 feet. What is the approximate area of the circle?

   a. 7 square feet

   b. 14 square feet

   c. 154 square feet

   d. 308 square feet

9. A circle has an area of 36π square meters. What is the radius of the circle?

   a. 6 m

   b. 18 m

   c. 72 m

   d. 1296 m

MP3 10. Jay used 16 sections of a circle to find a formula for the area of a circle.

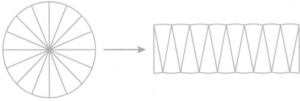

16 sections

Is Jay's formula correct? Explain.

length of rectangle $= C$
$C = \pi d = 2\pi r$
$A = $ length of rectangle • width of rectangle
$A = 2\pi r • r$
$A = 2\pi r^2$

Solve the problems.

MP2 **11.** Bizz is running for Student Senate. He designed this t-shirt logo for his campaign. The logo is made up of a square with 14-cm sides and four half circles. Use $\frac{22}{7}$ for π to approximate the area of the logo.

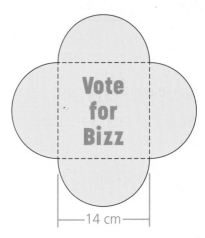

Vote for Bizz

—14 cm—

 **Show your work.**

Answer _____

MP7 **12.** The circumference of Earth is about 24,900 miles. Is the radius of Earth closer to 4,000 or 5,000 miles?

Answer _____

 **Justify your answer.**

MP8 **13.** The figure shows the target Anaya designed for the Archery Club. The diameter of the outermost circle (the target) is 50 centimeters. The diameter of the innermost circle (the bull's eye) is 10 centimeters. What percent of the whole target is the bull's eye?

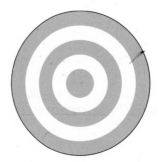

 **Show your work.**

Answer _____

Essential Question:
How can you use facts about supplementary, complementary, vertical, and adjacent angles to find the unknown angle measure in a figure?

7.G.5

Words to Know:
adjacent angles
opposite rays
vertical angles
complementary angles
right angle
supplementary angles
straight angle

Guided Instruction

In this lesson, you will learn facts about special angle pairs. You will use these facts and what you know about writing and solving equations to find unknown angle measures in a figure.

Two angles that have a common vertex and a common side (ray) but do not overlap are called adjacent angles.

Understand: Identifying pairs of adjacent angles

Name two pairs of adjacent angles in the figure at the right.

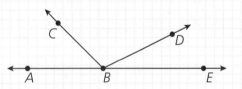

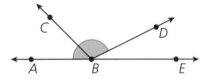

∠ABC and ∠CBD are adjacent angles.
The angles share vertex B and side BC.

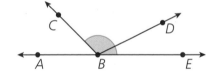

∠CBD and ∠DBE are adjacent angles.
The angles share vertex B and side BD.

∠ABC and ∠ABD are **not** adjacent angles because they overlap.
∠ABC and ∠DBE are **not** adjacent angles because they do not share a common side.

> Two pairs of adjacent angles are ∠ABC and ∠CBD; ∠CBD and ∠DBE.

Remember!
To name an angle, use the symbol ∠. Using the two rays and the vertex of the angle, write the letter for a point on one ray, then the letter for the vertex, followed by the letter for a point on the other ray. If there is only one angle at a vertex, you can use just the letter of the vertex.

Understand: Identifying pairs of vertical angles

Name two pairs of vertical angles in the figure at the right.

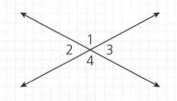

Two rays that form a straight line are called opposite rays. Two angles whose sides form two pairs of opposite rays are called vertical angles. We can think of vertical angles as opposite angles formed by an X.

∠1 and ∠4 are
vertical angles.

∠2 and ∠3 are
vertical angles.

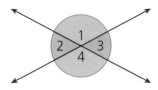

Angles can also be named using numbers.

▶ Two pairs of vertical angles are ∠1 and ∠4; ∠2 and ∠3.

Vertical angles always have the same measure. In the figure above:
m∠1 = 120°   m∠2 = 60°   m∠3 = 60°   m∠4 = 120°

Remember!
A short way to write "the measure of angle 1" is m∠1.

Understand: Using facts about complementary angles to write equations to find the unknown angle measure in a figure

Find the value of *x* in the figure at the right.

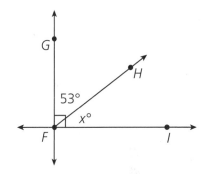

If the measures of two angles have a sum of 90°, the angles are called complementary angles. The two angles do not need to be adjacent angles, but when they are, they form a right angle.

∠GFI is a right angle. It measures 90°. ∠GFH and ∠HFI are complementary angles. We can use this fact to write an equation to find the value of *x*.

$$m\angle GFH + m\angle HFI = 90°$$
$$53° + x° = 90°$$
$$53 + x = 90$$
$$53 - 53 + x = 90 - 53$$
$$x = 37 \longleftarrow \text{The measure of } \angle HFI \text{ is } 37°.$$

Remember!
A right angle has a measure of 90°. Right angles are marked with this symbol, ⌐.

▶ The value of *x* is 37.

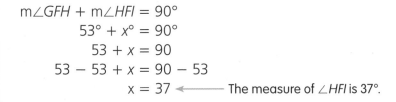 Suppose you know that two angles are complementary angles and you know that one of the angles has a measure of 23°. What is the measure of the other angle?

Guided Instruction

Understand: Using facts about supplementary angles to write equations to find the unknown angle measure in a figure

Find the value of d in the figure at the right.

If the measures of two angles have a sum of 180°, the angles are called supplementary angles. The two angles do not need to be adjacent angles, but when they are, they form a straight angle.

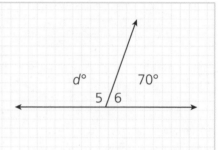

$\angle 5$ and $\angle 6$ in the figure above are supplementary angles. Together they form a straight angle. We can use this fact to write an equation to find the value of d.

$$m\angle 5 + m\angle 6 = 180°$$
$$d° + 70° = 180°$$
$$d + 70 = 180$$
$$d + 70 - 70 = 180 - 70$$
$$d = 110 \longleftarrow \text{The measure of } \angle 6 \text{ is } 110°.$$

➡ The value of d is 110.

✏ · Suppose you know that two angles are supplementary angles and you know that one of the angles has a measure of 49°. What is the measure of the other angle?

Connect: Using equations to solve multi-step problems involving an unknown angle measure

In the figure at the right, line JL is perpendicular to line KN. Find the value of a.

You can use equations to find the value of a.

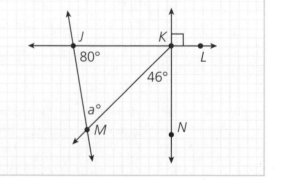

Method 1
Use two equations.

Step 1

Find m∠JKM.

Because line JL is perpendicular to line KN, ∠JKM and ∠MKN are complementary angles. The sum of their measures is 90°.

Write and solve an equation → $m\angle JKM + m\angle MKN = 90°$
to find m∠JKM.
Let x = m∠JKM in degrees. → $x + 46 = 90$
$$x + 46 - 46 = 90 - 46$$
$$x = 44$$

$$m\angle JKM = 44°$$

> After finding m∠JKM, you will know the measure of two angles in triangle JKM. When you know two angle measures in a triangle, you can find the measure of the third angle because the sum of the angle measures in a triangle is always 180°.

Step 2

Find a, the measure in degrees of ∠JMK.

Use the fact that m∠JKM is 44° (from Step 1) and the fact that the sum of the measures of the three angles in a triangle is 180°.

Write and solve an equation.

$$m\angle MJK + m\angle JKM + m\angle JMK = 180°$$
$$80 + 44 + a = 180$$
$$124 + a = 180$$
$$124 - 124 + a = 180 - 124$$
$$a = 56$$

$$m\angle JMK = 56°$$

Method 2
Use just one equation.

$$m\angle MJK + m\angle JKM + m\angle JMK = 180°$$
$$80 + (90 - 46) + a = 180$$
$$80 + 44 + a = 180$$
$$124 + a = 180$$
$$124 - 124 + a = 180 - 124$$
$$a = 56$$

$$m\angle JMK = 56°$$

▶ Using either method, the value of a is 56.

✏ Are ∠MJK, ∠JKM, and ∠JMK supplementary angles? Explain.

Guided Practice

For exercises 1–2, use the figure at the right to complete the statements.

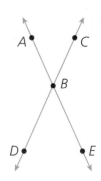

1. $\angle ABC$ and $\angle DBE$ form a pair of

   _____ angles.

2. $\angle ABC$ and $\angle ABD$ form a pair of _____

   and _____ angles.

Write and solve an equation to find the value of *x*.

3.

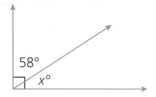

58°

x°

4.

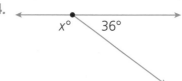

x°　36°

5.

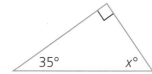

35°　x°

Equation

_____

x = _____

Equation

_____

x = _____

Equation

_____

x = _____

For exercise 6, use the figure at the right.

6. **a.** Write an equation to find the value of *x*.

   Equation _____

   b. Solve the equation from part a to find the value of *x*.

   x = _____

   c. Use your answer from part b to write an equation to find the value of *y*.

   Equation _____

   d. Solve the equation from part a to find the value of *y*.

   y = _____

60°

y°

x°

30°　40°

🤴 Think•Pair•Share

MP4　**7.** In Exercise 6, you used an equation to find the value of *x* and then used the value of *x* and another equation to find the value of *y*. Write just one equation that you could use to find the value of *y*. Solve the equation. Compare your solution to the solution in part d above.

Independent Practice

Write and solve an equation to find the value of x.

1.

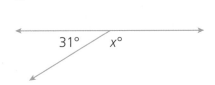

2.

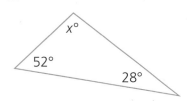

3.

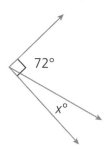

Equation

_____

x = _____

Equation

_____

x = _____

Equation

_____

x = _____

For exercises 4–7, find the values of the unknown variables.

4. x = _____

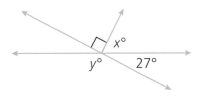

5. y = _____

6. a = _____

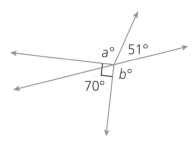

7. b = _____

For exercises 8–11, circle each correct answer.

8. Which angles in the figure are vertical angles?

   a. ∠ACB and ∠HCD

   b. ∠CDG and ∠EDF

   c. ∠CDE and ∠GDF

   d. ∠ACH and ∠BCD

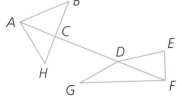

9. If a, b, c, and d are each greater than 0 and b + c = 90, which of the following must be true?

   a. c = d

   b. a + d = 90

   c. b + d = 90

   d. a < 90

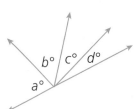

Independent Practice

10. Which equation can you use to find x?

a. $48 - (180 + 135) + x = 180$

b. $48 + (135 - 90) + x = 180$

c. $48 + (180 - 135) + x = 180$

d. $48 - (180 - 135) + x = 180$

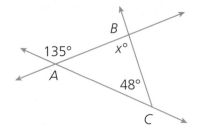

11. Which equation can you use to find z?

a. $85 + 59 + z = 90$

b. $85 + (90 - 31) + z = 180$

c. $85 + (180 - 31) + z = 180$

d. $85 + 59 + z = 180$

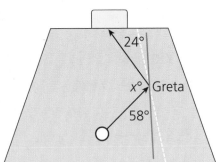

Solve the problems.

MP4 **12.** Greta deflected a soccer ball off her foot at an angle of 24°
to score a goal. The ball came at Greta at an angle of 58°.
Find x, the measure of the angle of Greta's deflection.

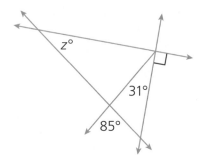

▦▶ **Show your work.**

Answer _____

MP2 **13.** The figure shows one face of the great Egyptian pyramid
of Cheops. Asef claims that the top angle, the angle with
measure $x°$, is a right angle. Do you agree or disagree
with Asef? Explain.

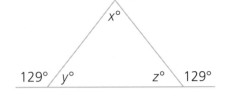

Answer _____

▦▶ **Justify your answer.**

Independent Practice

14. A right triangle has ∠*A*, ∠*B*, and right angle ∠*C*. Can ∠*A* and ∠*B* be complementary? Explain.

MP2 **15.** In the figure at the right, ∠*ABC* and ∠*CED* are both right angles. Luke claims that each of the angles in triangle *ABC* has the same measure as one of the angles in triangle *CED*. Liz says she agrees with Luke and claims that because of this, triangle *ABC* and triangle *CDE* must actually be the same triangle, that is, you could cut one out and fit it exactly onto the other. Do you agree with Luke? Explain. Do you agree with Liz? Explain.

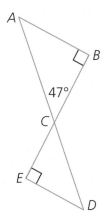

MP2 **16.** The pattern below is made from identical rectangles. What is the unknown angle measure?

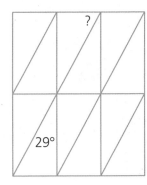

Answer _____

✏️ **Justify your answer.**

MP2 **17.** Angle 1 and angle 2 are complementary. The measure of ∠2 is 15° less than twice the measure of ∠1. What is the measure of each angle?

✏️ **Show your work.**

Answer _____

Problem Solving: Area, Volume, and Surface Area

Essential Question:
How can you solve real-world and mathematical problems involving area, volume, and surface area?

7.G.6

Words to Know:
surface area
prism
right prism
regular polygon
pyramid
right pyramid

Guided Instruction

In this lesson, you will learn how to solve real-world and mathematical problems involving area, volume, and surface area.

Understand: **Finding area of a two-dimensional shape**

The owners of Ace Diner build a large "A" to place outside their diner. The shape is made up of one triangle, two parallelograms, and a trapezoid. What is the area of the shape?

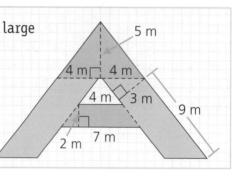

Find the area of each part and then add the areas together.

Find the area of the triangle.
The triangle has a base of 8 m (4 m + 4 m) and a height of 5 m.

$A = \frac{1}{2}(b \cdot h)$

$A = \frac{1}{2}(8 \cdot 5)$

$A = \frac{1}{2}(40)$

$A = 20$

The area of the triangle is 20 m².

Find the area of the two parallelograms.
First, find the area of one parallelogram.
The parallelogram has a base of 9 m and a height of 3 m.

$A = b \cdot h$
$A = 9 \cdot 3$
$A = 27$

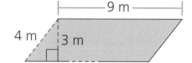

The area of the parallelogram is 27 m². Since there are two parallelograms that are exactly alike, the area of the two parallelograms is 2 • 27 m², or 54 m².

Find the area of the trapezoid.
The trapezoid has a base of 4 m, a base of 7 m, and a height of 2 m.

$A = \frac{1}{2}h(b_1 + b_2)$

$A = \frac{1}{2} \cdot 2(4 + 7)$

$A = 1(11)$

$A = 11$

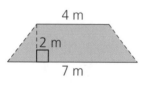

The area of the trapezoid is 11 m².

Add the areas together to find the total area.

20 m² + 54 m² + 11 m² = 85 m²

➡ The area of the shape is 85 m².

Understand: Finding the surface area of a three-dimensional object

Glen uses a right hexagonal prism and two right hexagonal pyramids to make a piñata. The base of the prism is a regular hexagon. How many square inches of paper does he need to cover the piñata?

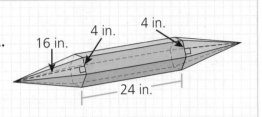

The total area of the surface of a three-dimensional object is called the surface area. Glen needs to find the surface area of the piñata.

Find the area of the faces of the prism that are part of the surface area.

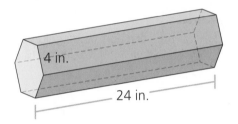

A prism is a three-dimensional figure that has two parallel bases, or ends, that are polygons with the same size and shape. In a right prism, the sides, or lateral faces of the prism are rectangles.

A prism is named by the shape of its base. So, Glen's prism is a hexagonal prism.

A regular polygon has all sides the same length and all angles the same measure.

A right hexagonal prism has 6 lateral faces that are rectangles. Because the base of Glen's prism is a regular hexagon, each rectangle is the same size. Each has a length of 24 inches and a width of 4 in.

$$A = \ell \cdot w \qquad A = 24 \cdot 4 \qquad A = 96$$

The area of each rectangular face is 96 square inches. The area of the 6 rectangular faces is 6 • 96, or 576 square inches.

Find the area of the faces of the pyramids that are part of the surface area.

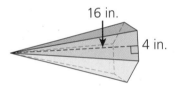

A pyramid is a three-dimensional figure that has a base that is a polygon. The sides, or lateral faces of the pyramid are triangles. In a right pyramid, the vertex is directly above the center of the base.

A pyramid is named by the shape of its base. So, Glen's pyramids are hexagonal pyramids.

In Glen's piñata, because the base of each pyramid is a regular hexagon, each hexagonal pyramid has 6 triangular faces that are all the same shape and size. So, there are 2 • 6, or 12, triangular faces in all. Each has a base of 4 inches and a height of 16 inches.

$$A = \frac{1}{2}(4 \cdot 16) \qquad A = \frac{1}{2}(64) \qquad A = 32$$

The area of each triangular face is 32 square inches. The area of the 12 triangular faces is 12 • 32, or 384 square inches.

Add the areas. 576 square inches + 384 square inches = 960 square inches

➡ Glen needs 960 square inches of paper to cover the piñata.

Guided Instruction

Understand: Finding the volume of a three-dimensional object

Selina is using modeling clay to make a log cabin. The model is made up of a right rectangular prism and a right triangular prism. How many cubic inches of modeling clay does Selena need to make the log cabin? The model will be solid, not hollow.

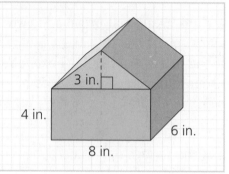

3 in.

4 in.

6 in.

8 in.

To find the number of cubic inches of modeling clay Selina needs, add the volume of the right rectangular prism and the volume of the right triangular prism.

Find the volume of the right rectangular prism.

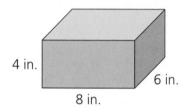

4 in.

8 in.

6 in.

$V = \ell \cdot w \cdot h$
$V = 8 \cdot 6 \cdot 4$
$V = 192$

Remember!

To find the volume of a right rectangular prism, you can use either of two formulas.

$V = \ell \cdot w \cdot h$
$V = B \cdot h$

B stands for the area of the base and h stands for the height of the prism.

The volume of the right rectangular prism is 192 cubic inches.

Find the volume of the right triangular prism.

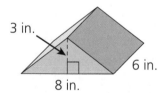

3 in.

6 in.

8 in.

The formula $V = B \cdot h$ (B is the area of the base) can be used for *any* prism.

In this prism, the base is a triangle with $b = 8$ in. and $h = 3$ in.

• First, find the area of the base of the prism.

$A = \frac{1}{2} \cdot b \cdot h$

$A = \frac{1}{2} \cdot 8 \cdot 3$

$A = 12$

In this formula, *b* is the base of the triangle and *h* is the *height of the triangle.*

The area of the base of the triangular prism is 12 square inches.

• Next, find the volume of the triangular prism. The height of the prism is 6 in.

$V = B \cdot h$

$V = 12 \cdot 6$

$V = 72$

In this formula, *B* is the area of the base of the triangular prism and *h* is *the height of the prism.*

The volume of the right triangular prism is 72 cubic inches.

Add the volumes. 192 cubic inches + 72 cubic inches = 264 cubic inches

➤ Selena needs 264 cubic inches (264 in.³) of modeling clay.

Connect: Solving a mathematical problem involving surface area

A right square pyramid has a base 12 m on each side. The surface area of the pyramid is 336 m². What is the height (h) in meters of each triangle that forms a lateral face?

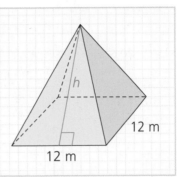

12 m

12 m

A right square pyramid has a square base and 4 triangular faces that are all the same shape and the same size. To find the height of each triangle, you need to first find the area of each triangle. Then you can use the area of a triangle formula to find the height of each triangle.

Step 1

Subtract the area of the base from the surface area, 336 m², to find the area of the 4 triangular faces.

The base is a square with side = 12 m.

$A = s \cdot s$
$A = 12 \cdot 12$
$A = 144$

The area of the base is 144 m².

336 m² − 144 m² = 192 m²

Step 2

Find the area of 1 triangular face.
192 m² ÷ 4 = 48 m²

Step 3

Use the formula for area of a triangle to find the height of the triangle.

$$48 = \frac{1}{2} \cdot (b \cdot h)$$
$$48 = \frac{1}{2} \cdot 12h$$
$$48 = 6h$$
$$48 \div 6 = \frac{6h}{6}$$
$$8 = h$$

The base of each triangle is the length of a side of the square base. So, the base of the triangle is 12 m.

➡ The height of each triangle is 8 m.

✏ Why do you divide by 4 in Step 2?

Guided Practice

For exercises 1–2, use the figure and information below.

The three-dimensional figure at the right is made up of a cube and a right triangular prism.

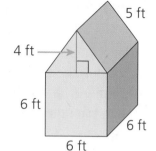

5 ft

4 ft →

6 ft

6 ft

6 ft

1. Follow the steps to find the surface area of the figure.

   a. Find the total area of the _____ square faces of the cube that are part of the surface area of the entire figure.

      $A = s \cdot s$

   _____

   b. Find the total area of the _____ triangular bases of the triangular prism.

      $A = \frac{1}{2} \cdot b \cdot h$

   _____

   c. Find the total area of the _____ rectangular faces of the triangular prism that are part of the surface area of the entire figure.

      $A = \ell \cdot w$

   _____

   d. Use your answers from parts 1a, 1b, and 1c to find the surface area of the three-dimensional figure.

      _____ + _____ + _____ = _____

2. Follow the steps to find the volume of the figure.

   a. Find the volume of the cube.

      $V = e \cdot e \cdot e$

   _____

   b. Find the volume of the triangular prism.

      $B = \frac{1}{2}(b \cdot h)$ $V = B \cdot h$

   _____

   c. Use your answers from parts 2a and 2b to find the volume of the three-dimensional figure.

      _____ + _____ = _____

 **Think•Pair•Share**

MP7 3. A right pyramid has a surface area of 232 square meters. The base is a regular octagon with an area of 72 square meters. What is the area of each triangular face? Explain.

Independent Practice

For exercises 1–2, use the figure and information below.

This is a right prism with a trapezoid as its base.

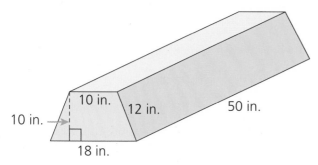

1. Find the surface area of the prism.

Answer _____

2. Find the volume of the prism.

Answer _____

3. This figure is made of a square rectangular prism and two identical right square pyramids. Find its surface area.

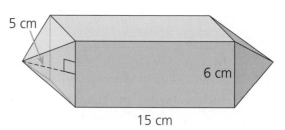

Answer _____

Independent Practice

For exercises 4–6, circle the correct answer or answers.

4. Which expression represents the surface area (in square feet) of the prism below?

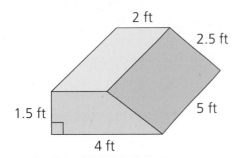

2 ft

2.5 ft

1.5 ft

5 ft

4 ft

   a. $2(\frac{1}{2} \cdot 2(1.5 + 4)) + 5(2 + 2.5 + 4 + 1.5)$

   b. $2(\frac{1}{2} \cdot 1.5(2 + 4)) + 5(2 + 2.5 + 4 + 1.5)$

   c. $2(\frac{1}{2} \cdot 1.5(2 + 4)) + 5(10)$

   d. $2(\frac{1}{2} \cdot 1.5(10)) + 5(6)$

5. Which describes the faces of a right octagonal pyramid?

   a. 1 octagon and 8 triangles

   b. 1 octagon and 6 triangles

   c. 2 octagons and 8 rectangles

   d. 2 octagons and 6 rectangles

6. The surface area of a cube is 384 cm². Which expression shows the volume of the cube in cubic centimeters?

   a. $8 \cdot 8 \cdot 8$

   b. $\left(\frac{384}{6}\right)$

   c. $\left(\frac{384}{6}\right)^2$

   d. $64 \cdot 8$

7. The volumes of two prisms are equal. Both prisms have the same height but they have different shape bases. What can you conclude about the two prisms? Explain.

8. Morgan says that the easiest way to find the surface area of a complex 3-dimensional shape is to break the shape into simpler 3-dimensional shapes such as prisms and pyramids, find the surface area of each shape separately, and then find the sum of all of the surface areas. Is Morgan's method a good one? Explain.

Independent Practice

For exercises 9–10, use the rectangular prism below.

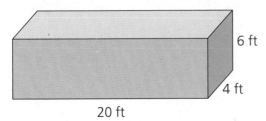

6 ft

4 ft

20 ft

MP4 **9.** Find another rectangular prism that has the same volume as the rectangular prism above. Are the surface areas of the two figures the same?

✏️ **Show your work.**

Answer _____

MP4 **10.** Find a right triangular prism that has the same height (20 feet) and the same volume as the rectangular prism shown above. Draw the triangular prism.

✏️ **Show your work.**

Answer _____

1. Find the value of *x*.

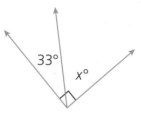

   x = _____

2. Find the area of the circle. Use 3.14 for π.

48 cm

   _____

3. A plane makes a slice perpendicular to the base of a square pyramid as shown. What is the best name for the shape made by the slice?

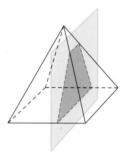

   _____

4. The rectangle is drawn on centimeter-grid paper. Find the scale of the drawing.

40 m

60 m

   1 cm = _____

5. Tell whether *exactly one triangle, more than one triangle*, or *no triangle* can be constructed from the three side lengths given.

   side lengths: 22 in., 14 in., 10 in.

   _____

6. Find the volume of the right triangular prism.

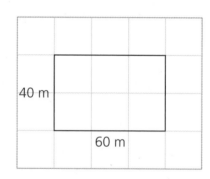

2.5 ft

3 ft

7 ft

   _____

7. Use a ruler and a protractor to draw two triangles with sides measuring $\frac{3}{4}$ in. and 1 in. and a 40° angle that is not between the two sides.

For exercises 8–13, circle the correct answer or answers.

8. For which of the following conditions can you draw *no triangle*?

   a. angle measures: 50°, 60°, and 70°

   b. side measures: 25 m, 50 m, and 60 m

   c. side measures: 25 m, 50 m, and 75 m

   d. angle measures: 70°, 20°, and 70°

9. Which of the following is true for a circle with a circumference of 10π cm?

   a. The radius is 5π cm.

   b. The diameter is 5 cm.

   c. The diameter is 10 cm.

   d. The area is 25π cm².

10. Which of the following is true for a scale drawing in which 2 cm represent 8 cm?

   a. A scale factor for the lengths is 5.

   b. A scale factor for the lengths is 4.

   c. A scale factor for the areas is 32.

   d. A scale factor for the areas is 16.

11. Which of the following is true about a pair of vertical angles?

   a. Angles must have the same measure.

   b. Angles may be complementary angles.

   c. Angles must be adjacent angles.

   d. Angles cannot be adjacent angles.

12. Which equation can you use to find *a*?

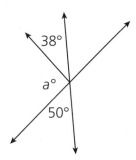

   a. $180 - (50 + 38) = a$

   b. $50 - 38 + a = 180$

   c. $180 + (50 + 38) = a$

   d. $50 + 38 + a = 180$

13. The scale drawing shows that side *DC* is 40 cm long. What is the length of side *AB*?

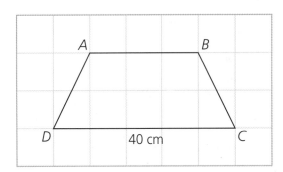

   a. 60 cm

   b. 24 cm

   c. 24 m

   d. 120 cm

For exercises 14–16, find the value of the unknown variables.

14. $x =$ _____

15. $y =$ _____

16. $z =$ _____

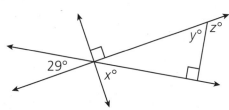

Solve the problems.

MP8 **17.** Nina slices a cube of cheese so that the cut is parallel to the bottom of the cube. What is the best name for the shape of the cross section?

Answer _____

MP5 **18.** On the centimeter grid, draw a scale drawing for a trapezoid-shaped room with bases 30 feet and 40 feet, and height 10 feet. Use the scale 1 cm : 5 ft.

MP6 **19.** Zeke builds a cabin in the shape of a cube with a roof in the shape of a triangular prism. What is the volume of the cabin?

✏ **Show your work.**

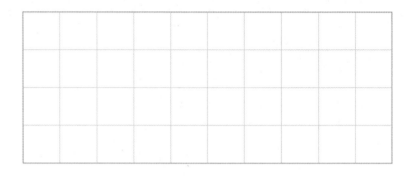

15 ft

18 ft

Answer _____

MP4 **20.** Lance will cut this trapezoidal prism in half and then paint both parts. The figure shows two different ways to cut the prism. Which cut will require more paint, Cut 1 or Cut 2? Explain.

Answer _____

✏ **Justify your answer.**

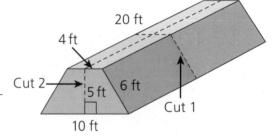

20 ft

4 ft

Cut 2 → 5 ft   6 ft

Cut 1

10 ft

Progress Check

Look at how the Common Core standards you have learned and will learn connect.

It is very important for you to understand the standards from the prior grade level so that you will be able to develop an understanding of statistics and probability in this unit and be prepared for next year. To practice your skills, go to sadlierconnect.com.

GRADE 6 — I Can...	Before Unit 5	GRADE 7 — Can I ?	After Unit 5	GRADE 8 — I Will...
6.SP.1 Decide if a question is a statistical question	☐	**7.SP.1; 7.SP.2** Understand the concept and purpose of statistical sampling; use data from random sampling to draw inferences about a population	☐	
6.SP.4 Display numerical data in dot plots, histograms, and box plots	☐	**7.SP.3** Assess the visual overlap of two numerical data distributions	☐	**8.SP.1** Construct scatter plots for bivariate data
6.SP.3 Understand the purpose of measures of center and of measures of variation	☐	**7.SP.4** Use measures of center and variability to compare two populations	☐	
	☐	**7.SP.5** Understand the probability of a chance event as a number between 0 and 1	☐	
	☐	**7.SP.6** Collect data on the process that produces a chance event to approximate its probability	☐	**8.SP.4** For categorical data, display frequencies and relative frequencies in a two-way table
	☐	Predict the relative frequency of a chance event given its probability	☐	
	☐	**7.SP.7** Develop probability models	☐	
	☐	**7.SP.8** Find probabilities of compound events	☐	

HOME◆CONNECT...

Your child will investigate some basic ideas in both statistics and probability in this unit.

The statistical ideas involve sampling and how sampling is used to draw inferences and to compare populations. Understanding these concepts will help your child analyze statistical information to decide whether the samples are representative of the population and whether the inferences are valid.

Probability is the chance of an event occurring. Probabilities range from 0 to 1. All calculations of probability are the same: the number of favorable outcomes divided by the total number of equally-likely outcomes.

Activity: Experimental probabilities are found by collecting data for a chance event. You and your child can carry out some simple probability experiments. Tossing coins requires only a few coins and paper and pencil. Try tossing a coin 24 times and recording the numbers of heads and of tails. See whether they are about same, indicating a probability of $\frac{1}{2}$. Then toss 2 coins 24 times and record the number of times 2 heads are tossed, 1 head and 1 tail are tossed, and 2 tails are tossed. See whether tossing 2 heads or 2 tails occurs about $\frac{1}{4}$ of the times and tossing 1 head or 1 tail occurs about $\frac{1}{2}$ of the time. The experimental probabilities may or may not be close to the expected probabilities but might be closer if more trials are made.

In this unit your child will:

- Develop and use ideas about sampling

- Use statistical displays to observe visual overlap of data

- Compare populations with sample statistics

- Understand probability and its relationship to relative frequency

- Use models to find theoretical and experimental probabilities

- Find probabilities of compound events

- Represent sample spaces for compound events and simulate compound events

NOTE: All of these learning goals for your child are based on the Grade 7 Common Core State Standards for Mathematics.

Ways to Help Your Child

A Fermi question is one that is best answered by using estimates because an exact answer is not easily found.

You and your child can estimate and discuss this Fermi-like question.

- How many light bulbs are in your home?

- Remind your child to consider the light bulbs in appliances, in holiday decorations, in flashlights, and in closets.

> **ONLINE**
> **For more Home Connect activities, continue online at** sadlierconnect.com

Focus on Statistics and Probability

Essential Question:
How can statistics and probability provide support when you need to make a decision?

Essential Question:
How can you take a representative sample of a population?

7.SP.1

Words to Know:
- data
- population
- sample
- sampling
- representative sample
- random sample
- biased sample
- inference

Guided Instruction

In this lesson, you will learn whether a sample of a population is likely to be representative of that population.

Understand: Judging if a sample is representative of a population

> Springfield's mayor wants to know if the town's residents are in favor of putting up more stop signs. On a Tuesday afternoon, he knocks on the doors of fifty residents in one neighborhood to ask: "Do you want more stop signs?" Are the opinions he gets likely to represent those of all residents of Springfield?

To determine if the opinions of his selected group are likely to represent those of the entire group, start by sorting through the facts given in the problem.

The information being collected, called data, will be all of the "yes" and "no" responses he receives to the question: "Do you want more stop signs?" The entire group of interest, called the population, is all residents of the town. Asking all residents their opinions would be time-consuming, so the mayor is asking only *part* of the population. The set of the population he collects data from is called a sample, and the method he uses to obtain this data is called sampling.

The most useful sample would be a small group whose opinions represent those of the entire population. This is called a representative sample. The best way to try to get a representative sample is to take a random sample. A sample is random if every member of the population has an equal chance of being selected. A random sample does not favor any small group within the population more than any other. Is the mayor's sample random?

No, it is not. Here are two reasons the sample is not random:

- He is only knocking on doors in one neighborhood. This one neighborhood may not be representative of all neighborhoods in his town.

- He is knocking at a time when many types of people, such as those at work, will not be home. The people who are home to answer his question may not be representative of all people.

The mayor's sample favors some individuals in the population more than others, so this is a biased sample.

▶ The mayor's sample is not likely to be a representative sample.

Understand: Choosing a sampling method

A factory manager wants to know how many of the 20,000 LED light bulbs made each day are defective. His employees suggest three possible ways for taking a sample of 200 bulbs:

- **Method 1:** Test the first two hundred bulbs made each day.
- **Method 2:** Test every one hundredth bulb made each day.
- **Method 3:** Assign the numbers 1 to 20,000 to the bulbs. Randomly select 200 numbers between 1 and 20,000, and test the bulbs with those numbers.

Which method will allow the manager to make the best guess of the total number of defective bulbs made each day?

To find the method that will allow the manager to make the best guess of the total number of defective light bulbs, find the method most likely to produce a representative sample. This will provide the most useful information about the population, or group of interest.

Start by identifying the population and the sample of interest. In this case, the population is the 20,000 bulbs made each day, and the goal is to find a 200 bulb sample that is representative of the population.

You can consider each method separately:

Method 1: Testing the first two hundred light bulbs might be an easy way to take a sample, but these bulbs may not represent bulbs made at different times of day. For example, workers might become tired later in the day and make more mistakes. So the sample taken by this method may not be a representative sample.

Method 2: Testing every one hundredth bulb uses a repetitive method to take the sample. It avoids the problems of Method 1. But what if a machine error caused every odd-numbered bulb to be defective? Using this method, none of those bulbs would be found. A repetitive sampling method can provide a representative sample in other situations, but not here.

Method 3: Randomly selecting which bulbs should be tested is most likely to produce a representative sample. Each bulb made during the day has an equal chance of being chosen. So, this method will best help the manager make an informed guess based on evidence about the total number of defective light bulbs.

▶ Method 3 will allow the manager to make the best guess of the total number of defective bulbs made each day.

An informed guess based on evidence is called an inference. To make a valid inference using a sample, the sample should be representative of the population.

Guided Instruction

Connect: Planning for a representative sample

> Reggie wants to find out the favorite websites of the 700 students in grades 7 through 9. His plan for taking a sample is to ask the first 20 male 8th graders on his school bus to name their favorite websites.
>
> a. Describe a better sampling method that Reggie can use.
>
> b. Do you think if he takes two random samples of the same size, he will get the same results?

a. To describe a better sampling method, first look for the shortcomings of Reggie's method.

Reggie's proposed sample is not likely to be representative of the population of 700 students in all three grades for the following reasons:

- Reggie will only ask male students. Their opinions may not be the same as those of female students.

- Reggie will only ask 8th graders. Their opinions may not be the same as those of 7th and 9th graders.

- Reggie will only ask students who take the bus. Their opinions may not be the same as those of students who use another method to get to school.

To find a better method, address these issues so that the opinions of those in the sample are more likely to represent those of all students in grades 7–9. The method should not limit the sample to males, 8th graders, and bus riders.

▶ A better sampling method would be to ask every twentieth student as they walk in the school door about their favorite website, regardless of their gender, grade, or mode of transportation to school.

b. To consider whether two random samples would have the same results, think about what a random sample means.

A random sample is likely to be representative of the population. So, each random sample is likely to approximate the same proportions of responses as those in the entire population. However, they are still just approximations. So the two random samples are likely to be similar to each other, but not exactly the same.

▶ No, two random samples are not likely to have exactly the same results.

✏ Reggie suggests another method. He will alphabetize the names of all students in the school and ask every twentieth student on the list about his or her favorite website. Is this method likely to give a representative sample?

In problem 1, follow the steps to evaluate the proposed sampling method.

1. At Jada's middle school, 8th grade students can choose to take a foreign language class, either Spanish or French, after school. Jada wants to know if 8th graders who take a foreign language after school also plan to take a foreign language class in high school. She considers three possible methods for taking a sample.

   Method 1: Ask every twentieth student who walks into school in the morning.

   Method 2: Ask every 8th grade student who leaves Spanish class.

   Method 3: Ask every tenth 8th grade student who enters Spanish and French classes.

   Which, if any, of these methods is likely to produce a random sample?

   a. Define the population in this situation.

   b. Define the sample of each method.

      Method 1:

      Method 2:

      Method 3:

   c. Is each sample likely to be representative of the population? Explain.

      Method 1:

      Method 2:

      Method 3:

2. An airline wants to know whether its customers are satisfied with their flights. Describe a sampling method they could use to determine this.

Think•Pair•Share

MP3 3. A park ranger wants to know if people from a nearby town would be more likely to visit her park if it had more nature trails. One Saturday, she asks every tenth park visitor: "Would more nature trails make you more likely to visit the park?" Will the ranger get a representative sample of the population of interest?

Independent Practice

In problem 1, follow the steps to evaluate the proposed sampling method.

1. The owner of a department store wants to know how many visitors to her store actually make purchases. She considers three different methods for taking a sample.

   Method 1: Ask the first hundred visitors to the store if they plan on making purchases.

   Method 2: Ask every 100th person who leaves the store if they made a purchase.

   Method 3: Call every 1,000th person on an alphabetical list of residents and ask if they usually make purchases when visiting department stores.

   Which, if any, of these methods is likely to produce a random sample?

   a. Define the population in this situation.

   b. Define each proposed sample.

      Method 1:

      Method 2:

      Method 3:

   c. Is each sample likely to be representative of the population? Explain.

      Method 1:

      Method 2:

      Method 3:

2. A factory manager wants to take a sample of 50 of the 5,000 cell phones built each day to make sure they work. Describe a sampling method that would produce a representative sample. Why would a representative sample be useful to the manager?

Independent Practice

3. The owner of FoodWorld Groceries wants to know the most popular grocery store in town. She decides to have the cashiers at her stores ask customers as they check out. Would these data allow her to make an inference about the most popular grocery store chain in town?

For exercises 4–6, refer to the following situation. Circle all correct answers.

The manager of the 24-Hour Diner wants to know how many of her customers would purchase breakfast dishes if they were served all day rather than just in the morning. To obtain a sample, she plans to leave comment cards at fifty tables in the afternoon with the question: "Would you like breakfast dishes served all day long?"

4. What is the population of interest to the manager?

   a. All customers of the restaurant.

   b. All customers who want breakfast dishes in the afternoon.

   c. All people who live in the nearby town.

   d. All people who want breakfast dishes at any hour.

5. Which of these are shortcomings of the proposed sampling method?

   a. The sample relies on voluntary responses by customers.

   b. The sample would not represent customers who come in at different times of day.

   c. The sample would consist of too much data if all 50 cards were returned.

   d. The sample would only tell her whether people would like breakfast dishes served all day, not that they would purchase them.

6. Which of these sampling methods would be the most useful for obtaining a representative sample?

   a. Asking every customer who comes into the restaurant between 8 A.M. and 9 A.M.

   b. Asking every customer who comes into the restaurant between 8 P.M. and 10 A.M.

   c. Asking every 25th customer who enters the restaurant over 24 hours.

   d. Asking every customer who spends more than $20 on his or her meal.

Independent Practice

7. Dennis wants to know the approximate number of books that each middle school student in his state reads every summer. Why would taking a random sample of middle school students in the state be the most practical way for him to find an answer?

MP3 8. A scientist studies the heights of redwood trees in California. She proposes entering in the locations of all redwood forests in the state into a computer program, and having the computer randomly select 200 small plots in these forests to measure redwood tree heights. Explain why her method is likely to produce a representative sample of the heights of all redwood trees in California.

MP3 9. Ms. Simon gives the 35 students in her math class a surprise quiz. Afterward, she asks the students with the top five scores whether they thought the quiz was easy or difficult. Since all five students answer "easy," she says that most students think the quiz was easy. What argument would you make against this being a valid inference?

MP3 10. Carl wants to know if the students in his school are planning to visit a new mall that will be opening in a few weeks. To get a sample of the students in his school, he places flyers around school that say "Are you planning to visit the new mall? Let me know!", and includes his email address. Will his sample be random? Will it be representative?

MP3 11. Gianni wants to determine the average grade on the last quiz in his Reading class. He decides to ask four of his friends. Each of his friends got a B on the quiz. Is that enough for him to say that the average grade on the last quiz in his Reading class was a B?

MP3 **12.** Vlad wants to determine the favorite beverage of his school's 8th graders, so he asks every tenth member of the school's 8th grade sports teams. His teacher tells him his sample will not be representative of the population. Vlad says he'll take another sample, this time asking every fifth member of the school's 8th grade sports teams. He says his new sample must be more representative because it includes more students from his grade. Is he correct?

Answer _____

✎ **Justify your answer.**

MP3 **13.** In this map of Martin's neighborhood, each small rectangle is one house. The nearby forest is going to be turned into a parking lot, so Martin wants to take a sample of his neighbors to find their opinions about this. He draws a circle (that includes his own house) on the map. He will ask residents from each house in the circle (the red houses) their opinions about the new parking lot. Why is his sample likely to be biased?

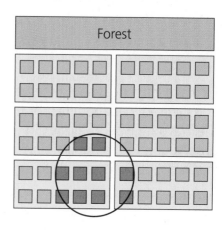

MP3 **14.** Ms. Danvers wants to know whether her employees are satisfied with their jobs. Instead of asking all 500 employees, which includes the 25 in the accounting department, the 50 in the shipping department, and the 425 factory workers, she decides to take a sample. She will ask each of the 50 employees in the shipping department to complete an anonymous survey about whether they are satisfied with their jobs. Is this a random sample?

Answer _____

✎ **Justify your answer.**

Use Sampling to Draw Inferences

Essential Question:

What does the data from a random sample tell you about a population?

7.SP.2

Words to Know:
variability

Guided Instruction

In this lesson, you will draw inferences about a population based on data from a random sample.

Understand: Drawing Inferences about a population from a random sample

Joanna uses a random sample of 50 students in her grade and asks them about their favorite type of movies. She writes the data in the table shown.

If there are a total of 500 students in her grade, what are two inferences you can make about the population?

Favorite Type of Movie	Number of Students
Action	10
Comedy	26
Drama	6
Fantasy	8

To make inferences about the population, start by making sense of the sample data. You can see that about half of the students in the sample said that comedies were their favorite type of movie. So you could make an inference by 'scaling up' this observation to the population. You could predict that about half of the students in the population are likely to say comedies are their favorite type of movies, too.

You can make more specific inferences as well. If a sample is representative of a population, then the ratios of the responses are likely to be similar in both the sample and the population. So, you can use a proportional relationship to make inferences about the population.

For example, you can find the unknown in a proportional relationship to predict the number of students in the population who would say that action movies are their favorite type.

the ratio of the number of sampled students who say action movies are their favorite to the total number of students in the sample

$$\frac{10}{50} = \frac{a}{500}$$
$$10 \cdot 500 = 50a$$
$$5,000 = 50a$$
$$\frac{5,000}{50} = \frac{50a}{50}$$
$$100 = a$$

the ratio of the total number of students who say action movies are their favorite, a, to the total number of students in the population

➡ Based on the sample, about half the students in her grade are likely to say that comedies are their favorite type of movie and about 100 of the 500 students in her grade would say action movies are their favorite.

Understand: Using multiple samples to make inferences about a population

The local library is open from 9:00 A.M. to 5:00 P.M., but is considering adding evening hours one day a week. Shania takes three different random samples of 50 visitors at the library to determine which day of the week should have evening hours. Her results are in this table.

Day	Sample #1	Sample #2	Sample #3
Sunday	9	11	8
Monday	7	5	6
Tuesday	6	5	5
Wednesday	14	17	18
Thursday	6	5	6
Friday	4	3	4
Saturday	4	4	3

a. What inferences can you make about the population based on these random samples?

b. Shania says visitors would prefer evening hours on Monday more than on Tuesday. Is this a valid statement?

a. To make inferences using multiple random samples, notice that the responses in the samples are similar, but not exactly the same. This is often true of multiple random samples. Recall that the proportion of responses in a random sample is close to the proportion of responses in the whole population. The difference between the corresponding values in random samples is called the sampling variability.

To account for the variability of samples, look for trends that are true for all samples:

• More visitors want evening hours on Wednesday than on any other day. This is true in each sample, so it is true across all samples. So, it is likely to be true of the whole population.

• The fewest visitors want evening hours added on Friday or Saturday than on any two days. This is also true in each sample, so it is also likely to be true of the population.

▶ More visitors want evening hours on Wednesday than on any other day. The fewest visitors want evening hours added on Friday or Saturday than on any other two days.

Continued»

Guided Instruction

b. To evaluate whether Shania's statement is true, examine the differences between the data for evening hours on Monday and Tuesday.

The data values are nearly the same. They could be the result of the variability expected of any group of random samples. The differences between samples for evening hours on Monday vs. Tuesday are not enough to make a reliable claim about the entire population.

▶ Shania's statement is not supported by the sample data.

Connect: Using the mean of random samples to make inferences about a population

The operators of the PlayPlace amusement park want to know how many first-time visitors plan to visit the park again in the next year. They take random samples of 600 first-time visitors as they exit the park asking them: "When do you plan to visit again?" The results are below.

	In the Next Year	Between 1 and 2 Years from Now	Between 2 and 5 Years from Now	More than 5 Years/Will Not Visit Again
Sample #1	84	128	326	62
Sample #2	76	116	364	44
Sample #3	80	119	345	56

PlayPlace has 720,000 first-time visitors each year. Based on these samples, about how many first-time visitors each year plan to visit the park again in the next year?

To use all three random samples to estimate the number of first-time visitors who will visit again in the next year, start by finding the mean number of these responses.

For the three samples, the mean number of first-time visitors who plan to visit again in the next year is $\frac{84 + 76 + 80}{3} = \frac{240}{3} = 80$. So the mean of the samples indicates that 80 of 600 first-time visitors plan to visit again in the next year.

You can use proportional reasoning to estimate the number of the 720,000 first-time visitors each year who plan to visit again in the next year.

If $\frac{80}{600} = \frac{n}{720,000}$ ⟶ $720,000 \left(\frac{80}{600}\right) = n$ ⟶ so $n = 96,000$.

▶ Based on the random samples, approximately 96,000 first-time visitors plan to visit again in the next year.

In exercises 1 and 2, follow the steps to answer the questions.

1. Camille takes a random sample of 40 of her 480 coworkers to learn their preferred workout. Her results are in this table.

   Based on this sample, what is an estimate for the number of coworkers for whom swimming is their preferred workout?

Preferred Workout	Number of Coworkers
Yoga	6
Swimming	5
Treadmill	19
Weightlifting	10

   a. Complete the proportional relationship.

   the ratio of the number of sampled ⟶ $\underline{} = \dfrac{s}{\underline{}}$ ⟵ the ratio of the number of
   coworkers who prefer swimming   coworkers who prefer swimming,
   to the total number of coworkers s, to the total number of coworkers
   in the sample   in the population

   b. Find the unknown from part a.

   Based on the sample, Camille can estimate that about ____ coworkers would name swimming as their preferred workout.

2. Camille takes another sample, in addition to the sample she took in exercise 1. The results of the second sample are in this table.

   Based on both samples, state two inferences that you can make about the population.

Preferred Workout	Number of Coworkers
Yoga	7
Swimming	7
Treadmill	16
Weightlifting	10

   ● _____

   ● _____

Think•Pair•Share

MP3 3. Chavon reads exercises 1 and 2, and says more coworkers prefer yoga to swimming. Is this a valid inference using both samples? Explain.

Independent Practice

In exercises 1 and 2, follow the steps to answer the questions.

1. Roger takes a random sample of 55 of the 880 students in his school about what time of day they feel most alert. His results are shown in the table.

   Based on this sample, what is an estimate for the number of classmates who feel most alert after 5 P.M.?

Time When Most Alert	Number of Students
Before noon	17
Between noon and 5 P.M.	23
After 5 P.M.	15

   a. Show the proportional relationship.

   the ratio of the number of sampled ⟶ $\underline{\hspace{1cm}} = \dfrac{n}{\hspace{0.5cm}}$ ⟵ the ratio of the number of
   students who said "After 5 P.M."   students who said "After 5 P.M.", n,
   to the total number of students   to the total number of students
   in the sample   in the population

   b. Find the unknown in part a.

   Based on the sample, Roger can estimate that about _____ students would say they are most alert after 5 P.M..

2. Roger takes a second sample, in addition to the sample he took in exercise 1. The results of the second sample are in this table.

   Based on both samples, state two inferences that you can make about the population.

Time When Most Alert	Number of Students
Before noon	21
Between noon and 5 P.M.	24
After 5 P.M.	10

   • _____

   • _____

3. Explain why the tables in the two random samples in exercises 1 and 2 do not have the same values, even though they have the same size and were taken from the same population.

For exercises 4–6, circle all correct answers.

4. Emma Rose took a random sample of 250 visitors to an art museum to ask them which exhibit they came to see.

Exhibit	Sculpture Garden	Modern Art Exhibit	Traveling Exhibit	Other Exhibit
Number of Responses	47	130	48	25

Which of these inferences about the population of visitors is well supported by her sample?

a. About half of all visitors came to the museum to see the modern art exhibit.

b. More visitors came to see the modern art exhibit than any other exhibit.

c. More visitors came to see the traveling exhibit than the sculpture garden.

d. More visitors came to see the sculpture garden or the traveling exhibit than came to see the modern art exhibit.

5. A journalist investigates user complaints about their new laptops. She takes a random sample of 5,000 new laptop buyers and asks them to describe their main complaint about their laptops.

Short Battery Life	Screen Too Small	Slow Speed	Other Complaints	No Complaints
2,015	428	477	896	1,184

Based on this sample, which is the most reasonable estimate for how many of the 15,600,000 new laptop buyers in the United States last year had no complaints?

a. 1,540,650 b. 2,095,520 c. 2,420,000 d. 3,694,080

6. A scientist studies one type of bird in its native forest. He takes two random samples of 500 birds and measures their beak lengths. There are a total of 4,500 of these birds in this forest.

Beak Length	Less than 1 inch	Between 1 and 2 inches	Between 2 and 3 inches	Greater than 3 inches
Sample #1	46	317	72	65
Sample #2	50	295	85	70

Based on both samples, which of these is most likely to be the number of birds in this forest with beak lengths between 1 and 2 inches?

a. 1,746 b. 2,055 c. 2,754 d. 3,853

Independent Practice

MP4 **7.** In the 8th grade student council election, Vincent's classmates will each cast one vote. The students who receive the greatest and second greatest numbers of votes will be president and vice-president. Vincent takes two random samples of 64 students each in which he asks "Which one of the six candidates will you vote for?"

	Sandra	Kwame	Jason	Bradley	Kendall	Karen
Sample #1	8	14	11	4	9	18
Sample #2	10	16	5	4	10	19

Predict which students will likely be elected president and vice-president.

MP5 **8.** A safety technician studies how long cars actually remain stopped at stop signs. Based on her results, she makes two computer-generated random samples, called *simulations*, of how long cars stay stopped at a stop sign for 500 cars.

	More than 4 seconds	Between 2 and 4 seconds	Between 1 and 2 seconds	Between 0 and 1 second
Sample #1	35	160	159	146
Sample #2	46	151	145	158

What two inferences can you make about all cars based on her simulated data?

MP3 **9.** Gerry wants to estimate the number of cars that are less than 3 years old in his city. He takes two random samples of cars and their ages in his city.

	Less than 3 Years	Between 3 and 6 Years	Between 6 and 10 Years	Older than 10 Years
Sample #1	67	131	111	191
Sample #2	43	107	88	162

He calculates the mean of the number of cars less than 3 years old in the samples to be $\frac{67 + 43}{2} = \frac{110}{2}$, or 55 cars. He concludes that $\frac{55}{500}$ of the cars in the city are less than 3 years old. What mistake did Gerry make in his work?

Solve the problems.

MP4 **10.** Jen reads that the mean of a random sample can be used as an estimate for the mean of a population. She takes a random sample of the heights (in inches) of 10 of the 50 students in her gym class. Her data set is: 58, 56, 57, 60, 64, 66, 70, 65, 62, 65. Estimate the mean height of the students in the class.

✏ **Show your work.**

Answer _____

MP2 **11.** Karol takes two random samples of the 650 students in her school, asking each to name his or her favorite color. Which is more likely to be representative of the population: Sample #1, Sample #2, or both samples together?

	Red	Orange	Yellow	Green	Blue	Purple
Sample #1	6	4	6	6	16	12
Sample #2	9	6	4	5	14	12

Answer _____

✏ **Justify your answer.**

MP3 **12.** An advertising agency takes two random samples of drivers aged 25–34 to determine the color of cars they are most interested in purchasing.

	Blue	Black	Silver	White	Red	Gray
Sample #1	123	215	183	88	122	117
Sample #2	132	199	177	85	130	108

The agency's report says drivers aged 25–34 are more interested in purchasing blue cars than red cars. Do you agree?

Answer _____

✏ **Justify your answer.**

32 Use Visual Overlap to Compare Distributions

Essential Question:
How can you compare data sets visually and then confirm your inferences?

7.SP.3

Words to Know:
distribution

Guided Instruction

In this lesson, you will learn to compare two data sets visually, and then use their measures of center and variability to verify your comparisons.

Understand: Comparing displays of data sets visually

A high school coach compares the weights of the boys tennis and basketball teams. The data set is in the table to the right.

Use dot plots of the data sets to visually compare the average weights and variability of the teams.

Tennis Team Weights (lb)

159, 160, 160, 163, 165, 165, 165, 165, 165, 170, 170, 174, 174, 180, 185

Basketball Team Weights (lb)

166, 175, 177, 182, 185, 185, 188, 188, 198, 198, 198, 199, 199, 203, 203

To compare the data sets, stack dot plots so one is directly above the other. Make sure their scales are the same, so you can visually compare the shapes and placements, or distribution, of data on both plots.

Tennis Team Weights (lb)

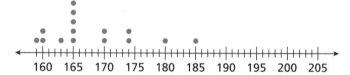

You can see that the data sets overlap, and that the range of the basketball team weights is greater.

Basketball Team Weights (lb)

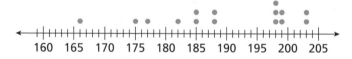

You can also see that much of the basketball weight data is to the right of the tennis team weight data. This suggests the mean of the basketball team is greater than the mean of the tennis team. You can also see that the basketball team data appear to be more spread out. This suggests the variability of weights is greater for the basketball team.

➡ By visual comparison, the mean weight and variability appear to be greater for the basketball team than for the tennis team.

Understand: Comparing data sets using their measures of center and variability

The coach in the previous example wants to support his comparisons of the teams. Do the measures of center and variability support the comparisons he made visually?

To determine if the measures of center and variability support his comparisons, start by calculating the mean.

For the tennis team, the mean is:

$$\frac{(159 + 160 + 160 + 163 + 165 + 165 + 165 + 165 + 165 + 170 + 170 + 174 + 174 + 180 + 185)}{15} =$$

$\frac{2{,}520}{15}$, or 168 pounds.

For the basketball team, the mean is:

$$\frac{(166 + 175 + 177 + 182 + 185 + 185 + 188 + 188 + 198 + 198 + 198 + 199 + 199 + 203 + 203)}{15} =$$

$\frac{2{,}844}{15}$, or 189.6 pounds.

The mean weight of the basketball team is $189.6 - 168 = 21.6$ pounds greater than the mean weight of the tennis team.

You can use these means to calculate the mean absolute deviation (MAD) for each set.

> **Remember!**
> The mean average deviation is the average of the absolute differences between each data value and the mean.

For the tennis team:

Weight	159	160	160	163	165	165	165	165	165	170	170	174	174	180	185
Abs. Diff. from Mean	9	8	8	5	3	3	3	3	3	2	2	6	6	12	17

The average of the absolute difference from the mean for the weights of members of the tennis team is:

$$\frac{(9 + 8 + 8 + 5 + 3 + 3 + 3 + 3 + 3 + 2 + 2 + 6 + 6 + 12 + 17)}{15} = \frac{90}{15} = 6.$$

The mean absolute deviation for the tennis team is 6 pounds.

For the basketball team, using the rounded value of 190 for 189.6:

Weight	166	175	177	182	185	185	188	188	198	198	198	199	199	203	203
Abs. Diff. from Mean	24	15	13	8	5	5	2	2	8	8	8	9	9	13	13

The average of the absolute difference from the mean for the weights of members of the basketball team is:

$$\frac{(24 + 15 + 13 + 8 + 5 + 5 + 2 + 2 + 8 + 8 + 8 + 9 + 9 + 13 + 13)}{15} = \frac{142}{15} \approx 9.5.$$

The mean absolute deviation for the basketball team is about 9.5 pounds.

The mean absolute deviation is about $9.5 - 6 = 3.5$ pounds greater for the basketball team than for the tennis team, so the basketball team has a greater variability in weight.

➡ The means and the mean absolute deviations support the inferences that the mean weight and variability are greater for the basketball team than for the tennis team.

Guided Instruction

Understand: Expressing a difference in means as a multiple of MAD

The tables show test-score data for Kent Middle School. For which subject was the improvement more significant?

Reading	Year 1	Year 2
Mean	580	630
MAD	160	150

Math	Year 1	Year 2
Mean	650	700
MAD	25	22

For each subject, find the difference in means for the two years.

Reading: 630 − 580 = 50   **Math:** 700 − 650 = 50   The difference is the same.

We can evaluate the significance of the difference in means for each subject by expressing that difference as a multiple of the MAD for each year's set of data.

Reading

$$\frac{\text{difference in means}}{\text{MAD for Year 1}} = \frac{50}{160} = 0.3125$$

$$\frac{\text{difference in means}}{\text{MAD for Year 2}} = \frac{50}{150} = 0.\overline{3}$$

In reading, the difference in means is about 0.3 times the MAD for either year.

Math

$$\frac{\text{difference in means}}{\text{MAD for Year 1}} = \frac{50}{25} = 2$$

$$\frac{\text{difference in means}}{\text{MAD for Year 2}} = \frac{50}{22} = 2.\overline{27}$$

In math, the difference in means is about 2 times the MAD for either year.

The greater the multiple, the more significant the difference in means is.

➡ The improvement was more significant in math.

> If the students' scores for each subject and for each year were shown on dot plots, the differences in the scores for the two years would be more obvious for math than for reading.

Connect: Using box plots to compare data sets

Two teams hold a free throw contest. The numbers of points scored by the players on each team are shown in the box plots. Compare the data sets using measures of center and variability.

Number of Points Scored

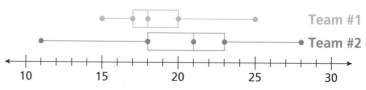

To compare data sets in a box plot, find the five-number summaries.
   Team #1: Min: 15, First Quartile: 17, Median: 18, Third Quartile: 20, Max: 25
   Team #2: Min: 11, First Quartile: 18, Median: 21, Third Quartile: 23, Max: 28

Team #2 has the greater median (21 compared to 18), range (17 compared to 10), and interquartile range (5 compared to 3).

> The greater range and interquartile range lets you infer that Team #2 has greater variability in its scores.

➡ Team #2 has a greater median and a greater variability in its scores than Team #1.

For exercise 1, follow the steps to compare the data sets.

1. Marion records the hours of overtime put in last month by the employees of two small companies.

   Company 1: 0, 3, 5, 6, 7, 7, 7, 8, 10, 10, 10, 11, 13, 15

   Company 2: 0, 1, 2, 3, 3, 6, 10, 10, 10, 12, 15, 19, 19, 20, 20

   Company 1: Overtime Hours Worked

   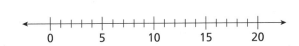

   Company 2: Overtime Hours Worked

   a. Complete a dot plot of each data set.

   b. Compare the two sets visually to complete these statements.
      The mean number of hours worked for Company 1 appears to be

      _____ the mean number of hours worked for Company 2.

      The variability of the data for Company 1 appears to be _____
      the variability of the data for Company 2.

   c. Compute the mean for each data set.

      Company 1: $\dfrac{(\qquad\qquad\qquad\qquad\qquad)}{14} = \underline{\quad}$

      Company 2: $\dfrac{(\qquad\qquad\qquad\qquad\qquad)}{15} = \underline{\quad}$

   d. Compute the mean absolute deviation (MAD) for each company.

      For Company 1:

Value	0	3	5	6	7	7	7	8	10	10	10	11	13	15
Abs. Diff. from Mean														

      The MAD is: $\dfrac{(\qquad\qquad\qquad\qquad\qquad)}{14} = \underline{\quad}$

      For Company 2:

Value	0	1	2	3	3	6	10	10	10	12	15	19	19	20	20
Abs. Diff. from Mean															

      The MAD is: $\dfrac{(\qquad\qquad\qquad\qquad\qquad)}{15} = \underline{\quad}$

 **Think • Pair • Share**

MP2 2. Do your answers to parts c and d above support your answer to part b? Explain.

Independent Practice

For exercise 1, follow the steps to compare the data sets.

1. Jane manages lacrosse teams for two schools. She records the number of points scored by players on each team last season.

   Team 1: 20, 20, 22, 22, 27, 27, 27, 28, 31, 36

   Team 2: 26, 28, 29, 29, 29, 31, 31, 32, 32, 33

   a. Complete a dot plot of each data set.

   b. Compare the two sets visually to complete these statements.

   The mean number of points scored by Team 1 appears to be _____ the mean number of points scored by Team 2. The variability of data for

   Team 1 appears to be _____ the variability of data for Team 2.

   Team 1: Points Scored

   Team 2: Points Scored

   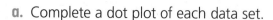

   c. Compute the mean for each data set.

   Team 1: $\dfrac{()}{10}$ = _____

   Team 2: $\dfrac{()}{10}$ = _____

   d. Compute the mean absolute deviation (MAD) for each team.

   For Team 1:

Value	20	20	22	22	27	27	27	28	31	36
Abs. Diff. from Mean										

   The MAD is: $\dfrac{()}{10}$ = _____

   For Team 2:

Value	26	28	29	29	29	31	31	32	32	33
Abs. Diff. from Mean										

   The MAD is: $\dfrac{()}{10}$ = _____

   e. Do your answers to parts c and d support your answer to part b? Explain.

Independent Practice

2. Use the values in exercise 1 to express the difference in means of both teams as a multiple of the variability for each team.

The difference in means is _____ time(s) the MAD for Team 1.

The difference in means is _____ time(s) the MAD for Team 2.

Exercises 3–6 refer to the following situation and data. Circle all correct answers.

Ms. Lopez gives the same math exam to her morning class and to her afternoon class. She keeps track of how many minutes it takes for the 18 students in each class to finish. The data sets and dot plots are shown.

Morning Class Finishing Times (minutes): 41, 44, 45, 45, 46, 46, 46, 48, 48, 48, 49, 49, 49, 49, 51, 52, 54, 54

Morning Class: Finishing Times (minutes)

Afternoon Class Finishing Times (minutes): 42, 47, 48, 48, 50, 51, 51, 52, 52, 52, 54, 54, 54, 55, 55, 55, 56, 60

Afternoon Class: Finishing Times (minutes)

3. Which of the following inferences are supported by visual comparison?

a. Some students in each class took between 55 and 60 minutes to finish the test.

b. The variability for the morning class data appears to be similar to the variability in the afternoon class data.

c. The mean finishing time for the morning class appears to be less than the mean finishing time for the afternoon class.

d. The ranges of the data sets are the same.

4. What is the actual difference in the means of finishing times between the morning class and afternoon class?

a. 4 min   **b.** 7 min   **c.** 11 min   **d.** 14 min

5. To the nearest minute, what is the difference in the mean absolute deviations of the data sets?

a. 0 min   **b.** 3 min   **c.** 6 min   **d.** 9 min

6. About how many times the variability of the finishing time for the afternoon class is the difference in the means of the finishing times for both classes?

a. 0.2 times   **b.** 1.3 times   **c.** 2.6 times   **d.** 3.5 times

Independent Practice

Solve the problems.

MP1 **7.** Jan records the points scored by members of the girls' soccer teams from two schools.

Franklin Middle School: 45, 48, 48, 51, 53, 54, 55, 55, 55, 56, 56, 60

Greenville Middle School: 53, 54, 54, 59, 59, 59, 60, 60, 61, 61, 63, 65

a. Make a dot plot of each data set, and compare the variability of the data sets visually.

Franklin Players: Points Scored

Greenville Players: Points Scored

b. Calculate the mean absolute deviations for both teams. Do they support your answer to part a?

✏️ **Show your work.**

Answer _____

MP3 **8.** Kim and Jeff compare their bowling scores over the last year in a box plot. Kim says she has the higher score on average, while Jeff says he is the more consistent bowler. Who is correct?

Bowling Scores

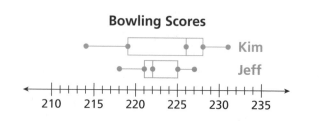

Answer _____

✏️ **Justify your answer.**

MP2 **9.** Since each student's score on the last exam was less than 90, Mr. Clark adds 10 points to each student's score. Think of the scores before these 10 points were added as Data Set #1, and the scores after the points were added as Data Set #2.

a. How would dot plots and means of the two data sets compare?

b. How would the variability differ in the two sets?

MP6 **10.** Carl makes a dot plot for each of the following data sets:

Data Set #1: 30, 32, 35, 35, 38, 38, 39, 40, 40, 40, 40, 42, 44, 44, 44, 49, 50

Data Set #2: 30, 33, 35, 35, 35, 38, 38, 40, 40, 40, 40, 44, 45, 45, 46, 46, 50

He finds that the mean of each data set is 40. He also sees that the ranges of the data sets are the same. So he concludes that the data sets have exactly the same variability. Is his conclusion correct?

Data Set #1

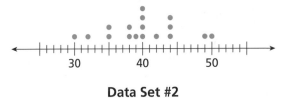

Data Set #2

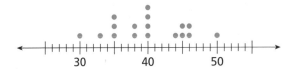

Answer _____

✏️ **Justify your answer.**

Essential Question:
How can you compare two populations using random samples drawn from each?
7.SP.4

Words to Know:
statistics

Guided Instruction

In this lesson, you will learn to compare two populations by comparing the measures of center and variability of random samples.

Understand: Selecting a measure of center to compare random samples

> Jasmine wants to compare rental costs in two apartment buildings. She takes a random sample of the monthly rent of eight apartments in each building.
>
> **Building #1:**
> $4,500; $1,750; $1,775; $1,850; $1,750; $1,750; $1,825; $1,825
>
> **Building #2:**
> $1,900; $1,850; $1,900; $1,950; $1,900; $1,875; $1,925; $1,875
>
> Which measure of center of the samples best allows you to compare the typical rents at these two buildings? Based on this measure, how do the typical rents compare?

To determine the best measure of center for comparing these data sets, start by looking for any outliers. For example, seven of the eight apartments in Building #1 have very similar rents. However, one rent is much greater than the others: $4,500. This could be a large top floor apartment that is not representative of any other apartments in the building. So, its rent would not be representative of the rents of the other apartments in that building. For that reason, the mean would not be a good choice for comparing rents at the two buildings.

Remember!
When an outlier is present, it can affect the calculation of the mean.

Consider comparing the medians of the rents instead. From low to high, the rents are:

Building #1: $1,750; $1,750; $1,750; $1,775; $1,825; $1,825; $1,850; $4,500

Building #2: $1,850; $1,875; $1,875; $1,900; $1,900; $1,900; $1,925; $1,950

So, the median rent of the samples for Building #1 is $\frac{(\$1,775 + \$1,825)}{2} = \$1,800$, and for Building #2 is $\frac{(\$1,900 + \$1,900)}{2} = \$1,900$. You have calculated medians for whole populations before. When measures of center and variability are calculated for samples, they are called statistics.

Remember!
When you have an even number of data values, the median is the mean of the two middle values.

▶ The median rents of the samples are better indicators of the typical rent in each building than the mean rents of the samples. The medians suggest that the typical rent is less expensive in Building #1 than in Building #2.

Understand: Using random samples to compare populations

Two teachers compare the number of extra credit points their students have earned. They each take a random sample of 12 of their 90 students from last year.

Based on these random samples, which class has a more consistent number of points earned?

Reading: Extra Credit Points
9, 10, 11, 14, 16, 20, 20, 20, 23, 24, 24, 25

Social Studies: Extra Credit Points
12, 13, 13, 15, 16, 17, 17, 17, 20, 21, 21, 22

To make inferences about the consistency of points earned in each class, compare the variability of the samples.

As before, you can make and stack two dot plots with the same scales to compare the data sets visually. The range of points earned is clearly greater for the Reading class sample, and those data values are more spread out. So, the Social Studies class appears to have earned a more consistent number of points.

Reading: Extra Credit Points

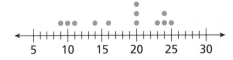

Social Studies: Extra Credit Points

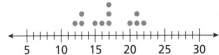

Now calculate the mean absolute deviation (MAD) of the two samples to see if they support the inference you made by visually comparing the data.

• The mean number of points for the Reading class sample is
$$\frac{(9 + 10 + 11 + 14 + 16 + 20 + 20 + 20 + 23 + 24 + 24 + 25)}{12} = 18.$$

So the MAD for the Reading class sample is
$$\frac{(9 + 8 + 7 + 4 + 2 + 2 + 2 + 2 + 5 + 6 + 6 + 7)}{12} = 5.$$

• The mean number of points for the Social Studies class sample is
$$\frac{(12 + 13 + 13 + 15 + 16 + 17 + 17 + 17 + 20 + 21 + 21 + 22)}{12} = 17.$$

So the MAD for the Social Studies class sample is
$$\frac{(5 + 4 + 4 + 2 + 1 + 0 + 0 + 0 + 3 + 4 + 4 + 5)}{12} = 2\frac{2}{3}.$$

Use what you have found about the samples to make inferences about the populations. Since the MAD of the Reading sample is almost twice the MAD of the Social Studies sample, you can predict that this variability will be true in the populations as well. Since the points earned in the Social Studies sample are closer to the mean, you can predict the points of all Social Studies students are more consistent than the points of all Reading students.

▸ Based on the random samples, the Social Studies class has a more consistent number of points earned.

Guided Instruction

Connect: Evaluating inferences about populations made from random samples

Dale takes random samples of 20 young people (age 13 to 17) in his neighborhood and 20 adults (18 or over) in his neighborhood. He asks "How many hours a week do you spend online?"

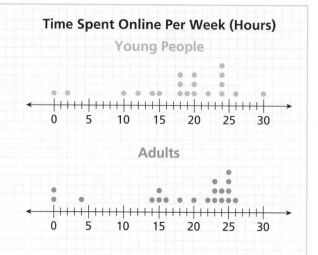

From his data (shown in the dot plots), Dale finds the mean time spent online per week for young people is 18 hours and for adults is 18.35 hours.

Dale decides that adults in the United States spend a greater mean number of hours online than young people. Does his inference about the difference in the populations based on the difference in samples make sense?

To evaluate whether Dale's inference is valid, consider whether the random samples are representative of the population described. The random samples are all taken from one neighborhood, so they more likely represent people who live there, and not all people in the United States.

Next, consider his sample sizes and the populations he describes. Sampling 20 people out of 100 might provide representative data, but sampling 20 people out of millions in the United States is not likely to get representative data.

Then, consider whether the difference between the sample means is large enough to make a claim about a difference between population means. Here, the difference of sample means is 0.35 hour. Recall that random samples of the same population are usually a little different just because of the variability of random sampling. So, this relatively small difference between the sample means may not describe an actual difference between means in the population.

Finally, consider whether the measures of center make sense for the data sets given. You can see outliers in both dot plots. So, the means are affected by these values. A better measure of center for comparing samples would be the median.

▶ Dale's inference is not valid, for the reasons described above.

For exercise 1, follow the steps to compare the data sets.

1. Carmella takes a random sample of the lengths of 15 comedy films and 15 drama films in her DVD collection. She makes these dot plots.

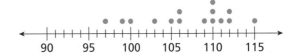

Comedy Film Length (minutes)

90   95   100   105   110   115

Drama Film Length (minutes)

90   95   100   105   110   115

   a. Compare the dot plots visually to make an inference about the means and variabilities of the data.

   b. To support your inferences, compute the mean for each data set.
      Mean (comedy film sample):

      (_____)
      ———————————————————————————————————————
                          15

      = _____ minutes

      Mean (drama film sample):

      (_____)
      ———————————————————————————————————————
                          15

      = _____ minutes

   c. Calculate the mean absolute deviation for each type of film.

      For comedy films, the MAD is:

      (_____)
      ———————————————————————————————————————
                          15

      ≈ _____ minutes

      For drama films, the MAD is:

      (_____)
      ———————————————————————————————————————
                          15

      = _____ minutes

 **Think•Pair•Share**

MP7 2. Do your calculations support your inferences you made in part a?

Independent Practice

For exercise 1, follow the steps to compare the data sets.

1. Salespeople at a used car dealership compare the numbers of cars sold by website auction with those sold by dealers in person. For each group, a random sample is taken for cars sold per week for 12 weeks in the previous year. The two dot plots show the data.

Cars Sold Per Week by Website Auction

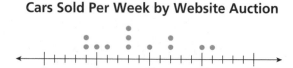

Cars Sold Per Week by Dealers in Person

   a. How do the dot plots of the samples compare visually? Compare the dot plots visually to make an inference about the means and variabilities of the data.

   b. Compute the mean for each data set.

   Mean (auction): $\dfrac{(\underline{\hspace{8cm}})}{12}$ = _____ cars

   Mean (in person): $\dfrac{(\underline{\hspace{8cm}})}{12}$ = _____ cars

   c. Calculate the mean absolute deviation for each data set.
   For cars sold by auction:
   For values 4, 4, 5, 6, 8, 8, 8, 10, 12, 12, 15, and 16, the absolute differences

   from the mean are ____, ____, ____, ____, ____, ____, ____, ____, ____, ____, ____,

   and ____.

   The MAD is: $\dfrac{(\underline{\hspace{7cm}})}{12}$ = _____ cars

   For cars sold in person:
   For values 5, 6, 6, 7, 9, 9, 9, 10, 10, 11, 12, and 14, the absolute differences

   from the mean are ____, ____, ____, ____, ____, ____, ____, ____, ____, ____, ____,

   and ____.

   The MAD is: $\dfrac{(\underline{\hspace{7cm}})}{12}$ = _____ cars

   d. Do your calculations support your inferences about how the number of all cars sold each week by website auction last year differs from the number of all cars sold weekly in person at this dealership last year? Explain.

Independent Practice

**For exercises 2–3, circle all correct answers.
Both exercises refer to the following situation.**

A company considers two new types of touchscreen keyboards for their employees' phones. Two groups of 10 employees each are selected from their 60 employees. Each group is given phones with one of these keyboards, and the phones keep track of how many typing errors each person makes. (An error is considered to be when a letter or number is typed and then deleted). At the end of one day, the following data set is used to make the two dot plots.

Number of Mistakes Per Day

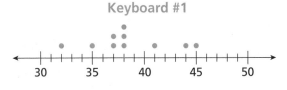

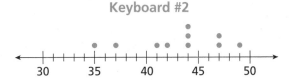

Keyboard #1 (number of mistakes):
32, 35, 37, 37, 38, 38, 38, 41, 44, 45

Keyboard #2 (number of mistakes):
35, 37, 41, 42, 44, 44, 44, 47, 47, 49

2. Based on the sample data, what inferences can you make about the mean number of errors that would be made by all employees on these keyboards?

   a. The difference in sample means is 4.5 errors, so employees using Keyboard #1 would make fewer mistakes.

   b. The difference in sample means is 4.5 errors, so employees using Keyboard #2 would make fewer mistakes.

   c. The difference in sample means is 0.5 error, so employees using Keyboard #1 would make fewer mistakes.

   d. The difference in sample means is 0.5 error, so employees using Keyboard #2 would make fewer mistakes.

3. What evidence could be used to support the claim that all employees using Keyboard #1 would make more consistent numbers of errors?

   a. The range is much smaller for Keyboard #1.

   b. The mean absolute deviation is slightly less for Keyboard #1.

   c. The range is much smaller for Keyboard #2.

   d. The mean absolute deviation is slightly less for Keyboard #2.

Independent Practice

MP2　**4.** You have compared populations in two ways: by examining population data and by examining sample data. How does making comparisons using these data differ?

MP3　**5.** Dana takes random samples of 20 heights each from the 500 8th graders and 500 9th graders in her school. She compares them using a measure of center and a measure of variability for each sample. Would larger random samples from each population help her be more confident in her inferences? Explain.

Solve the problems.

MP6　**6.** High school students are raising money for the school band. Some students stand at the mall entrance, while others stand on the sidewalk closer to the street. They take a random sample of 10 students from each group to find how much each student raised per day. The data sets below show each student's daily total rounded to the nearest dollar.

Mall Entrance (Amount raised in $): 15, 20, 20, 24, 24, 25, 26, 28, 28, 35
Street Sidewalk (Amount raised in $): 22, 26, 28, 28, 28, 29, 30, 30, 32, 32

Find the measures of center and variability to suggest where a student should stand to raise more money.

　Show your work.

Answer _____

Independent Practice

MP4 **7.** Alice is trying to choose between jobs at two companies. To give her an idea of what she would earn, the presidents of each company send her random samples of 6 employees' salaries.

Company #1: $54,550; $55,000; $58,000; $61,550; $62,750; $385,425
Company #2: $63,800; $67,200; $68,240; $69,150; $70,000; $72,000

a. Why would the president of Company #1 suggest Alice make her decision using the mean of the data sample?

b. Which measure of center should Alice use to get an idea of the salary she would earn?

c. Based on your answer to part b, which company should she choose based on the salary alone, and what is your estimate of the salary based on the random sample?

Answer _____

✏️ **Show your work.**

MP3 **8.** A tablet manufacturer wants to compare its two best-selling models. The company takes random samples of 20 customers of Model A and 20 customers of Model B and asks: "How many times per week do you have to restart your tablet because it freezes?" The data is shown in this box plot. Based on the samples, is there a sufficient difference between the sample data sets to state which model is more reliable for the average user?

Number of Restarts Per Week

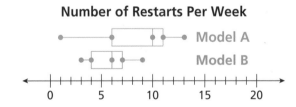

Answer _____

✏️ **Justify your answer.**

34 Describe the Probability of a Chance Event

Essential Question:
How can you describe the probability of a chance event?

7.SP.5

Words to Know:
likelihood
experiment
event
probability

Guided Instruction

In this lesson, you will learn to understand and describe the probability of a chance event.

Understand: The probability of an event

Each letter of the alphabet is printed on a square tile. The tiles are placed in a bag and one is drawn out without looking. Which number best describes the likelihood of drawing out a tile with a consonant: 0.2, 0.5, or 0.8?

To decide which number describes the likelihood, think about how likely it is to draw a tile with a consonant. The likelihood of something happening tells how possible it is to happen. Something can never happen, happen less than half of the time, happen half of the time, happen more than half of the time, or always happen.

Some words have different meanings when they are used in probability. Reaching in without looking and drawing a tile from the bag is an experiment. An experiment has outcomes that happen by chance. Getting a tile with a consonant is an event. An event is one or more desired outcomes of an experiment.

The probability of an event is a number between 0 and 1 that represents the likelihood that the event will happen, or occur.

> The number line shows how a probability expressed as a number from 0 through 1 describes how likely it is that an event will occur.

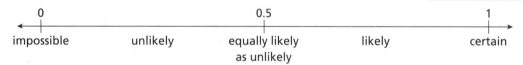

0		0.5		1
impossible	unlikely	equally likely as unlikely	likely	certain

- A probability of 0 means that an event cannot occur and so is impossible.

- A probability of 1 means that an event will definitely occur and so is certain.

- Halfway between 0 and 1 is 0.5 or $\frac{1}{2}$. This probability means that an event is as likely to occur as to not occur.

- Probabilities between 0 and 0.5 describe events that are unlikely to occur.

- Probabilities between 0.5 and 1 describe events that are likely to occur.

> The closer the probability is to 0, the more unlikely that the event will occur.
>
> The closer the probability is to 1 the more likely that the event will occur.

Now think about the letter tiles in the bag. There are 21 consonants out of the 26 tiles in the bag, so there are 21 out of 26 chances that a tile with a consonant will be drawn. This means that drawing a tile with a consonant is a very likely outcome. Of the 3 numbers to choose from, only 0.8 describes a likely situation.

➡ The number that best describes the likelihood of drawing a consonant is 0.8.

Understand: Find the probability of a certain event

> For a probability experiment, tiles with the letters A, B, C, D, E, and F, each on its own tile, are placed in a bag. What is the probability of reaching into the bag once and taking out a tile with a letter that comes before G in the alphabet?

To find the probability, you can think about what is happening in this probability experiment. You need to find the number of possible outcomes and the number of desired outcomes.

The number of possible outcomes is the number of tiles in the bag. When you reach in and take out 1 tile, there are 6 possible tiles you might take out. The number of desired outcomes, or the event, is the number of tiles with the letters that come before G. You are looking for the probability of this event.

Notice that *all* of the letters on the tiles come before G in the alphabet. So it is certain that the tile you take out will have a letter that comes before G. There are 6 out of 6 chances of taking out a tile with a letter that comes before G. To describe the probability of an event that is certain, you use the number 1.

▶ The probability of choosing a tile with a letter that comes before G is 1.

Understand: Find the probability of an impossible event

> For a probability experiment, tiles with the letters A, B, C, D, E, and F, each on its own tile, are placed in a bag. What is the probability of reaching into the bag once and taking out a tile with a letter that comes after F in the alphabet?

To find the probability, you can think about what is happening in this probability experiment. Start by the number of possible outcomes and the number of desired outcomes. Then see how often a desired outcome happens out of all the outcomes.

The number of possible outcomes is the number of tiles in the bag, so there are 6 possible tiles to take out. The number of desired outcomes, or the event, is the number of tiles with the letters that come after F. You are looking for the probability of this event.

Notice that *none* of the letters on the tiles come after F in the alphabet. So it is impossible to take out a tile with a letter that comes after F. To describe the probability of an impossible event, you use the number 0.

▶ The probability of choosing a tile with a letter that comes after F is 0.

Guided Instruction

Connect: Fractions and probability

> A coin is tossed. Which event is more likely to occur, the coin lands on heads or the coin lands on tails? What is the probability of each event?

You can use fractions as well as decimals to describe probabilities. As with decimals, probabilities described with fractions show the likelihood of an event.

0     $\frac{1}{2}$ 1

impossible   unlikely   equally likely or unlikely   likely   certain

Remember!

The probability of an event ranges from being impossible with a probability of 0 to being certain with a probability of 1.

When tossing a coin, there are two possible outcomes, heads or tails. Because the events are equally likely, you can use $\frac{1}{2}$ to describe the probability of either event. So the probability of tossing heads is $\frac{1}{2}$ and the probability of tossing tails is also $\frac{1}{2}$.

➡ The probability of a tossed coin landing on heads is $\frac{1}{2}$. The probability of a tossed coin landing on tails is $\frac{1}{2}$.

> If you toss a 1–6 number cube, what is the probability of tossing an even number?

First look at the possible outcomes. You can toss the numbers 1, 2, 3, 4, 5, or 6. Of these numbers, 2, 4, and 6 are even, and 1, 3, and 5 are not even. So the likelihood of tossing an even number is the same as the likelihood of tossing a number that is not even. This means that the probability of tossing an even number is $\frac{1}{2}$.

➡ The probability of tossing an even number is $\frac{1}{2}$.

> The likelihood of drawing a blue marble from a bag of marbles is $\frac{5}{6}$. The likelihood of drawing a red marble from the same bag is $\frac{1}{8}$. How does the number of blue marbles compare to the number of red marbles in the bag?

A probability of $\frac{5}{6}$ means that drawing a blue marble is very likely. A probability of $\frac{1}{8}$ means that drawing a red marble is very unlikely. So the bag has more blue marbles than red marbles.

➡ The number of blue marbles is greater than the number of red marbles.

1. The 10 tiles in a bag show 7 squares and 3 circles. Which number best represents the probability of drawing a tile with a circle with one pick from the bag, 0.3, 0.5, or 0.7? Explain your answer.

2. A teacher has 6 blue markers and 3 red markers. The teacher picks one marker without looking. Which number best represents the probability the teacher picks a blue marker, $\frac{1}{3}$ or $\frac{2}{3}$? Explain your answer.

For exercises 3 and 4, circle the correct answer. Choose all that apply.

3. Which of the following numbers represent the probability of an event that is more likely to occur than not occur?

   a. 0.2   b. $\frac{1}{4}$

   c. 0.5   d. $\frac{3}{4}$

4. Which of the following numbers represent the probability of an event that is less likely to occur than not occur?

   a. $\frac{1}{5}$ b. 0.25

   c. $\frac{1}{2}$ d. 0.75

Find the probability.

5. A bag contains tiles with the numbers 1, 3, 5, 7, and 9. What is the probability of taking out a tile with an even number?

_____

6. A bag contains tiles with the numbers 4, 8, 12, 16, and 20. What is the probability of taking out a tile with a multiple of 4?

_____

 Think•Pair•Share

MP6 7. From a set of tiles printed with circles and squares, Giselle thought that the probability of drawing a tile with a circle was 0.7. Max thought that the probability of drawing a tile with a square was 0.8. Is it possible for both Giselle and Max to be correct? Explain.

Independent Practice

Draw lines to match.

Hillary has 10 picture cards in a stack. There are 5 cards showing dogs, 3 cards showing cats, 1 card showing a gerbil, and 1 card showing a rabbit. If she chooses one card without looking, what is:

1. the likelihood of it showing a gerbil?

2. the likelihood of it showing a dog or a cat

3. the probability of it showing an animal?

4. the probability of it showing a bird

5. the likelihood of it showing a rabbit?

6. the probability that it will show a dog?

a. likely

b. 0

c. unlikely

d. $\frac{1}{2}$

e. 1

Write the answer.

7. A box contains 9 red pens and 1 blue pen. If you take one item out of the box, how likely is it that it will be a red pen?

_____

8. A box contains 9 yellow pencils and 1 red pencil. If you take one item out of the box, what is the likelihood that it will be a red pencil?

_____

9. A box contains only 6 blue pens. What is the probability that if you pick a pen out of the box it will be a blue pen?

_____

10. A box contains only 6 blue pens. What is the probability that if you pick a pen out of the box it will be a red pen?

_____

11. A box contains 6 blue pens and 5 red pens. Which is more likely, that you will pick a blue pen or a red pen out of the box?

_____

12. A box contains 10 blue pens and 10 red pens. Which is more likely, that you will pick a blue pen or a red pen out of the box?

_____

Circle the correct answer for exercises 13–18. Choose all that apply.

13. Which of the following numbers represent the probability of an event that is unlikely to occur?

    a. 0.3   **b.** $\frac{1}{5}$

    c. 0.6   **d.** $\frac{5}{6}$

14. Which of the following numbers represent the probability of an event that has an equal likelihood of either occurring or not occurring?

    a. 1   **b.** 0.5

    c. 0   **d.** $\frac{1}{2}$

Use the spinner at the right for exercises 15–18.

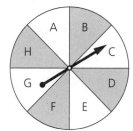

15. What is the likelihood of the spinner shown at the right landing on space F?

    a. unlikely   **b.** likely

    c. certain   **d.** impossible

16. What is the likelihood of the spinner landing on a space with a letter of the alphabet?

    a. impossible   **b.** certain

    c. unlikely   **d.** likely

17. What is the probability of the spinner shown at the right landing on a shaded space?

    a. 1   **b.** 0.5

    c. $\frac{1}{2}$ **d.** $\frac{1}{8}$

18. What is the probability of the spinner landing on Z?

    a. 1   **b.** $\frac{1}{2}$

    c. 0.25   **d.** 0

19. From the set of numbers {1, 2, 3, 4, 5, 6}, what is the probability of choosing a number that is greater than 10?

    _____

20. From the set of numbers {5, 10, 15, 20, 25}, what is the probability of choosing a number that is divisible by 5?

    _____

Independent Practice

Identify each event as *likely, unlikely, certain,* or *impossible*. Assign a probability to each event and explain why you chose that probability.

21. John goes to the mall only once each week. Today John is at the mall.

    Likelihood: _____

    Probability: _____

22. Millie was born on the 30th of the month. Millie was born in February.

    Likelihood: _____

    Probability: _____

23. Thanksgiving will come before New Year's Eve this year.

    Likelihood: _____

    Probability: _____

24. Thanksgiving will come before Fourth of July this year.

    Likelihood: _____

    Probability: _____

25. December will be a colder month than October.

    Likelihood: _____

    Probability: _____

26. December will have more rainy days than November.

    Likelihood: _____

    Probability: _____

MP2 27. Describe an event that you think is certain to happen and has a probability of 1. Explain why this event is certain.

MP2 28. Describe an event that you think cannot possibly happen and has a probability of 0. Explain why this event is impossible.

Independent Practice

MP2 **29.** Describe an event that you think is neither certain nor impossible and has a probability between 0 and 1. Explain why this event is likely or unlikely.

Use the information below for exercises 30–32. Use the terms *certain*, *likely*, *unlikely*, and *impossible* to describe the likelihood of an event and explain your reasoning.

Nora has a bag containing 2 red and 8 blue marbles. There are 10 marbles in all. Nora pulls out 1 marble at a time without looking, records the color, and returns the marble to the bag.

MP3 **30.** Describe the likelihood that Nora pulls out a blue marble.

MP3 **31.** Describe the likelihood that Nora pulls out a green marble.

MP3 **32.** Describe the likelihood that Nora pulls out a red or a blue marble.

Use the information below for exercises 33–35. Use the terms *very likely*, *likely*, *unlikely*, and *very unlikely* to describe the likelihood of an event and explain your reasoning.

A seventh-grade homeroom has 15 boys and 13 girls. The teacher writes each student's name on a slip of paper and then puts all the slips in a bag. The teacher draws out a slip when a helper is needed. Each time, the slip is put back in the bag.

MP2 **33.** The teacher wants someone to take a note to the office. Henry wonders whether his name will be drawn. What is the likelihood that Henry takes the note to the office?

MP2 **34.** The teacher wants someone to collect homework papers. What is the likelihood that a slip with a girl's name will be drawn?

MP2 **35.** On a day when the teacher needs a student to be a hall monitor, two students are home because they have a cold. Describe the likelihood that the teacher does not draw the name of an absent student.

Relate Relative Frequency and Probability

Essential Question:
How are relative frequency and probability related?

7.SP.6

Words to Know:
outcome
frequency
relative frequency

Guided Instruction

In this lesson, you will learn how to relate relative frequency and probability.

Understand: Finding approximate probability using relative frequency

Jake knows that when he tosses a coin, the probability of heads is $\frac{1}{2}$ and the probability of tails is $\frac{1}{2}$ because tossing heads and tossing tails are both equally likely. He wonders what the probabilities are for tossing a thumbtack. Is the probability of the thumbtack landing point up $\frac{1}{2}$? Jake decides to carry out an experiment, so he tosses a thumbtack 200 times and records his data in this table.

Use the data in the table to approximate the probability that a thumbtack will land point up and the probability that a thumbtack will land point down.

Thumbtack Position	Number of Times
point up	25
point down	175

Jake's table shows the two possible outcomes of his experiment and how many times each outcome occurs. The number of times a particular outcome occurs is called its frequency.

The relative frequency of an outcome is the ratio of the frequency of that outcome to the total frequency of all of the outcomes. Calculate the relative frequency of each outcome.

relative frequency (point up) $= \frac{\text{frequency of point up}}{\text{total frequency}} = \frac{25}{200} = \frac{1}{8}$

You can also write the relative frequency as a decimal, 0.125, or as a percent, 12.5%.

relative frequency (point down) $= \frac{\text{frequency of point down}}{\text{total frequency}} = \frac{175}{200} = \frac{7}{8}$

This relative frequency can also be written as a decimal, 0.875, or as a percent, 87.5%.

The relative frequency of an outcome is an approximation for the probability of that outcome.

➡ The approximate probability that the thumbtack will land point up is $\frac{1}{8}$ and the approximate probability that it will land point down is $\frac{7}{8}$.

✏ · Do you think that if Jake tossed the thumbtack 200 more times he would get the same relative frequencies?

Understand: Using a known probability to predict the frequency of a given outcome

> Andy tosses a coin 500 times. He knows that the probability of the coin landing heads up is $\frac{1}{2}$. How many times out of 500 can he expect the coin to land heads up?

You have used relative frequencies to approximate probabilities. To solve this problem, you work backwards. You use a known probability as the relative frequency so that you can predict the frequency of a particular outcome when you know the total frequency.

$$\text{relative frequency} = \frac{\text{frequency of an outcome}}{\text{total frequency}}$$

If you multiply both sides of the equation by the total frequency, you have an equation for finding the frequency of an outcome.

$$\text{relative frequency} \cdot \text{total frequency} = \text{frequency of an outcome}$$

Substitute the numbers from the problem in the equation.

$$\frac{1}{2} \cdot 500 = 250$$

> Use $\frac{1}{2}$ for the relative frequency and 500 for the total frequency.

➡ Andy can expect the coin to land heads up 250 times.

Do these results mean that the coin *will* actually land heads up 250 times? No—the actual results may be different. This is just the best prediction we can make with the information we have.

The actual data are likely to be close to, but different from, the expected data. In general, the greater the number of total outcomes in an experiment, the closer the actual data will be to the expected values.

✏ How could you use what you know about proportional reasoning to solve the problem above?

Guided Instruction

Connect: Using approximate probabilities to make predictions

Keisha spins a spinner 100 times and gets the results shown in the table. If Keisha then spins the spinner 2,000 times, predict how many times you think the spinner would land on red, how many times it would land on yellow, and how many times it would land on blue.

Outcome	Frequency
red	25
yellow	8
blue	67

To solve this problem, calculate the relative frequencies for each outcome to approximate the probability for each color. Then use the approximate probabilities to predict the results for 2,000 spins.

Step 1

Calculate the relative frequency for each color.

relative frequency of red $= \frac{25}{100} = 0.25$

relative frequency of yellow $= \frac{8}{100}$ or 0.08

relative frequency of blue $= \frac{67}{100} = 0.67$

The relative frequencies are approximations of the probabilities.

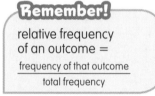

Remember!

relative frequency of an outcome =

$\frac{\text{frequency of that outcome}}{\text{total frequency}}$

Step 2

Use the approximate probabilities to predict the results of 2,000 spins.

For each color, multiply the approximate probability by the total number of trials.

Red: $0.25 \cdot 2{,}000 = 500$

Yellow: $0.08 \cdot 2{,}000 = 160$

Blue: $0.67 \cdot 2{,}000 = 1{,}340$

In this case, it may be easier to use the decimal numbers than the fractions.

➡ The best prediction is that the spinner will land on red 500 times; it will land on yellow 160 times; and it will land on blue 1,340 times.

Using the results of a small experiment to predict what would happen in a large experiment is similar to using the results of a small representative random sample to make predictions about a population. When we use probability in this way, we call it statistics. Statistics and probability are closely related.

✏ Describe what you think the spinner in the above problem might look like.

Shape cards are placed into a bag and one card is drawn out and then replaced. This is repeated and the results are recorded. Use the results to find the relative frequency of each shape.

1. 3 circles and 5 triangles are drawn.

   Circle _____

   Triangle _____

2. 8 circles, 7 squares, and 5 triangles are drawn.

   Circle _____

   Square _____

   Triangle _____

Solve the problems.

3. A bag contains 5 red marbles and 5 blue marbles. After 60 picks (replacing the picked marble each time), how many times would you expect each color marble to be picked?

   Red _____

   Blue _____

4. A spinner is divided into 2 equal sections. One section is green and the other section is orange. After 600 spins, how many times would you expect each color to be the result?

   Green _____

   Orange _____

   White _____

5. A bag contains solid color marbles and striped marbles. For his experiment of picking one marble and replacing it, Henry recorded picking a solid color marble 4 times and a striped marble 16 times. If he repeated the experiment and picked 100 marbles, predict how many would be solid and how many would be striped.

   _____

★♥ **Think•Pair•Share**

MP6 6. If you toss a 1–6 number cube 60 times, how many times do you expect to toss an even number? Toss a 1–6 number cube 60 times and record the results. Do your results match your expected results? Why or why not? Combine your results with the results of your classmates. What would be the expected number of times for each number to occur? Do the actual results match the expected numbers?

Independent Practice

Use the data below for exercises 1–6.

Josie spins a spinner and records her results in this table.

Outcome	Purple	Yellow	Green	Orange
Frequency	9	17	2	22

1. How many times did Josie spin the spinner? _____

For exercises 2–5, write the relative frequency of each color as a fraction, as a decimal, and as a percent.

2. purple _____ _____ _____

3. yellow _____ _____ _____

4. green _____ _____ _____

5. orange _____ _____ _____

6. Predict the number of times the spinner would land on purple out of 200 spins.

_____

Solve the problems.

7. Greg flips a coin 60 times. How many times would you expect it to land heads up?

_____

8. Al rolls a 1–6 number cube 10 times. How many times would you expect him to get a number greater than 10?

_____

9. Boyd spins a spinner with sections labeled A-H a total of 96 times. The letter A comes up 12 times. What is the relative frequency of A as a percent?

_____

10. Boyd spins a spinner with two sections, red and blue. He spins red 30 out of 75 times. What is the relative frequency of red written as a decimal?

_____

11. A bag contains both red and blue tokens. Tanya takes out a token and returns it to the bag 120 times. She draws a red token 40 times. What is the relative frequency for red?

_____

12. A bag contains both red and blue tokens. Rosa takes out a token and returns it to the bag 20 times. She draws a blue token 9 times. Out of 100 times, how many times would you expect blue?

_____

Independent Practice

Circle the correct answer for exercises 13–18. Choose all that apply.

13. Ky tosses a 1–6 number cube 150 times. How many times should she expect to get an even number?

 a. 25

 b. 50

 c. 75

 d. 150

14. Ky tosses a 1–6 number cube 150 times. How many times should she expect to get a number less than 7?

 a. 0

 b. 1

 c. 75

 d. 150

15. Ky tosses a coin 150 times. How many times would you expect the coin to land heads up?

 a. $\frac{1}{2}$

 b. 150

 c. 75

 d. 0.5

16. Ky tosses a coin 300 times. Which expression shows the number of heads she should expect?

 a. $\frac{1}{2} \cdot 300$

 b. $\frac{1}{2} \cdot 150$

 c. $0.5 \cdot 300$

 d. $0.5 \cdot 150$

17. Last summer it was over 100 degrees for 13 out of 91 days. What is the relative frequency for temperatures over 100 degrees?

 a. 13

 b. $\frac{13}{91}$

 c. $\frac{1}{6}$

 d. $\frac{1}{7}$

18. In baseball, Robinson Cano got 8 hits in 25 at bats. At this rate, how many hits would you expect Cano to have in 600 at bats?

 a. 160

 b. $\frac{8}{25}$

 c. 192

 d. 0.32

Solve the problem.

19. A website that sells shoes reports that the relative frequency of shoppers returning a pair of shoes because of a problem is $\frac{2}{25}$. Each return costs the company $2.50 in shipping. How much should the company plan for return shipping costs if it sells 8,000 pairs of shoes next month?

Independent Practice

MP2 **20.** Maurice flipped a coin 40 times and got 24 heads and 16 tails. How do Maurice's actual results compare with his expected results? Explain.

MP7 **21.** Monica spun a spinner and got the results shown in the table.

a. The spinner shown is not colored in. Use Monica's results to color in the spinner with red, yellow, blue, and green. Explain why you chose each color.

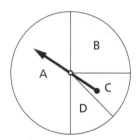

Red	Yellow	Blue	Green
16	33	14	57

b. Monica tried 150 spins of a different spinner and got the results shown in this table. Draw sections in the spinner and label each section with a color. Explain your thinking.

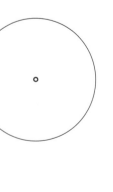

Red	Yellow	Blue	Green
50	25	50	25

MP2 **22.** Carlos works at Gamer Net, a website that sells video games. He collected data from 7th graders about their favorite video game among the top four titles.

Game	Artificial Earth IV	Fútbol! Fútbol!	Car Chase 2025	Doggie Town
Number	55	90	40	115

The website sells about 4,500 games each month. Of those 4,500 games, about 4,000 are sales of the top four titles. Carlos's boss wants Carlos to predict how many copies of each title will be sold next month.

a. Based on the data given, how many copies of Artificial Earth IV will be sold next month?

Show your work.

Answer _____

b. Based on the data given, how many copies of Fútbol! Fútbol! will be sold next month?

Show your work.

Answer _____

c. Based on the data given, how many copies of Car Chase 2025 will be sold next month?

Show your work.

Answer _____

d. Based on the data given, how many copies of Doggie Town will be sold next month?

Show your work.

Answer _____

e. Show how you can check the calculations you made in parts a–d.

36 Finding Theoretical Probability

Essential Question:
How can you use a model to find theoretical probability?

7.SP.7a

Words to Know:
favorable outcome
theoretical probability

Guided Instruction

In this lesson, you will learn how to find theoretical probability by analyzing a model for a probability situation.

Understand: Calculate theoretical probability

A spinner is divided into 8 equal sections. Three sections are blue, four are red, and one section is yellow. What is the probability that on the next spin the arrow will stop in a blue section?

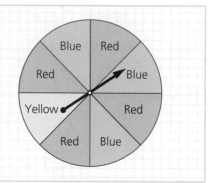

You can answer this question by analyzing the spinner and the possible outcomes of spinning the arrow. For the spinner, there are 8 possible outcomes, since there are 8 possible sections in which the arrow could stop. A favorable outcome is an event, or particular outcome, for which you want to know the probability.

When each of the outcomes is equally likely, the model for the theoretical probability of an event is the ratio of the number of favorable outcomes to the total number of possible outcomes.

$$\text{Probability (event)} = P(\text{event}) = \frac{\text{number of favorable outcomes}}{\text{total number of possilble outcomes}}$$

You write P for *probability* and use parentheses to show the event for which you are finding the probability.

In this problem, the event is the arrow stopping in a blue section. On the spinner, there are 3 blue sections, or 3 favorable outcomes, out of the total of 8 sections.

$$P(\text{blue section}) = \frac{3}{8}$$

➡ The theoretical probability of the arrow stopping in a blue section on the spinner is $\frac{3}{8}$.

The theoretical probability is based on the possible outcomes and shows what results can be expected for an experiment. It cannot tell exactly what the results of an experiment will be.

Remember!
Outcomes are equally likely if each outcome has the same chance of occurring. Since each section of the spinner is the same size, the arrow is equally likely to stop in each section.

What is $P(\text{red section})$? What is $P(\text{yellow section})$?

Understand: Random drawings

In order to select one student to be the class representative, a teacher writes the name of each student on a separate slip of paper and places all of the slips in a box. One slip will be drawn from the box to choose the class representative. In the class, there are 8 boys and 12 girls. What is the theoretical probability that the class representative will be a girl?

You can use the ratio model of favorable outcomes to total outcomes to find the theoretical probability since each name has an equal chance of being selected.

There are 12 slips with girls' names, so there are 12 favorable outcomes. The probability that a slip with a girl's name is picked is:

$$P(\text{girl}) = \frac{12}{20} = \frac{3}{5}$$

➡ The theoretical probability that the class representative will be a girl is $\frac{3}{5}$.

✏ What is the theoretical probability that the class representative will be a boy?

Understand: Probability and a number cube

If you toss a 1–6 number cube, what is the theoretical probability of tossing an even number?

You can use the ratio of favorable outcomes to total outcomes to calculate the theoretical probability since the outcomes are all equally likely.

On a 1–6 number cube, there are a total of 6 possible outcomes: 1, 2, 3, 4, 5, and 6. For the event of tossing an even number, there are 3 favorable outcomes: 2, 4, and 6.

$$P(\text{even}) = \frac{3}{6} = \frac{1}{2}$$

➡ The theoretical probability of tossing an even number is $\frac{1}{2}$.

Notice that theoretical probability model is based *only* on the set-up of an experiment and not on collecting data. You might roll a number cube many times and *not* obtain an even number half of the time. But the theoretical probability model shows that you can expect to get an even number half the time.

✏ What is the theoretical probability of tossing a number greater than 4?

Guided Instruction

Connect: Predicting the number of occurrences

A bag contains 5 red marbles, 3 blue marbles, and 2 green marbles. George picks one marble, records the color, then puts the marble back into the bag. He then repeats the process 200 times. How many times can George expect to pick each color marble?

You can calculate the theoretical probability of picking each color and then multiply it by 200, the number of trials to make the prediction.

Remember!
You can use probability to make predictions.

Step 1

Find the theoretical probability of picking each color.
There are 10 marbles in the bag. Each has an equal chance of being picked.

$P(\text{red}) = \frac{5}{10}$ or $\frac{1}{2}$ $\qquad$ $P(\text{blue}) = \frac{3}{10}$ $\qquad$ $P(\text{green}) = \frac{2}{10}$ or $\frac{1}{5}$

Step 2

Multiply the probability of each color by the total number of trials.

$\text{Red} = \frac{1}{2} \cdot 200 = 100$ $\qquad$ $\text{Blue} = \frac{3}{10} \cdot 200 = 60$ $\qquad$ $\text{Green} = \frac{1}{5} \cdot 200 = 40$

You could also use proportional reasoning and solve this equation: $\frac{1}{2} = \frac{x}{200}$.

▶ George can expect to pick a red marble 100 times, a blue marble 60 times, and a green marble 40 times.

A 1–6 number cube is tossed 120 times. How many times would you expect to get a number less than 3?

You can use the theoretical probability model to solve this problem.

There are 6 possible equally likely outcomes. There are 2 favorable outcomes: tossing a 1 or tossing a 2.

$P(\text{number less than 3}) = \frac{2}{6}$ or $\frac{1}{3}$

Then multiply the theoretical probability by 120, the total number of trials.
$\frac{1}{3} \cdot 120 = 40$

▶ You would expect to toss a number less than three 40 times.

Guided Practice

A spinner is divided into 12 equal sections and has 4 colors, as shown. Find the probability of the events of the arrow stopping on each color.

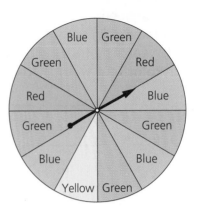

1. P(yellow) = _____

2. P(red) = _____

3. P(blue) = _____

4. P(green) = _____

A 1–6 number cube is tossed. Find the probability.

5. P(odd number)

6. P(number greater than 4)

7. P(number less than 6)

_____   _____   _____

A bag contains picture cards. There are pictures of 6 apples, 9 oranges, and 10 bananas. One card is chosen without looking. Find the probability.

8. P(apple)

9. P(orange)

10. P(banana)

_____   _____   _____

11. A spinner has 8 equal sections. Four sections are blue, 3 are red, and 1 section is yellow. Ollie spins 400 times and records the results. How many times can he expect to spin each color? Show your work.

Answer _____

⛹ Think•Pair•Share

MP1 **12.** For an experiment, toss a 1–6 number cube 30 times. Before you start, predict how many times you can expect to toss an even number and how many times you can expect to toss a number greater than 4. Keep a record of your results. Do your results match or come close to your predictions?

Independent Practice

A seat in Section A of the stadium is chosen at random. The fan seating in that seat receives two free tickets to next week's game. Find the probability that a person in each color seat would receive the free tickets.

1. P(yellow) = _____

2. P(red) = _____

3. P(blue) = _____

4. P(blue or yellow) = _____

5. P(red or blue) = _____

Seats in Section A

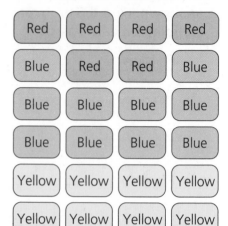

Red	Red	Red	Red
Blue	Red	Red	Blue
Blue	Blue	Blue	Blue
Blue	Blue	Blue	Blue
Yellow	Yellow	Yellow	Yellow
Yellow	Yellow	Yellow	Yellow

Dave wrote a whole number greater than 0 and less than 11 on a piece of paper. Find the probability that Dave's number is each of the following.

6. P(7)

7. P(less than 5)

8. P(odd)

_____   _____   _____

9. P(less than 1)

10. P(greater than 10)

11. P(divisible by 2 or 3)

_____   _____   _____

You draw a card from a deck that has 12 star cards, 8 yellow moon cards, 6 blue moon cards, 9 planet cards, and 1 sun card. Find each of the following.

12. P(moon)

13. P(star)

14. P(blue moon or planet)

_____   _____   _____

15. A board game has 26 tiles labeled with alphabet letters. Players draw 1 tile at a time. Over 260 different drawings, how many times are players likely to draw either a vowel or the letter Y?

Independent Practice

Use the spinner for exercises 16–21. Sections 1–4 are green, 5–7 are purple, 8–12 are yellow, and 13–16 are red. Circle the correct answer for exercises 16–21. Choose all that apply.

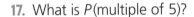

16. What is P(red)?

   a. $\frac{1}{4}$ b. 0.25

   c. $\frac{4}{12}$ d. $\frac{1}{3}$

17. What is P(multiple of 5)?

   a. $\frac{1}{16}$ b. $\frac{3}{16}$

   c. $\frac{3}{5}$ d. $\frac{11}{16}$

18. What is P(less than 9)?

   a. $\frac{9}{16}$ b. $\frac{2}{3}$

   c. $\frac{1}{2}$ d. 0.5

19. How many times would you expect to spin green in 200 spins?

   a. $\frac{1}{2}$ b. 25

   c. 50   d. 60

20. How many times would you expect to spin purple in 240 spins?

   a. 25   b. 35

   c. 45   d. 55

21. How many times would you expect to spin yellow or red in 400 spins?

   a. $\frac{9}{16}$ b. 125

   c. 200   d. 225

Solve the problem.

22. In a TV game show, one game always starts with 32 suitcases. Twenty of the suitcases contain some kind of prize; 12 suitcases contain nothing. At each show, one contestant chooses a suitcase at random. After 160 shows, how many contestants would you expect to choose a suitcase with nothing?

Answer _____

Independent Practice

23. Ricardo has a spinner with 20 equal sections. Ten of the sections are red and 10 are yellow. He calculates the probability that the spinner will land on yellow in this way:

$$P(\text{yellow}) = \frac{20 \text{ favorable outcomes}}{10 \text{ possible outcomes}} = \frac{2}{1}$$

What is wrong with Ricardo's calculation? Explain.

24. Wolf says that there is no difference between an event and a favorable outcome. Manesh disagrees and says that the two terms are different and can be distinguished. Who is right? Explain and give an example to support your explanation.

25. Wolf and Manesh also disagree about the difference between the total number of possible outcomes and the total number of trials in a probability experiment. Manesh says both totals identify the same concept. Wolf claims that both totals are not the same. Who is right? Explain and give an example to support your explanation.

Solve the problems.

MP1 26. Hal forgot the last two digits in Kyle's phone number. Hal knows that the two digits are identical and odd. What is the probability that Hal will dial Kyle's number correctly on the first try?

   ✏ **Show your work.**

   Answer _____

MP4 **27.** The table shows data for a spinner with 8 equal sized sections and 3 colors, red, blue, and yellow.

Red	Blue	Yellow
39	13	52

Suppose the data shows the theoretical probabilities of each color exactly.
Draw the spinner.

Show your work.

MP2 **28.** A computer scientist wanted to test to see if the passwords people chose are random. He had 5,000 people submit the first letter of their password into a data bank and found the data below for letters A, B, C, M, P, Q, and X. The scientist claimed that people choose their passwords randomly. Do you agree?

A	B	C	M	P	Q	X
200	191	186	203	344	190	195

Answer _____

Justify your answer.

Finding Experimental Probability

Essential Question:
How can you use a model to find experimental probability?

7.SP.7b

Words to Know:
experimental probability

Guided Instruction

In this lesson, you will learn how to use a model to find experimental probability.

Understand: Experimental probability

Ursula drew marbles one at a time out of a bag containing an unknown number of red and blue marbles, each time replacing the marble in the bag. After 4 draws, Ursula estimated that the probability of picking a red marble is $\frac{1}{2}$, since she picked the same number of red and blue marbles.

After 30 draws Ursula picked a red marble 10 times and a blue marble 20 times. What does Ursula find when she uses the new data to recalculate the experimental probability of picking a red marble?

You can think about the meaning of probability to answer this question.

For Ursula's first estimate, she had very few data to work with. Since the same number of red and blue marbles were picked, $\frac{1}{2}$ seemed like a reasonable estimate for the probability of picking a red marble.

With more data after 30 draws, Ursula can recalculate the probabilities. Since red was drawn 10 times and blue 20 times, Ursula used these calculations.

$$P(\text{red}) = \frac{10}{30} = \frac{1}{3} \qquad P(\text{blue}) = \frac{20}{30} = \frac{2}{3}$$

Remember!
The probability is the relative frequency, the ratio of the number of times an outcome occurs to the total number of outcomes.

These probabilities are based on the results of the experiment. When a probability is based on the results from doing an experiment, it is called experimental probability. Finding an experimental probability always involves collecting data. Theoretical probability, on the other hand, is based on the experiment's possible outcomes—such as the number of marbles of each color—and not on actual experimental results.

➡ When Ursula uses the new data to recalculate the probability, she finds that the results suggest the probability of picking red is closer to $\frac{1}{3}$.

As more data are collected and analyzed during an experiment, the experimental probabilities change. For most experiments, as more data are collected, the experimental probabilities should come close to the theoretical probabilities.

Understand: Finding experimental probability

From a set of shapes cards containing circles, triangles, and squares, Dave drew one card from the box. He recorded the result, then placed the card back into the box. After 40 trials, Dave had recorded cards with 20 circles, 7 triangles, and 13 squares. What is the probability that on the next pick Dave will get a card with a square?

You can use the experimental probability based on collecting data to make predictions about future events.

Like theoretical probability, experimental probability is the ratio of favorable outcomes to total outcomes. When you collect data, each trial is a separate outcome so:

Theoretical Probability

$$P(\text{event}) = \frac{\text{favorable outcomes}}{\text{total number of outcomes}}$$

Experimental Probability

$$P(\text{event}) = \frac{\text{favorable outcomes}}{\text{total number of trials}}$$

Dave carried out 40 trials: $20 + 7 + 13 = 40$. Based on his results, he calculated the probability of drawing each shape.

A circle was drawn 20 times. $\longrightarrow$ $P(\text{circle}) = \frac{20}{40} = \frac{1}{2}$

A triangle was drawn 7 times. $\longrightarrow$ $P(\text{triangle}) = \frac{7}{40}$

A square was drawn 13 times. $\longrightarrow$ $P(\text{square}) = \frac{13}{40}$

➡ The probability that Dave draws a card with a square on the next pick is $\frac{13}{40}$.

✏ Suppose Dave drew 50 more cards from the box. How many of them would you expect to be triangle cards?

✏ Suppose Dave drew 50 more cards from the box and 8 of them were cards with squares. How can you explain this result?

Guided Instruction

Connect: Use probability to make a prediction

The results of a survey of 60 students asking how many pets they have at home are shown in the table. Based on these data, predict how many of the 300 students in the school have no pets, 1 pet, 2 pets, or 3 or more pets?

Number of pets	Number of students
0	16
1	21
2	8
3 or more	15

You can use your understanding of experimental probability to analyze these results and answer the question.

Step 1

Find the experimental probability of having each number of pets.

$P(0 \text{ pets}) = \frac{16}{60} \text{ or } \frac{4}{15}$

$P(1 \text{ pet}) = \frac{21}{60} \text{ or } \frac{7}{20}$

$P(2 \text{ pets}) = \frac{8}{60} \text{ or } \frac{2}{15}$

$P(3 \text{ or more pets}) = \frac{15}{60} \text{ or } \frac{1}{4}$

Step 2

Multiply each experimental probability by the total number of students.

For 0 pets $\longrightarrow \frac{4}{15} \cdot 300 = 80$

For 1 pet $\longrightarrow \frac{7}{20} \cdot 300 = 105$

For 2 pets $\longrightarrow \frac{2}{15} \cdot 300 = 40$

For 3 or more pets $\longrightarrow \frac{1}{4} \cdot 300 = 75$

➤ A prediction based on the results of the survey says that 80 students have 0 pets, 105 students have 1 pet, 40 students have 2 pets, and 75 students have 3 or more pets.

✏ In the school lunch line, 15 students took an apple, 8 students took an orange, and 7 students took a banana. Based on these data, how many of the 150 students in the lunch line took each type of fruit?

1. From a bag of marbles, Joe picked one marble, recorded the color, then put the marble back in the bag. After many draws, Joe had picked 12 red marbles and 18 blue marbles. What is the probability that Joe will pick a red marble on the next draw?

   Step 1: How many draws are there? $12 + 18 = $ _____

   Step 2: How many times did Joe draw a red marble? _____ times

   Step 3: What is $P(\text{red})$? _____

   On the next draw, the probability that Joe will pick a red marble is _____.

2. The results of a survey are shown in the table. Based on these data, how many of the 600 students at the school would choose each sport?

Favorite Sport	Number of Students
Basketball	30
Football	10
Baseball	5
Other	15

   Step 1: Find the experimental probabilities.

   $P(\text{basketball}) = \dfrac{30}{60}$ or _____

   $P(\text{football}) = $ _____ or _____

   $P(\text{baseball}) = $ _____ or _____ $P(\text{other}) = $ _____ or _____

   Step 2: Find the number of students who would choose each sport.

   Basketball: $\dfrac{1}{2} \cdot 600 = $ _____   Baseball: _____ • _____ = _____

   Football: _____ • $600 = $ _____   Other: _____ • _____ = _____

   _____ students would choose basketball, _____ would choose football,

   _____ would choose baseball, and _____ would choose a different sport.

ᵛᴵᵂ Think•Pair•Share

MP6 3. If you toss a 1–6 number cube, what is the theoretical probability of tossing each number? Toss a number cube 30 times. Record each result. Find the experimental probability of tossing each number. Explain any differences between the theoretical and experimental probabilities.

Independent Practice

The table shows sales at the Tech Central store for the new u-Phone. The phone comes in 5 great colors, can be safely submerged underwater, and floats.

1st Week Sales	
u-Phone color	Number sold
Ice Blue	56
Pumpkin	21
Pomegranate	42
Tuxedo Black	70
Chalk	91

1. What is the experimental probability that a u-Phone sold will be Ice Blue? _____

2. What is the experimental probability that a u-Phone sold will be Pomegranate? _____

3. What is the experimental probability that a u-Phone sold will be Chalk? _____

4. Based on sales at Tech Central, if 50,000 u-Phones are sold nation-wide, how many of them will be Tuxedo Black? _____

5. Based on sales at Tech Central, if 50,000 u-Phones are sold nation-wide, how many more Pomegranate phones will be sold than Pumpkin phones? _____

6. A different Tech Central store sold a total of 300 phones. How many Tuxedo Black phones would you predict that this store sold? _____

7. A Mr. Software shop sold a total of 200 phones. How many of the phones would you expect to be Ice Blue? _____

8. Thirty-two of the 200 phones that the Mr. Software shop sold were Pumpkin. How does the experimental probability at Mr. Software sales compare to the experimental probability at Tech Central? Explain.

Circle the correct answer for exercises 9–13. Choose all that apply.

A total of 840 babies were born this year at City Hospital. Some of the top baby names are shown in the graph.

9. What was the experimental probability that a baby born would be named Jayden?

   a. 0.025

   b. 21

   c. $\frac{1}{40}$

   d. 2.5%

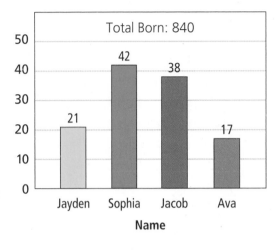

10. If half the babies born were girls, what was the experimental probability that a girl baby born would be named Sophia?

    a. 0.01

    b. 0.1

    c. 1%

    d. 10%

11. If 4,000,000 babies are born in the U.S. this year, how many of them would you expect to be named Jayden?

    a. 200,000

    b. 150,000

    c. 100,000

    d. 75,000

12. If 4,000,000 babies are born in the U.S. this year, how many of them would you expect to be named Sophia or Jacob?

    a. about 38,000

    b. about 220,000

    c. about 380,000

    d. about 440,000

13. If 4 million babies are born this year, about how many of them will not be named Jayden, Sophia, Jacob, or Ava? Give your answer to the nearest whole number.

Independent Practice

14. Marjory says that the theoretical probability for many real world problems cannot be measured. However, the experimental probability for these same problems can be successfully measured. Give an example of the type of problem Marjory is referring to.

15. Pablo claims that for a coin flip there is no difference between theoretical and experimental probability. Each side of the coin has a probability of exactly $\frac{1}{2}$ and that precise theoretical probability is confirmed when data is collected. Is Pablo right? Explain.

Use the table for exercises 16–17.

Failure rates for Bling brand light bulbs are shown.

MP2 **16.** What is the failure rate for Bling light bulbs in a time frame of under 2,000 hours? Give your answer to the nearest tenth of a percent.

    ➤ **Show your work.**

Bling Light Bulbs	
Time	Number Failed
after 1 hour	53
after 100 hours	14
after 200 hours	7
after 1,000 hours	4
after 1,500 hours	13
after 2,000 hours	505
after 2,100 hours	116
after 2,200 hours	92
after 2,300+ hours	96
Total 900	

    Answer _____

MP1 **17.** A light bulb has been burning for exactly 2,000 hours. What is the probability that it will fail within the next 100 hours? Within the next 300 hours? Give your answers to the nearest tenth of a percent.

    ➤ **Show your work.**

    Answer _____

Independent Practice

Use the batting record of Homer "Home Run" Jones for exercises 18–20.

MP2 **18.** When Homer comes to the plate, what is the probability that he will not make an out?

✏ **Show your work.**

Homer Jones	
Home runs	42
Doubles	48
Triples	6
Singles	98
Walks	116
Strikeouts	121
Fly outs	137
Ground outs	132

Answer _____

MP3 **19.** In the play-offs Homer comes to the plate 80 times and hits only 6 home runs. Should his fans be disappointed in his performance?

Answer _____

✏ **Justify your answer.**

MP3 **20.** Mike is creating a spinner for a baseball board game that divides up Homer's batting record into 5 categories: Home runs, Other hits, Walks, Strikeouts, and Other outs. Label each section in the spinner at the right. Write the approximate percent of the spinner that each section represents.

✏ **Show your work.**

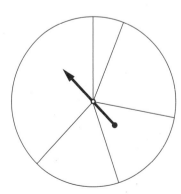

Finding Probabilities of Compound Events

Essential Question:
How can you find probabilities of compound events?

7.SP.8a

Words to Know:
compound events
tree diagram

Guided Instruction

In this lesson, you will learn how to find probabilities of compound events.

Understand: **Compound events and tree diagrams**

> A coin is tossed and the result, heads or tails, is recorded. Then the coin is tossed again. What is the probability that the result of two tosses is heads, then tails?

To find the probability, you have to learn about compound events.

Compound events are two or more events that both occur, one after another or at the same time. Each time the coin is tossed is an event, so tossing the coin twice is a compound event.

On the first toss, the result can be either heads or tails, each of which is equally likely. If the first toss is heads, the second toss can be heads or tails. If the first toss is tails, the second toss can be heads or tails. There are a total of four possible outcomes, shown in the tree diagram.

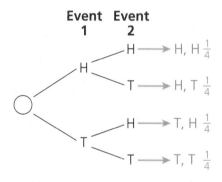

There are four possible outcomes and each is equally likely. So the theoretical probability of tossing heads, then tails, is $\frac{1}{4}$.

▶ The probability of tossing heads, then tails, is $\frac{1}{4}$.

✏️▸ What is the probability that both tosses are tails?

Understand: Using multiplication to find the probability of a compound event

A spinner has 8 equal sections; 3 are red, 2 are blue; 2 are yellow, and 1 is green.

A coin is tossed and the spinner is spun. What is the probability of the coin turning up heads and the spinner landing on red?

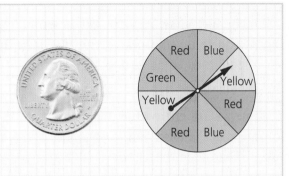

To solve this problem, you can make a tree diagram or use multiplication.

• You can make a tree diagram to show all of the possible outcomes.

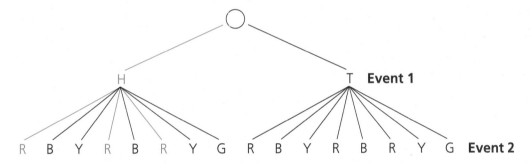

You can count that there are 16 possible outcomes. The outcome heads and red occurs 3 times. So the probability of the compound event of tossing heads and spinning red is $\frac{3}{16}$.

Making a tree diagram is useful when there are not too many possible outcomes.

• When there are a large number of outcomes, you can find the probability of a compound event by multiplying.

For two events A and B, the probability of A and B both occurring is $P(A) \cdot P(B)$.

First, find the probability of each event separately.

$P(\text{heads}) = \frac{1}{2}$ and $P(\text{red}) = \frac{3}{8}$

Now multiply the two probabilities.

$P(\text{heads}) \cdot P(\text{red}) = \frac{1}{2} \cdot \frac{3}{8} = \frac{3}{16}$

➡ The probability of tossing heads and spinning red is $\frac{3}{16}$.

What is the probability of tossing tails and spinning yellow?

Guided Instruction

Connect: Experimental probability for compound events

Jillian has a bag of tiles. Some of the tiles are red, some are blue, and some are yellow. She conducted an experiment in which she picks one tile without looking, records the color, and places the tile back into the bag. After a while, she had recorded 25 red, 10 blue, and 15 yellow.

Jackson also has a bag of tiles. Some of the tiles are green, some are orange, and some are purple. He conducted an experiment in which he picks one tile without looking, records the color, and places the tile back into the bag. After a while, he had recorded 35 green, 12 orange, and 3 purple.

Based on their picks so far, what is the experimental probability that on their next picks, Jillian will pick a red tile and Jackson will pick a purple tile?

Both Jillian and Jackson made 50 picks.

Based on Jillian's results, $P(\text{red}) = \frac{25}{50} = \frac{1}{2}$.

Based on Jackson's results, $P(\text{purple}) = \frac{3}{50}$.

The experimental probability of the compound event that Jillian picks a red tile and Jackson picks a purple tile is

$$P(\text{red and purple}) = P(\text{red}) \cdot P(\text{purple})$$

$$= \frac{1}{2} \cdot \frac{3}{50}$$

$$= \frac{3}{100}$$

➡ The experimental probability that Jillian picks a red tile and Jackson picks a purple tile is $\frac{3}{100}$.

▸ What is the experimental probability that Jillian picks a yellow tile and Jackson picks an orange tile?

For exercises 1–5, a coin is flipped and the spinner is spun.

 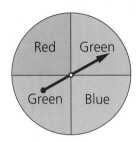

1. Complete the tree diagram to show the possible outcomes of 1 coin flip and 1 spin.

2. Find *P*(heads and green). _____

3. Find *P*(tails and blue). _____

4. Find *P*(heads and red). _____

5. Find *P*(tails and green). _____

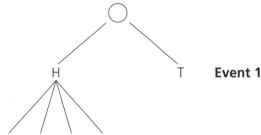

Event 1

Event 2

A bag contains 6 blue marbles, 9 yellow marbles, and 5 orange marbles. Without looking, a marble is picked, then put back into the bag. Use multiplication to find the probability of the compound events.

6. *P*(blue and blue) _____

7. *P*(yellow and orange) _____

8. *P*(blue and yellow) _____

9. *P*(orange and orange) _____

 **Think•Pair•Share**

MP8 **10.** Look back at exercise 2. Show how to find the probability by using multiplication rather than by using the tree diagram.

Independent Practice

A coin is flipped and a number cube is tossed.

1. Draw a tree diagram showing the outcomes of 1 coin flip and 1 number cube toss.

2. What is the probability of getting heads, then a 3? _____

3. What is the probability of getting tails,

   then an odd number? _____

4. What is the probability of getting heads,

   then a number that is less than 5? _____

5. What is the probability of getting heads or tails, then a 4? _____

6. If you flip the coin and roll the cube 60 times each,

   how many times would you expect tails and a 6 to come up? _____

7. If you flip the coin and roll the cube 60 times each, how many times would you expect heads and a number

   greater than 1 to come up? _____

8. Show a second way to draw the tree diagram. The first event in the tree diagram you drew above was the coin toss. Now draw a tree diagram starting with the number cube toss. Do you get the same outcomes? Explain.

Independent Practice

Circle the correct answer or answers for exercises 9–13. Use the information below and the table for exercises 9–14.

Baseball standings are shown for the American League East. Assume that teams are not playing each other.

9. What is the probability that both the Red Sox and the Yankees will win their next game?

a. $\dfrac{3}{4} \cdot \dfrac{2}{3}$

b. $\dfrac{15}{32}$

c. $\dfrac{3}{4} \cdot \dfrac{5}{8}$

d. $\left(\dfrac{3}{4}\right)^2$

Standings		
Team	Won	Lost
Red Sox	12	4
Yankees	10	6
Orioles	8	8
Blue Jays	6	10
Rays	4	12

10. What is the probability that the Orioles will win their next game and the Blue Jays will also win?

a. $\dfrac{5}{16}$

b. $\dfrac{3}{16}$

c. $\dfrac{1}{2} \cdot \dfrac{3}{8}$

d. $\left(\dfrac{1}{4}\right)^2$

11. What is the probability that the Rays, Yankees, and Orioles will all lose their next game?

a. $\dfrac{9}{25}$

b. $\left(\dfrac{3}{8}\right)^2$

c. $\dfrac{9}{64}$

d. $\dfrac{3}{4} \cdot \dfrac{3}{8} \cdot \dfrac{1}{2}$

12. After 64 games are played, how many more games would you expect the Red Sox will win than the Yankees?

a. 48

b. 40

c. 8

d. 0

13. Nick flips a coin. What is the probability that the coin will come up heads and the Orioles will win their next game?

a. $\dfrac{1}{4}$

b. $\dfrac{1}{8}$

c. $\dfrac{1}{16}$

d. $\left(\dfrac{1}{2}\right)^2$

14. Suppose the Yankees win their next 2 games and the Red Sox lose their next 2 games. How will their experimental probabilities change? What would be the probability that both teams would win their next game after the Yankees won 2 games and the Red Sox lost 2 games?

Independent Practice

Solve the problems.

MP6 **15.** Both Claire and Andre took a blue marble out of 2 different bags, each containing 3 red marbles and 3 blue marbles. Claire put the marble back into her bag. Andre did not replace the marble that he took out of his bag. Now both students take out another marble. What is the probability that both take out a blue marble?

> **Show your work.**

Answer _____

MP8 **16.** Richie forgot the password for his computer. He knows that the password is set up as: vowel, even digit less than 5, odd digit greater than 2. What is the probability that he will guess the right password on the first try?

> **Show your work.**

Answer _____

MP8 **17.** Billy is playing a board game. To win, Billy needs to spin the spinner at the right two times and have a total of 6. What is the probability that Billy will win? Draw a tree diagram to find your answer.

> **Show your work.**

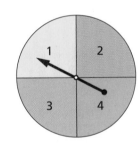

Answer _____

Use the table for problems 18–19.

MP8 **18.** Which probability is greater, that it will be mostly rainy for the next 2 days or that it will be mostly sunny for the next 3 days? Explain.

April Weather	
Weather	Days
Mostly sunny	6
Mostly rainy	10
Mostly cloudy	12
Mostly foggy	2

Answer _____

➤ **Justify your answer.**

MP8 **19.** Rhonda is trying to schedule her outdoor 3-day weekend get-away. What is the probability that it will be neither mostly rainy nor mostly foggy for the next 3 days?

➤ **Show your work.**

Answer _____

MP8 **20.** LaMarcus generally makes 80 percent of his free throws. Bronson generally makes 70 percent of his free throws. Which is more likely, that LaMarcus will make his next 3 free throws, or Bronson will make his next 2 free throws?

Answer _____

➤ **Justify your answer.**

Lesson

39 Represent Sample Spaces for Compound Events

Essential Question:
How can you represent sample spaces for compound events?

7.SP.8b

Words to Know:
sample space

Guided Instruction

In this lesson, you will learn how to represent sample spaces for compound events.

Understand: Using a table to show a sample space

Darlene tossed two number cubes. How can she show all of the possible outcomes? What is the probability that the sum of the two numbers is 8?

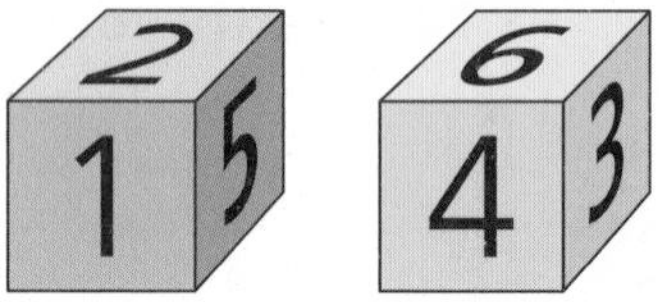

To solve this problem, you have to know about sample spaces.

A sample space is the set of all possible outcomes for an event. The outcomes may be listed, shown in a tree diagram, or shown in a table.

Remember!
In the previous lesson, you used a tree diagram to show the number of possible outcomes of tossing a coin and spinning a spinner. The tree diagram showed the sample space for the compound event.

To show the outcomes of tossing two number cubes and the sums, a table might be the most efficient way.

		Cube 1					
		1	2	3	4	5	6
Cube 2	1	2	3	4	5	6	7
	2	3	4	5	6	7	8
	3	4	5	6	7	8	9
	4	5	6	7	8	9	10
	5	6	7	8	9	10	11
	6	7	8	9	10	11	12

The table shows that there are 36 possible outcomes when two number cubes are tossed. Each combination is equally likely to occur. To find the probability that the sum will be 8, count the number of times 8 appears as the sum in the table. There are 5 occurrences of the sum 8—2 and 6, 3 and 5, 4 and 4, 5 and 3, and 6 and 2.

The outcome 2 and 6 and the outcome 6 and 2 are considered different outcomes.

➡ The probability of tossing a sum of 8 is $\frac{5}{36}$.

✏ What is the probability of tossing a sum of 3?

Understand: Using a tree diagram to show a sample space

Five pennies are tossed. What is the probability that exactly 4 of the pennies will land on heads?

To solve this problem, use what you know about finding the sample space for a compound event.

A tree diagram is an efficient way to show all of the possible outcomes of tossing five coins.

> Tossing 5 coins will have the same set of possible outcomes as tossing one coin 5 times.

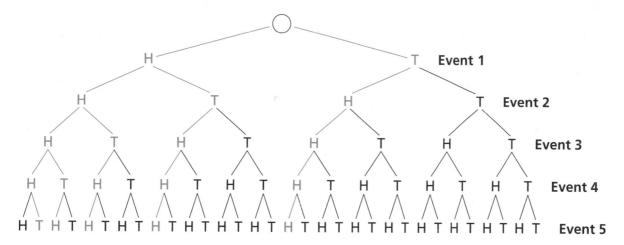

From this sample space, you can count that there are 32 possible outcomes, each of which is equally likely. Count the number of times H occurs exactly 4 times. There are 5 occurrences: HHHHT, HHHTH, HHTHH, HTHHH, and THHHH.

➡ The probability that exactly 4 pennies will land heads up is $\frac{5}{32}$.

✎ What is the probability that exactly 3 pennies will land tails up?

Guided Instruction

Connect: Sample spaces for different kinds of events

A coin is tossed. A number cube is tossed. A spinner is spun.

The spinner is divided into 4 equal sections, 1 red (R) section, 1 green (G), 1 blue (B) section, and 1 yellow (Y) section.

What is the probability of getting tails, an odd number, and red?

 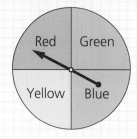

To show the sample space, make an organized list.

H, 1, R	H, 2, R	H, 3, R	H, 4, R	H, 5, R	H, 6, R
H, 1, G	H, 2, G	H, 3, G	H, 4, G	H, 5, G	H, 6, G
H, 1, B	H, 2, B	H, 3, B	H, 4, B	H, 5, B	H, 6, B
H, 1, Y	H, 2, Y	H, 3, Y	H, 4, Y	H, 5, Y	H, 6, Y
T, 1, R	T, 2, R	T, 3, R	T, 4, R	T, 5, R	T, 6, R
T, 1, G	T, 2, G	T, 3, G	T, 4, G	T, 5, G	T, 6, G
T, 1, B	T, 2, B	T, 3, B	T, 4, B	T, 5, B	T, 6, B
T, 1, Y	T, 2, Y	T, 3, Y	T, 4, Y	T, 5, Y	T, 6, Y

> The outcome H, 1, R means the coin lands heads up, the number cube lands with the number 1 on top, and the spinner lands on red.

There are a total of 48 possible outcomes.

There are 3 outcomes that are favorable:
T, 1, R   T, 3, R   T, 5, R

➡ The probability of getting tails, an odd number, and red is $\frac{3}{48} = \frac{1}{16}$.

✏ What is the probability of getting heads, an even number, and yellow?

What is the probability of getting tails, a number greater than 2, and either blue or red?

For exercises 1–4, a coin is tossed three times. Find each probability.

1. Create a sample space for the possible outcomes.

2. P(exactly 1 heads)

   _____

3. P(more than 1 tails)

   _____

4. P(3 heads)

   _____

Two number cubes are tossed. Find the probability of the given sum.

5. P(6) _____

6. P(12) _____

7. P(odd) _____

8. P(14) _____

A coin is tossed and two spinners are spun. One spinner has three equal sections, each with a different shape: circle, square, triangle. The other spinner has 6 equal sections: 3 red, 2 blue, and 1 yellow. Find the probability of each compound event.

9. P(heads, triangle, blue)

   _____

10. P(tails, circle, red)

    _____

11. P(heads, square, yellow)

    _____

Think•Pair•Share

MP8 12. Look back at the tree diagram on page 339. It shows the outcomes for tossing 5 coins. Now consider tossing 7 coins. How would the sample space be different? How many possible outcomes would there be? Look for a pattern. Now consider tossing 10 coins. How many possible outcomes would there be? What is the probability of all 10 coins landing heads up?

Independent Practice

One coin is tossed and two spinners like the ones shown are spun. Use this information for exercises 1–9.

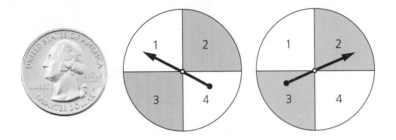

1. How many outcomes are in the sample space? _____

2. Use an organized list to show the sample space.

3. What is the probability of getting heads and two 3s? _____

4. What is the probability of getting tails and two numbers that match? _____

5. What is the probability of getting heads and a sum that equals 3? _____

6. What is the probability of getting tails and a sum that equals 6? _____

7. What is the probability of getting heads and a sum that is even? _____

8. What is the probability of getting tails and a sum that is greater than 4? _____

9. Suppose you added a second coin to the event above. You will now toss 2 coins and spin 2 spinners. How would the size of the sample space change?

For exercises 10–15, circle the correct answer or answers. Use the information below for exercises 10–16.

The Eagles are trying to qualify for the play-offs. Assume that for each game the Eagles have an equal likelihood of winning or losing.

10. To avoid being eliminated from the play-offs, the Eagles need to win at least 2 of the next 3 games. What is the probability that they will avoid elimination?

   a. $\frac{1}{32}$

   b. $\frac{3}{32}$

   c. $\frac{1}{8}$

   d. $\frac{1}{2}$

11. What is the probability that the Eagles will neither win all 3 of their next games nor lose all 3?

   a. $\frac{1}{4}$

   b. $\frac{1}{2}$

   c. $\frac{3}{4}$

   d. $\frac{7}{8}$

12. For the next 4 games, what is the size of the sample space for the Eagles as far as winning or losing?

   a. 8 outcomes

   b. 16 outcomes

   c. 24 outcomes

   d. 32 outcome

13. What is the probability that the Eagles will either win all four or lose all 4 of their next 4 games?

   a. $\frac{1}{32}$

   b. $\frac{1}{16}$

   c. $\frac{1}{8}$

   d. $\frac{3}{8}$

14. What is the probability that the Eagles will win exactly 2 of their next 4 games?

   a. $\frac{1}{4}$

   b. $\frac{3}{8}$

   c. $\frac{7}{16}$

   d. $\frac{1}{2}$

15. To finish in first place the Eagles need to win at least 3 of the next 4 games. What is the probability that they will finish in first place?

   a. $\frac{1}{4}$

   b. $\frac{5}{16}$

   c. $\frac{1}{3}$

   d. $\frac{1}{2}$

16. Suppose that on Friday the Eagles still need to win 3 of their next 4 games to finish in first place. Then they win the game on Saturday. What is the probability that the Eagles now will finish in first place? Explain.

Independent Practice

17. Mitch claims that he can compute the size of the sample space for events simply by taking the number of outcomes for each event to the power of the number of events. For example, there are 2 outcomes for every coin toss, so the sample space for 3 coin tosses is: $2^3 = 8$. Four coin tosses would give a sample space of $2^4 = 16$. Five coin tosses would give a sample space of $2^5 = 32$. Is Mitch's method valid? Explain.

18. Monica has flipped a coin 6 times and it has come up heads every time. Monica calculates that the chance of HHHHHH occurring is $\frac{1}{64}$. Monica is almost sure that her next flip will come up tails, since the chance of HHHHHHH occurring is $\frac{1}{128}$. Is Monica correct to assume that there is very little chance of heads turning up? Explain.

MP3 **19.** Phoebe is the coach of the top-seeded player at a tennis tournament. To win the tournament, a player needs to win 4 matches in a row. Phoebe computed the sample space as:

WWWW, WWWL, WWLW, WLWW, WWLL, WLWL, WLLW, WLLL, LWWW, LWWL, LWLW, LLWW, LWLL, LLWL, LLLW, LLLL

Phoebe then concluded that the top seed had only a $\frac{1}{16}$ chance of winning, since WWWW was the only outcome that resulted in a championship. However, Phoebe is confused because in the past 10 years the top seed has won 7 times. How could top seeds have won 7 out of 10 times? Was it just luck, or is Phoebe's calculation incorrect in some way? Explain.

Independent Practice

Solve the problems.

MP4 **20.** In a board game, when a player goes to jail, one way he or she can get out is by rolling "doubles"—both number cubes come up with the same number. Ned is currently "in jail." What is the probability that he will get out of jail on his next roll of two number cubes?

▭▸ **Show your work.**

Answer _____

MP4 **21.** A spinner has 4 equal-size sections labeled 1–4. A second spinner has 3 equal-size sections labeled 1–3. What is the probability of spinning both spinners and getting a sum that is an odd number?

▭▸ **Show your work.**

Answer _____

MP4 **22.** Hannah wants to have 5 children. Hannah would like to have at least one girl and at least one boy. Assuming that Hannah has 5 children and that the probability of having a boy or a girl is equal, what is the probability that Hannah will have at least one boy and at least one girl?

▭▸ **Show your work.**

Answer _____

40 Simulate Compound Events

Guided Instruction

In this lesson, you will learn how to simulate compound events.

Understand: Using a random number generator in a simulation

> On any given day, about 30% of the students in Terry's class wear a blue shirt. What is the probability that the next two students who walk into the classroom will be wearing a blue shirt?

To find out, you have to know how to set up a probability simulation.

In a simulation, you create a mathematical model of a real-world situation so you can carry out a probability experiment and use it to predict outcomes.

So the probability that a student has on a blue shirt is 30%, or 3/10, or 3 out of 10. This means that you need a simulation with 10 possibilities. The digits 0 through 9 give 10 possibilities. Assign three of the digits, such as 7, 8, and 9, to represent a student with a blue shirt. Then the digits 0, 1, 2, 3, 4, 5, and 6 represent a student not wearing a blue shirt.

Since the question asks about the next two students, use a calculator or software to generate a random two-digit number, from 00 to 99. Do this 50 times, or perform 50 trials, to generate some data.

To analyze the data, look for numbers that have both digits 7, 8, or 9. The numbers are highlighted in the data in the table. These two-digit numbers represent two students wearing blue shirts.

This data set generated 4 favorable outcomes out of 50 trials. Based on the data, you can find the experimental probability that the next two students to walk into the classroom will be wearing a blue shirt.

50 Trials of 2 Students

07	94	38	88	22
97	38	15	11	35
31	38	40	11	84
50	62	59	12	01
40	22	42	53	78
23	55	79	23	85
10	26	15	08	25
96	73	13	45	82
22	35	54	24	27
15	72	40	93	52

P(next two students are wearing blue shirts) $= \frac{4}{50} = \frac{2}{25}$, or 0.08.

▶ Based on the simulation, the probability that the next two students to enter the classroom wearing blue shirts is $\frac{2}{25}$ or 0.08.

▬▬▸ Perform the simulation again. Were your results the same? Explain.

Understand: Using number cubes in a simulation

At the local library, 1 out of every 6 patrons who check out materials checks out audio-visual (AV) materials only. What is the probability that exactly two out of the next three patrons will check out AV materials only?

To find out, set up a probability simulation.

To represent 1 out of 6 patrons, a standard number cube can be used. Assign one of the numbers, such as 3, to represent a patron who checks out only AV materials. Then the numbers 1, 2, 4, 5, and 6 represent patrons who check out material that is not AV. Then for 3 patrons, use 3 number cubes. Roll the 3 number cubes, and record the outcome. Repeat for 40 trials.

Or, instead of rolling number cubes, you could use a random-number generator to generate a list of 40 random three-digit numbers, using the digits 1, 2, 3, 4, 5, and 6.

A set of 40 trials might look as shown in the table.

To analyze the data, look for numbers that have exactly two 3s. The numbers are highlighted in the data in the table. These numbers represent exactly two out of the next three patrons who check out only AV materials.

This data set generated 3 favorable outcomes out of 40 trials. Based on the data, you can find the experimental probability that two out of the next three patrons will check out AV materials only.

40 Trials of 3 Library Patrons

515	232	451	152	463
143	166	156	461	662
563	222	522	434	362
655	356	343	626	611
411	214	424	325	434
353	324	144	245	235
632	663	365	546	661
251	654	642	566	633

P(two of the next three patrons check out AV materials only) $= \frac{3}{40}$, or 0.075.

▸ Based on the simulation, the probability that two of the next three patrons check out AV materials only is $\frac{3}{40}$ or 0.075.

▸ Perform the simulation again. Were your results the same? Explain.

Guided Instruction

Connect: Design a simulation

About 50% of the students in your school have a pet.

Design a simulation and generate 50 trials to estimate the probability that the next two students who enter the school will have a pet.

Since about 50% of the students have a pet, there are two possible outcomes that are close to equally likely. So, tossing a coin can be used for the simulation.

Assign Heads to represent a student with a pet and Tails to represent a student without a pet. When you toss 2 coins, a favorable outcome for the simulation is both coins landing heads up.

A set of 50 trials is shown in the table below. The highlighted outcomes represent the favorable outcomes.

50 Trials of 2 Students

H, T	T, T	T, T	T, T	H, H	T, T	T, H	T, H	H, T	H, T
H, H	H, T	T, H	H, H	T, T	H, H	T, T	H, T	T, H	T, H
H, H	T, H	H, T	T, T	T, H	H, T	H, H	T, T	H, H	H, H
T, H	H, H	T, T	T, H	H, T	T, H	T, T	T, H	T, H	T, T
H, T	T, T	H, H	T, T	H, H	T, H	T, T	H, H	H, T	T, H

This data set generated 12 favorable outcomes out of 50 trials. Based on this data, you can find the experimental probability that the next two students that enter the school will have a pet.

P(the next two students will have a pet) $= \frac{12}{50}$, or $\frac{6}{25}$, or 0.24

⮕ Based on this simulation, the probability that the next two students who enter the school will have a pet is $\frac{12}{50}$, or $\frac{6}{25}$, or 0.24.

✏ Design a second possible simulation for this experiment.

For exercises 1–5, follow the steps to solve the problem below.

In Renee's school, about 2 out of every 6 students are in the school band. Design a simulation and generate 50 trials to estimate the probability that the next two students to enter the lunchroom are in the school band.

1. How will you represent 2 out of every 6 students?

2. How will you generate the data?

3. Generate the data and record it in the table.

50 Trials of 2 students

4. Describe the favorable outcomes.

_____

5. Count the number of favorable outcomes in your data. What is the probability that the next two students who enter the lunchroom will be in the school band?

_____

Think•Pair•Share

MP4 6. Make an observation about the students in your classroom or school, estimating the number or percent of students supporting your observation. Then design a simulation to predict the probability that 2 out of the next 3 students chosen at random meet your observation. Then generate 50 trials of the simulation and estimate the probability that 2 out of the next 3 students chosen at random meet your observation.

Independent Practice

For exercises 1–3, follow the steps to solve the problem below.

A survey shows that 60 percent of 7th grade students ride the bus to school. Design a simulation and generate trials to estimate the probability that the first 2 students who enter the class today will have taken the bus.

1. Using a random number generator, which digits can you assign to students who took the bus?

2. Identify the favorable outcomes from the random data generated below.

50 Trials of 2 Students

64	98	47	24	43	37	29	04	88	27
54	91	22	43	83	46	66	11	34	36
07	16	58	77	22	31	90	59	56	50
23	74	87	61	53	08	65	19	14	84
81	34	13	72	29	02	33	28	00	60

3. Based on the 50 trials above, what percent of the time would you expect the next 2 students to have ridden the bus?

4. Twenty percent of 7th graders start their homework as soon as they get home from school. Using the simulation above, what percent of the time would you expect 2 students chosen randomly to have started their homework as soon as they got home from school?

5. Suppose for exercise 3 above you wanted to determine how likely the next 3 students who walk into class—rather than the next 2 students—rode the bus. How would your simulation change? Explain.

Independent Practice

Circle the correct answer or answers for exercises 6–11. Use the information below.

Data collected shows that 1 of every 8 students in 7th grade write their own blog.

6. Which model would work best to generate random numbers to simulate data for this situation?

   a. 1 flip of a coin

   b. 2 flips of a coin

   c. 3 flips of a coin

   d. 4 flips of a coin

7. What percent of the time would you expect to encounter a student who wrote his or her own blog?

   a. 12.5%

   b. 37.5%

   c. 50%

   d. 62.5%

8. Using coin flips, which outcomes could you assign to be favorable outcomes for "student writes blog?"

   a. HHH

   b. HHH and TTT

   c. HHH, HTT, TTH

   d. THT

9. Out of 50 flips, how many favorable outcomes would you expect?

   a. about 13

   b. about 12

   c. about 6

   d. about 3

10. Using a random number generator for this simulation, which digits might you include?

    a. 1, 2, 3, 4

    b. 1, 2, 3, 4, 5, 6

    c. 1, 2, 3, 4, 5, 6, 7, 8

    d. 1, 2, 3, 4, 5, 6, 7, 8, 9, 0

11. Using the random number generator in exercise 10, which outcomes could you assign to be favorable outcomes for "student writes blog?"

    a. 1

    b. 2

    c. 5

    d. 6, 7, 8

12. Suppose that instead of 1 of 8, a survey found that 3 of every 8 students actually wrote a blog. How would that change your simulation? Explain.

Independent Practice

MP4 **13.** Donna's record shows that she makes $\frac{1}{3}$ of her shots in basketball. She wants to know the probability that she will make at least 2 of her next 3 shots.

    a. Describe a spinner that could be used in a simulation. What spin would represent making a shot?

    b. For each trial, how many times will you spin the spinner? What will be a favorable outcome?

    c. Show the sample space for the outcomes. Which of the outcomes represent favorable outcomes?

    d. Based on the sample space, what is the theoretical probability that Donna will make at least 2 of her next 3 shots?

    e. Predict how many of the 50 trials in the simulation will have favorable outcomes.

    f. Create your spinner. Use your spinner to collect data for 50 trials. Record the data in the table below.

50 Trials of 3 Shots

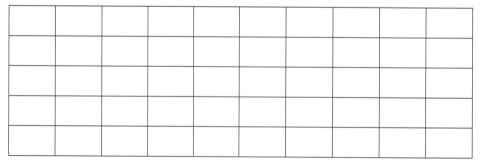

    g. Analyze your data. Does your simulation agree with the prediction you made in part e above?

MP4 **14.** According to polls, $\frac{3}{4}$ of voters say they will vote to re-elect Mayor Bramson.

a. To find the probability that exactly 2 of the next 3 voters to enter the voting booth will vote for Bramson, describe a spinner you could use in a simulation. Describe the favorable outcomes for a trial.

b. Show the sample space for the simulation. How many outcomes in the sample space are favorable outcomes?

c. Based on the sample space, find the probability that 2 out of the next 3 voters to enter the voting booth will vote for Bramson. Use your answer to predict the number of favorable outcomes in 50 trials of your simulation.

d. Make and use your spinner to collect and record data for 50 trials.

50 Trials of 3 Voters

e. Analyze your data. Use the results of your simulation to calculate the probability that 2 out of the next 3 voters to enter the voting booth will vote for Bramson. Compare the probability with the probability from part c.

f. Do the number of favorable outcomes from your simulation agree with the prediction you made in part c?

1. Which event would be closest to having a probability of occurring of 0.8?

   a. choosing a vowel from the set {a, e, i, o, u}

   b. choosing an odd number from the set {2, 4, 6, 8, 9}

   c. choosing a consonant from the set {b, c, d, e, f}

   d. choosing an even number from the set {1, 3, 5, 7, 9}

2. Ben wanted to survey the students in his school about their favorite sport. Which method would give him the most representative sample?

   a. asking every 5th student who passes through the lunch line

   b. asking all the students in one fourth-grade class

   c. asking all of the students on the basketball team

   d. asking every third girl that walks into school that day

3. A spinner is divided into 12 equal sections. Three of the sections are blue, 7 sections are yellow, and 2 sections are red. What results would you predict for 360 spins?

A set of tiles in a bag show 5 squares, 12 circles, and 8 triangles. One tile is chosen without looking. Find each of the following.

4. P(circle)

   _____

5. P(triangle)

   _____

6. P(square)

   _____

A bag contains 10 red marbles, 7 green marbles, and 8 striped marbles. A marble is picked, then put back into the bag. Use multiplication to find the probability of each compound event.

7. P(red and red)

   _____

8. P(green and striped)

   _____

Circle the correct answer.

9. The results of a survey are shown in the table. Based on this data, how many of the 300 students at the school would choose basketball?

   a. 90 students

   b. 85 students

   c. 75 students

   d. 60 students

Favorite Sport	Number of Students
Basketball	18
Football	15
Baseball	10
Other	17

The sample space shows the results of tossing two number cubes and finding the product of the numbers showing. Find the probability for each product.

Cube 1						
	1	2	3	4	5	6
1	1	2	3	4	5	6
2	2	4	6	8	10	12
3	3	6	9	12	15	18
4	4	8	12	16	20	24
5	5	10	15	20	25	30
6	6	12	18	24	30	36

Cube 2

10. P(odd) _____

11. P(greater than 25) _____

12. P(exactly 7) _____

13. Elliott took a random sample of 250 visitors to a zoo to ask them which animal they especially came to see.

Animal	Giraffes	Elephants	Bears	Dolphins
Number of Responses	47	25	48	130

Which of these inferences about the population of visitors is supported by his sample?

a. About half of all visitors came to the zoo to see the dolphins.

b. More visitors came to see the giraffes and bears than the dolphins.

c. More visitors came to see the elephants than the bears.

d. About the same number of visitors came to see the giraffes as the bears.

14. The box plot compares the bowling scores of Keith and Jane for their last 30 games.

Which of the following statements are true?

Bowling Scores

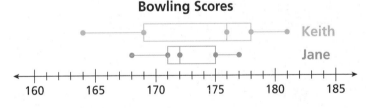

a. Jane's lowest score was higher than Keith's lowest score.

b. Keith had more scores between 169 and 178 than Jane had scores between 171 and 175.

c. Jane was a more consistent bowler than Keith.

d. Jane's high score was greater than Keith's high score.

15. About 67% of the families in a neighborhood have a minivan or similar vehicle. Describe a simulation you could use to determine the probability that two families chosen at random both have a minivan or similar vehicle.

For exercises 16–19, think about the experiment of tossing a coin 4 times.

16. Make a sample space of the possible outcomes.

17. What is P(all heads)? _____

18. What is P(exactly 3 heads)? _____

19. What is P(all heads or all tails)? _____

MP3 20. The marketing department of a car manufacturer takes two random samples of drivers aged 21–32 to determine the color of cars they are most interested in purchasing. The results of the samples are given in the table.

	Green	Black	Silver	Blue	Red	Yellow
Sample #1	123	215	183	88	122	117
Sample #2	132	199	177	85	130	108

The marketing department's report says that drivers aged 21–32 are more interested in purchasing green cars than red cars. Do you agree?

Answer _____

✏ **Justify your answer.**

7.RP.1, 7.RP.2a, 7.RP.2b, 7.RP.3, 7.NS.1c, 7.NS.1d, 7.NS.2c, 7.NS.2d, 7.NS.3, 7.EE.4a, 7.EE.4b

Performance Tasks

Performance Tasks show your understanding of the mathematics that you have learned. You will be doing various Performance Tasks as you complete your work in this text, **Common Core Progress Mathematics**.

Beginning This Task

The next five pages provide you with the beginning of a Performance Task. You will be given 5 items to complete, and each item will have two or more parts. As you complete these items you will:

I Demonstrate that you have mastered mathematical skills and concepts

II Reason through a problem to a solution, and explain your reasoning

III Use models and apply them to real-world situations.

Extending This Task

Your teacher may extend this Performance Task with additional items provided in our online resources at sadlierconnect.com.

Scoring This Task

Your response to each item will be assessed against a rubric, or scoring guide. Some items will be worth 1 or 2 points, and others will be worth more. In each item you will show your work or explain your reasoning.

Performance Task 1

Walk, Don't Run

1. The Walking Club is one of the after-school activities at Jefferson Middle School. It consists of three groups of walkers. Each group walks at a different pace. All groups begin together and walk the same 4-mile trail.

   a. Wendy is new to the club. She asks each group how fast they walk. Each group gives the answer in a different way. Find the speed of each group in miles per hour.

   Group 1: We walk $2\frac{1}{2}$ miles per hour.

   Group 2: We walk a mile in 20 minutes.

   Group 3: We take 2 hours to walk the trail.

   b. Which group will finish first? Explain how you know.

   c. How long will it take Group 1 to complete the trail?

   d. If each group starts promptly at 2:30 P.M., what time will Group 2 finish?

Zesty Black Bean Salsa

2. The Chef's Club is making black bean salsa.

   The recipe they are using has just two ingredients.

   > **Zesty Black Bean Salsa**
   > 30 ounces canned black beans
   > 16 ounces tomato salsa

   a. Using the above recipe, how many ounces of black beans will be used for every ounce of tomato salsa?

   b. The members of the club have decided that they will make $\frac{3}{4}$ of the recipe. How many ounces of black beans will they use? How many ounces of tomato salsa will they use?

   c. Several members decide that they would like to try the recipe at home. They record the amounts of each ingredient that they will use.

   Which members' black bean salsa will have the same ratio of beans to tomato salsa as the original recipe?

Name	Black Beans (ounces)	Tomato Salsa (ounces)
Jackson	8	10
Tamisha	20	$10\frac{2}{3}$
Logan	7.5	4
Samina	45	24
Lily	10	$5\frac{1}{3}$

   d. Carrie decides to make a graph of the ordered pairs of numbers in the table in part c. She uses the *x*-axis to represent the number of ounces of black beans and the *y*-axis to represent the number of ounces of tomato salsa. Will all of the points lie on a straight line? Explain.

Performance Task 1

Virtual Investments

3. Each member of the Stock Market Club begins with $5,000 in virtual money. Each week, members compare their virtual portfolio values with other members of the club.

Sophia buys shares in Fly Away Airlines. During the first week, the stock drops $0.75 (0.75 point) per share. During the second week, the stock goes up $0.50 (0.5 point) per share.

a. What is the total change in points per share of Fly Away Airlines stock during the first two weeks?

b. Explain why your answer to part a is positive or why it is negative.

c. On the number line below, draw a point to represent the change in the first week and a point to represent the change in the second week.

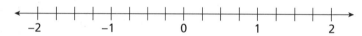

d. What is the difference between the change in the first week and the change in the second week? Explain how the number line in part c shows the difference.

e. The stock market is open for trading 5 days per week, Monday through Friday. For the two-week period, what is the average change for Fly Away Airlines per day of trading?

Trivia Time

4. The Trivia Club is open to seventh and eighth graders only. Members practice weekly and participate in monthly competitions between the seventh and the eighth grade teams.

   a. There are a total of 45 club members. There are 25% more eighth graders than seventh graders. How many members are from each grade?

   b. During the first half of each monthly competition, each correct answer is worth 15 points. During the second half of the competition, each correct answer is worth 25 points. In this month's competition, the seventh grade team answers 30 questions correctly during the first half and has a total of 1,450 points at the end of the competition. How many questions does the team answer correctly during the second half?

   Let q equal the number of questions the team answered correctly during the second half. Write and solve an equation to solve the problem.

   c. Use substitution to check your solution to the equation you wrote in part b.

   d. Use the information from part b. In this month's competition, the eighth grade team scores 10% fewer points than the seventh grade team. How many points does the eighth grade team score?

Digital Video Festival

5. Members of the Digital Video Club produce short videos. At the end of each school year, the club presents a Digital Video Festival at a local theater to show the community their 25 best videos.

   a. The club has learned from experience over the years that when they do not charge an admission fee, attendance is 800 people. For every dollar charged in admission, the attendance drops by 8 people. Write an inequality that can be used to find the price p in dollars that the club should charge so that at least 750 people will attend the film festival.

   b. Solve the inequality you wrote in part a.

   c. Explain in words what the solution to the inequality means in terms of the situation. Explain why the direction of the inequality sign in the solution makes sense.

   d. Use a number line to show the amount in dollars, p, that the club can charge and have at least 750 people attend the festival.

7. NS.3, 7.G.1, 7.G.2, 7.G.4, 7.G.5, 7.G.6, 7.SP.3, 7.SP.8a, 7.SP.8b

Performance Tasks

Performance Tasks show your understanding of the mathematics that you have learned. You will be doing various Performance Tasks as you complete your work in this text, **Common Core Progress Mathematics**.

Beginning This Task

The next five pages provide you with the beginning of a Performance Task. You will be given 5 items to complete, and each item will have two or more parts. As you complete these items you will:

I   Demonstrate that you have mastered mathematical skills and concepts

II   Reason through a problem to a solution, and explain your reasoning

III   Use models and apply them to real-world situations.

Extending This Task

Your teacher may extend this Performance Task with additional items provided in our online resources at sadlierconnect.com.

Scoring This Task

Your response to each item will be assessed against a rubric, or scoring guide. Some items will be worth 1 or 2 points, and others will be worth more. In each item you will show your work or explain your reasoning.

Performance Task 2

Whispering Willows

1. Each summer, Kim and her family spend a week at Rapid River Campground. This year, their campsite is in a section called Whispering Willows. The figure at the right is a scale drawing of this section of the campground.

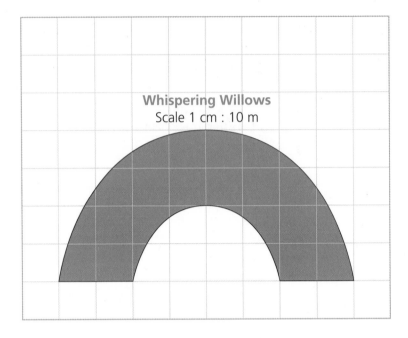

Whispering Willows
Scale 1 cm : 10 m

a. What is the distance around Whispering Willows? Use 3.14 for π.

b. Kim and her sister Lola walk around Whispering Willows twice. Do they walk more or less than 0.5 kilometer? Explain.

c. What is the area of Whispering Willows? Use 3.14 for π.

d. If each of the 16 campsites in Whispering Willows is approximately the same size, what is the approximate area of each campsite? Round your answer to the nearest square meter.

Bike Ride at the Campground

2. Kim and her mother bike to the swimming pool and back.

   a. They begin at their campsite and ride $\frac{3}{4}$ mile directly west to the camp store and then ride directly north 1 mile to the swimming pool. In the space at the right, draw their path. Label the point for the camp store and the point for the swimming pool. Use a ruler and the scale for your drawing.

Scale 1 in. : $\frac{1}{4}$ mile

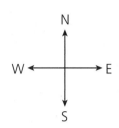

   b. They take the shortest path back from the swimming pool to the campsite. The path is a straight line. Draw the path. How many miles is it? Explain.

•
Campsite

   c. What is the total distance of the bike ride?

   d. The three points form a triangle. The angle of the triangle that is at the campsite has a measure (to the nearest degree) of 53°. Without using a protractor, find the measure (to the nearest degree) of the angle of the triangle that is at the swimming pool. Explain your method.

Performance Task 2

Comparing Tents

3. Kim's family has pitched two tents at their campsite. The shapes and dimensions of the tents are shown below.

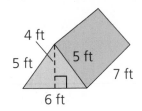

Tent A
Right Triangular Prism

4 ft
5 ft
5 ft
6 ft
7 ft

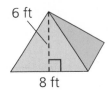

Tent B
Right Square Pyramid

6 ft
8 ft

a. How much floor space does each tent have?

Tent A _____

Tent B _____

b. Kim claims that Tent B has at least 50% more floor space than Tent A. Do you agree? Justify your answer.

c. What is the surface area of each tent?

Tent A _____

Tent B _____

d. Both tents are made from the same nylon material. Kim claims that at least 50% more nylon was needed to make Tent B than Tent A. Do you agree? Justify your answer.

Exit Surveys at Rapid River Campground

4. When checking out of Rapid Rivers Campground, campers are randomly selected to rank their camping experience on a scale of 0–10.

The dot plots show the rankings given by 12 youth campers (age 5–17) and 10 adult campers (age 18 and over).

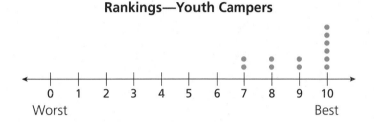

Rankings—Youth Campers

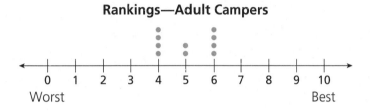

Rankings—Adult Campers

a. Find the mean ranking for each group of campers.

Youth mean _____

Adult mean _____

b. Find the mean absolute deviation (MAD) for the rankings of each group.

Youth MAD _____

Adult MAD _____

c. Did one of the groups show more variation in their rankings? If so, which group? Explain.

d. The camp manager claims that the difference between the means for the two groups is significant because it is about three times the variability of either group. Do you agree? Explain.

Performance Task 2

Souvenirs for Everyone

5. As campers check out, each is given a free souvenir from Rapid Rivers Campground.

   a. To determine which souvenir a camper receives, the camper spins the spinner shown at the right. What is the probability that Kim will receive a t-shirt?

   b. Use an organized list, a tree diagram, or a table to show the sample space for this compound event: Kim spinning the spinner and her sister Lola spinning the spinner.

   c. Use the sample space from part b. What is the probability that both Kim and Lola will get the same souvenir?

   d. Use the sample space from part b. What is the probability that both Kim and Lola will both get a t-shirt?

   e. Use the sample space from part b. What is the probability that neither Kim nor Lola will get a t-shirt?

A review of prerequisite mathematics needed to understand the concepts and skills of Grade 7.

A. Understand: What a unit rate is

Jackson runs 12 miles in 2 hours. His friend Roger says that Jackson is running at 6 miles per hour. What does Roger's statement mean?

To understand what 6 miles per hour means, you need to think about the reasoning behind Roger's statement.

A ratio tells how many units of a quantity there are for a number of units of another quantity. A ratio that tells how many units of a quantity there are for 1 unit of another quantity is a unit rate.

The ratio of miles Jackson runs to hours is 12 miles to 2 hours or $\frac{12}{2}$.

When you divide both parts of a ratio by the same number, the ratio relationship stays the same. Notice that dividing by 2 gives a denominator of 1.

$$\frac{12 \text{ miles}}{2 \text{ hours}} = \frac{12 \text{ miles} \div 2}{2 \text{ hours} \div 2} = \frac{6 \text{ miles}}{1 \text{ hour}}$$

The ratio now shows that Jackson runs 6 miles in 1 hour or 6 miles per hour.

B. Understand: Using ratio tables to compare ratios

Yoshi and his grandfather like to walk. Yoshi walks 2 miles in 30 minutes. His grandfather walks 3 miles in 60 minutes. Who walks at a faster rate?

To find who walks at a faster rate, you can use ratio tables to compare the rates of walking.

You can compare the ratios with the same distance.

Yoshi	
Distance (mi)	Time (min)
2	30
4	60
6	90
8	120

Grandfather	
Distance (mi)	Time (min)
3	60
6	120
9	180
12	240

Grandfather takes longer to walk the same distance, so Yoshi walks faster.

C. Understand: Finding a percent of a quantity

Fumi collects tiny wooden and fabric cats. Her grandmother has made 30% of the 20 cats she has collected. How many cats has her grandmother made for her?

You can use an equation to find the answer. A percent situation has three components: the Percent, the Whole, and the Part. These components are related by this equation: percent · whole = part.

Identify the values given in the problem.
percent: 30%   whole: 20 cats   part: unknown

Write the percent equation with the known values. Use a letter for the unknown value: $30\% \cdot 20 = p$

Solve the equation.

$30\% \cdot 20 = p$

$\dfrac{30}{100} \cdot 20 = p$ ◀—————— Rewrite 30% in fraction form.

$6 = p$ ◀—————— Multiply to find p.

Fumi's grandmother made 6 cats for her.

D. Understand: Renaming the dividend to divide a fraction by a fraction

Red Pine Park has the shape of a rectangle and an area of $\dfrac{5}{8}$ square mile. This park is $\dfrac{2}{3}$ mile long. How wide is Red Pine Park?

To solve this problem, you need to divide $\dfrac{5}{8}$ by $\dfrac{2}{3}$, but you cannot divide the numerators and the denominators. What you can do is rename $\dfrac{5}{8}$ so that its numerator is divisible by 2 and its denominator is divisible by 3.

$\dfrac{5}{8} \div \dfrac{2}{3} = \dfrac{5}{8} \cdot \dfrac{2}{2} \cdot \dfrac{3}{3} \div \dfrac{2}{3}$ ◀—— Multiply $\dfrac{5}{8}$ by $\dfrac{2}{2} \cdot \dfrac{3}{3}$, which is the same as $\dfrac{5}{8} \cdot 1 \cdot 1$, to rename $\dfrac{5}{8}$.

$= \dfrac{5 \cdot 2 \cdot 3}{8 \cdot 2 \cdot 3} \div \dfrac{2}{3}$ ◀—— Write the new dividend as one fraction.

$= \dfrac{5 \cdot 2 \cdot 3 \div 2}{8 \cdot 2 \cdot 3 \div 3}$ ◀—— Divide the numerator of the dividend by 2. Divide the denominator of the dividend by 3.

$= \dfrac{5 \cdot 3}{8 \cdot 2}$ ◀—— Simplify. $2 \div 2 = 1$, $3 \div 3 = 1$

$= \dfrac{5}{8} \cdot \dfrac{3}{2}$ ◀—— Write the multiplication with 2 fraction factors.

$= \dfrac{15}{16}$ ◀—— Multiply.

Red Pine Park is $\dfrac{15}{16}$ mile wide.

E. Understand: Operations with multi-digit decimals

- To add and subtract decimals, write the decimals in a column, aligning the decimal points. Then use the standard algorithms to add or subtract. You may use zeros as placeholders.

$$\begin{array}{r} 2.5 \\ 3.25 \\ +1.125 \\ \hline 6.875 \end{array} \qquad \begin{array}{r} 2.500 \\ 3.250 \\ +1.125 \\ \hline 6.875 \end{array}$$

- To multiply two decimals, multiply as you would with whole numbers, count the decimal places in the factors, then place the decimal point so that the number of decimal places in the product equals the total number of decimal places in the factors.

$$\begin{array}{r} \overset{1\ 2}{2.25} \\ \times\ 1.5 \\ \hline 1\ 1\ 2\ 5 \\ 2\ 2\ 5 \\ \hline 3.375 \end{array}$$

- To divide decimals, change the division to an equivalent division with a whole-number divisor.

$$2.5\overline{)23.75} \longrightarrow 25\overline{)237.5}$$

Divide, and place the decimal point in the quotient directly above the decimal point in the dividend.

$$\begin{array}{r} 9.5 \\ 25\overline{)237.5} \\ 225 \\ \hline 125 \\ 125 \\ \hline 0 \end{array}$$

F. Understand: Positive and negative numbers, opposites, and absolute value

- On a number line, positive numbers are to the right of 0 and negative numbers are to the left of 0.

- Look at -0.75 and 4.25 on the number line. The number 4.25 will be to the right of 4, but not past 5. The number -0.75 will be to the left of 0 but not past -1.

- The numbers 2 and -2 are opposites. Numbers that are opposites are the same distance from 0 on a number line.

- To determine which of two points, Point A or Point B, is farther from zero, use absolute values. Point A, -5, is 5 units to the left of 0. Point B, 3, is located 3 units to the right of 0. Distance has to be a positive quantity or 0. To work with a positive value of a number, use its absolute value. The absolute value of a number is written inside absolute value bars and means the positive value of the number. The two numbers can be written as $|3| = 3$ and $|-5| = 5$. Now compare the distances of both points from 0. Point A is located farther from 0 than point B.

G. Understand: Evaluating algebraic expressions

In the expression $t - 12$, t represents a daytime temperature. If the daytime temperature is 70 degrees, what is the temperature at night?

To evaluate an expression, you replace the variable with a specific value. The value 70 represents a daytime temperature, so it can be used in place of the t in the expression. Then the expression becomes $70 - 12$, which is 58.

The temperature at night is 58 degrees.

H. Understand: Using expressions to write an equation

Betty knew that a certain square had a side length of either 6 inches, 9 inches, or 11 inches. She knew that the perimeter of the square was 36 inches. Which side length was the correct length of the square?

To solve this problem, you need to use expressions to write an equation.

Betty uses the expression $4s$, where s is the length of one side of the square, to find the perimeter of the square. She also knows that the perimeter of the square is 36 inches.

Betty uses the equation $4s = 36$ to represent the situation.

What value of s makes this equation true? Try each of the three given values for s. Substitute each value in place of s in the equation and see if any of the values result in an equation that is true.

For $s = 6$,	For $s = 9$,	For $s = 11$,
$4s = 36$	$4s = 36$	$4s = 36$
$4 \cdot 6 = 36$	$4 \cdot 9 = 36$	$4 \cdot 11 = 36$
$24 = 36$	$36 = 36$	$44 = 36$
The value 6 results in an equation that is false.	The value 9 results in an equation that is true.	The value 11 results in an equation that is false.

The length of one side of the square was 9 inches.

I. Understand: Solving equations of the forms $x + p = q$ and $px = q$

Let x represent an unknown number. What is the solution to the equation $x + 8 = 17$?

To solve an equation is to get the variable (with a coefficient of 1) by itself on one side of the equation.

$x + 8 = 17$

$x + 8 - 8 = 17 - 8$ ⟵ Subtract 8 from both sides.

$x = 9$ ⟵ Simplify on both sides. The solution to the equation is $x = 9$.

Let x represent an unknown number. What is the solution to the equation $3x = 18$?

In the equation $3x = 18$, the term with the variable x is on a side by itself, but the coefficient is not 1—the coefficient is 3. To get x to have a coefficient of 1, divide $3x$ by 3. Then $1x = x$, and x would be by itself.

$3x = 18$

$\dfrac{3x}{3} = \dfrac{18}{3}$ ⟵ Divide by 3 on both sides.

$x = 6$ ⟵ Simplify on both sides. The solution to the equation is $x = 6$.

- -

J. Understand: Finding areas of parallelograms and triangles

Ian made this drawing of his backyard. How can Ian find the area of his backyard? To solve this problem, use the formula for the area of a parallelogram where b is the base and h is the height: $A = b \cdot h$. The base is 50 ft and the height is 20 ft.

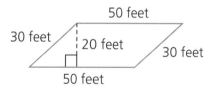

$A = b \cdot h$

$\quad = 50 \cdot 20$ or $1{,}000$ ⟵ The area of Ian's backyard is 1,000 ft².

Ian made a drawing of the flower garden in his backyard. What is the area of Ian's flower garden?

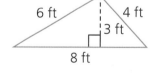

To solve the problem, use the formula for the area of a triangle where b is the base and h is the height:

$A = \dfrac{1}{2}(b \cdot h)$

$A = \dfrac{1}{2}(b \cdot h)$

$\quad = \dfrac{1}{2}(8 \cdot 3)$

$\quad = \dfrac{1}{2}(24)$ or 12

> When using the formula, the base (b) is the side that is perpendicular to the given height (h).

The area of Ian's flower garden is 12 ft².

K. Understand: Finding volumes of rectangular prisms

Small cubes with each side being $\frac{1}{4}$ foot long
are stacked so there are 4 layers of cubes.
Each layer is 3 cubes wide and 2 cubes deep.
What is the volume of the stack of cubes?

Find the length, width, and height of the stack.
Then find the product of length times width
times height.

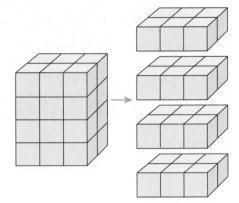

length $= 3 \cdot \frac{1}{4} = \frac{3}{4}$ width $= 2 \cdot \frac{1}{4} = \frac{2}{4}$ or $\frac{1}{2}$

height $= 4 \cdot \frac{1}{4} = \frac{4}{4}$ or 1

Volume $= \frac{3}{4} \cdot \frac{1}{2} \cdot 1 = \frac{3}{8}$ The volume is $\frac{3}{8}$ ft³.

L. Understand: Statistical questions and describing data

Describe how the two questions below are different.
Question 1: How many servings of fruits and vegetables did you eat today?
Question 2: How many servings of fruits and vegetables do students in my
class eat each day?

To understand how the questions are different, think about how you would
answer them. Question 1 has one specific answer, so it is not a statistical question.

Question 2 is an example of a statistical question. Answering a statistical
question involves collecting and analyzing different data values.

When data are organized, it is easier to see trends and patterns. One way to
organize data is by making a line plot.

0	5	2	2	1	3
2	0	8	5	4	0
1	0	2	5	2	1
3	3	2	2	1	2

Servings of Fruits and Vegetables

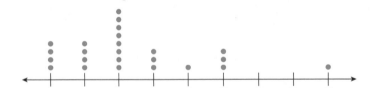

Things to consider as you look at the distribution of data values are the overall
shape, clusters, peaks, and gaps.

- The data values range from 0 servings to 8 servings, with many more smaller
  values than larger values.

- Most of the data values cluster between 0 and 3 servings, and there is only
  one value greater than 5 servings.

- There is a peak at 2 servings, indicating that it was the most common response.

374   Foundational Skills Handbook

You can use this model to solve problems.

Read

Read the problem.
Focus on the facts and the questions.

- What facts do you know?
- What do you need to find out?

Plan

Outline a plan.
Plan how to solve the problem.

- What operation will you use?
- Do you need to use 1 step or 2 steps?
- Will you draw a picture?
- How have you solved similar problems?

Solve

Follow your plan to solve the problem.

- Did you answer the question?
- Did you label your answer?

Check

Test that the solution is reasonable.

- Does your answer make sense? If not, review and revise your plan.
- How can you solve the problem a different way? Is the answer the same?
- How can you estimate to check your answer?

A Vanishing Cash Problem

> Before going to work, Dad took half the money that Mom left in an envelope on the kitchen counter. Later, Susan took half of what was in the envelope when she left for school. Still later, Wally took half of what was left when he went to school. When Mom retrieved the envelope upon returning from work that afternoon, she found exactly $12 in it. How much money was originally in the envelope?

Read

Visualize the problem as you reread it.
Focus on the facts and the question.

Facts: Three members of the family successfully took half the money in an envelope. After this $12 remained.

Question: How much money did the envelope initially hold?

Plan

Use the strategy *Work Backward*. You can start from the amount that remains at the end of the day and figure out how much was in the envelope at the beginning of the day.

Solve

Apply the strategy.

• Because Wally left $12 in the envelope he must have taken $12. So there was $24 in the envelope before he got to it.

• When Susan saw the envelope it must have held exactly $48 (twice $24). She would have taken half of the money, or $24, and left half, $24, in the envelope.

• It follows that Dad would have seen twice this $48, or $96, in the envelope. He took $48 and left $48 in the envelope.

Therefore, Mom must have initially left $96 in the envelope.

Check

You can check your solution by running through the scenario from start to finish.

• Mom left $96 in the envelope.

• Dad takes half of $96, or $48, and leaves $48 in the envelope.

• Susan takes half of $48, or $24, and leaves $24 in the envelope.

• Wally takes half of $24, or $12, and leave $12 in the envelope.

The answer checks.

Not Your Average Problem

> After taking six tests worth 100 points each, Mia's test average is 88. What is the lowest possible test score Mia could have received?

Visualize the problem as you reread it.
Focus on the facts and the question.

   Facts: Mia's average on six 100-point tests is 88.

   Question: What is the lowest test score Mia could have received?

Plan

You could use the strategy *Consider Extreme Cases*.
Is it possible that Mia could have received a 0 on one test?

Solve

Apply the strategy.

Suppose Mia had received a 0 on one of the tests.

Let a, b, c, d, and e represent Mia's scores on the other five tests. Then the average of the scores would be:

$$\frac{a + b + c + d + e + 0}{6} = 88$$

Multiplying both sides by 6 gives $a + b + c + d + e + 0 = 528$, or equivalently, $a + b + c + d + e = 528$. However, this is impossible because even if she had received 100 on each of the other five tests, the total score would be only 500, which is 28 short of 528. This reasoning leads to the answer.

The lowest possible score Mia could have received is 28, not 0.

That is, had Mia scored 100 on five of her tests, she would have had to score exactly 28 on the sixth test to have an average of 88.

So 28 is the lowest possible test score Mia could have received

Check

Suppose that Mia's scores were 100, 100, 100, 100, 100, and 28.
Her average score would then be:

$$\frac{100 + 100 + 100 + 100 + 100 + 28}{6} = \frac{528}{6} = 88$$

So the answer checks.

Common Core State Standards for Mathematical Practice

The Standards for Mathematical Practice, identified here, are an important part of learning mathematics. They are covered in every lesson in this book.

MP1 Make sense of problems and persevere in solving them.

- Analyze and plan a solution
- Relate to a similar problem
- Assess progress
- Use concrete objects or pictures
- Check solutions

MP2 Reason abstractly and quantitatively.

- Pay attention to all mathematical language
- Represent problems using symbols
- Consider units in problem solving
- Use properties of operations and objects

MP3 Construct viable arguments and critique the reasoning of others.

- Analyze a problem situation
- Share reasoning with others
- Explain an approach to a problem
- Construct arguments by using drawings or concrete objects

MP4 Model with mathematics.

- Relate mathematics to everyday problems
- Make assumptions and estimations
- Explain the relationship of quantities
- Use concrete tools to explain operations
- Interpret the solution in the context of a situation

MP5 Use appropriate tools strategically.

- Consider the range of available tools (e.g., place-value charts, graphs, clocks, etc.)
- Decide on appropriate tools to use for each situation
- Use tools carefully and strategically

MP6 Attend to precision.

- Communicate with precision
- Identify the meaning of symbols
- Use measurement units appropriately
- Calculate accurately
- Carefully formulate full explanations

MP7 Look for and make use of structure.

- Search for patterns or structure
- Evaluate the structure or design of a problem
- Discuss geometric shapes in terms of their similarities and differences

MP8 Look for and express regularity in repeated reasoning.

- Make generalizations in computation
- Obtain fluency using patterns
- Look for patterns with shapes and designs
- Use patterns to relate operations
- Evaluate reasonableness of answers

Key: MP = Mathematical Practice

378 Common Core State Standards for Mathematical Practice

Length

Metric

1 millimeter (mm) = 0.001 meter (m)   1 kilometer (km) = 1000 meters
1 centimeter (cm) = 10 millimeters   1 meter = 100 centimeters = 1000 millimeters
1 centimeter = 0.01 meter

Customary

1 foot (ft) = 12 inches (in.)   1 mile = 1,760 yards
1 mile (mi) = 5,280 feet   1 yard = 36 inches
1 yard (yd) = 3 feet

Metric to Customary   ### Customary to Metric

1 kilometer ≈ 0.62 mile   1 mile ≈ 1.609 kilometers
1 meter ≈ 39.37 inches   1 inch = 2.54 centimeters

Liquid Volume

Metric

1 milliliter (mL) = 0.001 liter (L)   1 liter = 1000 milliliters
1 kiloliter (kL) = 1000 liters   1 liter = 1000 cubic centimeters (cm^3)

Customary

3 teaspoons (tsp) = 1 tablespoon (tbsp)   1 quart = 4 cups
1 quart (qt) = 2 pints (pt)   1 pint = 2 cups
1 cup (c) = 8 fluid ounces (fl oz)   1 gallon (gal) = 4 quarts

Metric to Customary   ### Customary to Metric

1 liter ≈ 0.264 gallons   1 gallon ≈ 3.785 liters

Weight

Metric

1 milligram (mg) = 0.001 gram (g)   1 gram = 1000 milligrams
1 kilogram (kg) = 1000 grams   1 metric ton (t) = 1000 kilograms

Customary

1 pound (lb) = 16 ounces (oz)   1 ton (T) = 2,000 pounds

Metric to Customary   ### Customary to Metric

1 kilogram ≈ 2.2 pounds   1 pound ≈ 0.454 kilograms

Time

1 century = 100 years	1 leap year = 366 days	1 day = 24 hours (h)
1 year = 12 months	1 year = 52 weeks	1 hour = 60 minutes (min)
1 year = 365 days	1 week = 7 days	1 minute = 60 seconds (s)

Formulas

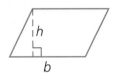

Area of a Parallelogram = bh

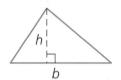

Area of a Triangle = $\frac{1}{2} bh$

Area of a Circle = πr^2
Circumference of a Circle = $2\pi r$ or πd

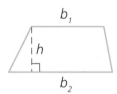

Area of a Trapezoid = $\frac{1}{2} h (b_1 + b_2)$

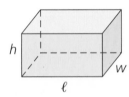

Volume of a Right Rectangular Prism = ℓwh
Volume of a Right Rectangular Prism = Bh

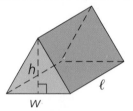

Volume of a Right Triangular Prism = $\frac{1}{2} \ell wh$
Volume of a Right Triangular Prism = Bh

Volume of a Right Circular Cylinder = $\pi r^2 h$
Volume of a Right Circular Cylinder = Bh
Surface Area = $2\pi rh + 2\pi r^2$

Volume of a Right Circular Cone = $\frac{1}{3} Bh$
Volume of a Right Circular Cone = $\frac{1}{3} \pi r^2 h$

Properties of Addition and Multiplication	
Associative Property of Addition $(a + b) + c = a + (b + c)$	Associative Property of Multiplication $(a \times b) \times c = a \times (b \times c)$
Commutative Property of Addition $a + b = b + a$	Commutative Property of Multiplication $a \times b = b \times a$
Identity Property of Addition $a + 0 = a$	Identity Property of Multiplication $a \times 1 = a$
Additive Inverse Property $a + (-a) = 0$	Multiplicative Inverse Property $a \times \frac{1}{a} = 1$
Distributive Property Multiplication over Addition $a \times (b + c) = (a \times b) + (a \times c)$	Distributive Property Multiplication over Subtraction $a \times (b - c) = (a \times b) - (a \times c)$

absolute value   The distance of a number from zero on a number line.

additive inverses   Two numbers whose sum is 0.

adjacent angles   Two angles with a common vertex and a common side that do not overlap.

algebraic solution   A solution found by writing and solving an equation.

circumference   The distance around a circle.

coefficient   A number multiplied by a variable in an expression.

complex fraction   A fraction with a fraction in the numerator, denominator, or both.

complementary angles   Two angles whose measures have a sum of 90°.

compound events   Two or more events that both occur, one after another or at the same time.

consecutive integers   Integers that follow each other in order.

constant term   A numerical term in an expression.

constant of proportionality   The constant value of the ratio of two proportional quantities.

cross section   The two-dimensional shape that is made by slicing through a three-dimensional figure with a plane.

data   Information collected for observation or analysis.

diameter   The distance across a circle through the center point.

event   A set of one or more outcomes of an experiment.

expand   To rewrite an expression without parentheses by distributing factors across terms.

experiment   A procedure that has outcomes that happen by chance.

experimental probability   Probability based on actual results from an experiment.

factor   To rewrite an expression as a product of factors.

frequency   The number of times an outcome occurs.

inference   An informed guess based on evidence.

integers   The set of whole numbers and their opposites.

irrational number   A number that cannot be written in the form $\frac{a}{b}$, where a and b are integers and b is not 0.

likelihood   The chance that an event will occur.

like terms   In an expression, two terms that are all constants or that have the same variable or variables.

linear expression   The sum of terms that are either rational numbers or the product of a rational number and a variable.

opposite rays   Two rays that form a straight line.

Order of Operations   A set of rules to follow when evaluating expressions.

origin   The point (0, 0) on a coordinate plane where the x- and y-axes intersect.

outcome   A result of an experiment.

parallel planes   Two planes that do not intersect.

percent decrease   When a quantity decreases, the ratio of the amount of decrease to the original amount, expressed as a percent.

percent error   A percent that indicates how close a measured value is to an actual or desired value.

percent increase   When a quantity increases, the ratio of the amount of increase to the original amount, expressed as a percent.

perpendicular planes   Two planes that intersect at right angles.

pi (π)   The ratio of the circumference of a circle to the diameter of the circle.

plane   A two-dimensional surface that extends without end in all directions.

plane section   The two-dimensional shape that is made by slicing through a three-dimensional figure with a plane.

population In data collection, the group of interest.

prism A three-dimensional figure that has two parallel bases that are polygons with the same size and shape and lateral faces that are rectangles or parallelograms.

probability A number from 0 to 1 that describes the likelihood that an event will occur.

proportional relationship A relationship in which the ratio of two quantities has a constant unit rate.

pyramid A three-dimensional figure that has a base that is a polygon and sides that are triangles.

radius $\frac{1}{2}$ the length of the diameter of a circle.

random sample Data collected from a subset of a population that is chosen randomly.

ratio A comparison of two quantities, A and B, that can be written as A to B, $A : B$, or $\frac{A}{B}$.

rational numbers A number that can be written in the form $\frac{a}{b}$, where a and b are both integers, and b is not zero.

regular polygon A polygon that has all sides the same length and all angles the same measure.

relative frequency The ratio of the number of times a particular outcome occurs to the total number of outcomes.

repeating decimal A decimal whose digits continue forever in a repeating pattern.

representative sample In data collection, a sample whose values are representative of the entire population.

right angle An angle with measure 90°.

right prism A prism with lateral faces that are rectangles.

right pyramid A pyramid with a vertex positioned directly over the center of the base.

right rectangular prism A right prism with rectangular bases.

right rectangular pyramid A right pyramid with a rectangular base.

sample Data collected for analysis.

sample space The set of all possible outcomes of an experiment.

sampling Collecting data from a subset of a population.

scale The ratio of a length in a scale drawing to the corresponding length in the actual figure.

scale drawing A smaller or larger representation of an actual figure on paper.

scale factor The ratio of the lengths of corresponding sides of a scale drawing and its original figure.

semicircle $\frac{1}{2}$ of a circle.

simplify To rewrite an expression with as few terms as possible.

simulation A probability experiment that models a real-world scenario.

statistics Collection and analysis of data.

straight angle An angle with measure 180°.

supplementary angles Two angles whose measures have a sum of 180°.

surface area The total area of the surface of a three-dimensional object.

term A constant number, a variable, or a grouping of numbers and variables in an expression.

terminating decimal A decimal with a finite number of digits.

theoretical probability The ratio of the number of favorable outcomes to the total number of possible outcomes when all outcomes are equally likely.

unit rate Tells how many units of a quantity there are for 1 unit of another quantity.

variability A measure of how much the values in a data set vary from each other or from a measure of center.

variable term The product of a rational number and a variable in an expression.

vertex The point at which two or more sides or planes meet.

vertical angles Two angles whose sides form two pairs of opposite rays.

M

Measure of center, 282–289, 290–297

Multiplication
of integers, 96–103

N

Number System
operations with integers, 72–79, 80–87, 96–103, 104–111
operations with rational numbers, 88–95, 112–119, 120–127, 128–135

O

Order of Operations, 128–135

Outcome, 306–313

P

Performance Task, 357–368

Pi (π), 235–243

Plane section, 228–235

Plane
parallel, 228–235
perpendicular, 228–235

Population, 266–273

Probability, 298–305, 306–313

Problem solving
area, volume, and surface area, 252–259
linear equations, 174–181
linear inequalities, 190–197
ratios, 50–57
rational numbers, 158–165

Problem–Solving Model, 375–377

Progress Check, 7, 69, 139, 201, 263

Properties of triangles, 212–219, 220–227

Proportional relationship, 18–25
on a coordinate plane, 18–25
represented with equations, 34–41
graphs of, 42–49

R

Radius, 235–243

Random sample, 266–273, 290–297

Ratio, 10–17

Rational numbers, 72–79
addition and subtraction of, 88–95
convert to decimal form, 120–127
multiplication and division of, 112–119

Ratios and Proportional Relationships
proportional relationships, 18–25, 26–33, 34–41, 42–49
ratios and unit rates, 10–17, 50–57

Rays, 244–251

Relative frequency, 306–313

Repeating decimal, 120–127

Representative sample, 266–273

Right angle, 244–251

S

Sample, 266–273

Sample space, 338–345

Scale drawing, 204–211

Scale factor, 204–211

Simulation, 346–353

Solve linear equations, 166–173

Solve linear inequalities, 182–189

Statistics, 290–297

Statistics and Probability

comparing distributions, 282–289
comparing populations, 290–297
compound events, 338–345, 346–353
probability, 298–305, 306–313, 314–321, 322–329, 330–337
sampling and inferences, 266–273, 274–281

Straight angle, 244–251

Subtraction
of integers, 80–87

Supplementary angles, 244–251

T

Term, 142–149
constant term, 142–149
like terms, 142–149
variable term, 142–149

Terminating decimal, 120–127

Theoretical probability, 314–321

Tree diagram, 330–337

U

Unit rate, 10–17

V

Variability, 274–281

Vertical angles, 244–251